AIRBORNE MICROBES

*Other Publications of the
Society for General Microbiology**

THE JOURNAL OF GENERAL MICROBIOLOGY

<hr>

SYMPOSIA

* Published by the Cambridge University Press, except for the first Symposium, which was published by Blackwell's Scientific Publications Limited.

AIRBORNE MICROBES

SEVENTEENTH SYMPOSIUM OF THE
SOCIETY FOR GENERAL MICROBIOLOGY
HELD AT THE
IMPERIAL COLLEGE, LONDON
APRIL 1967

CAMBRIDGE

Published for the Society for General Microbiology
AT THE UNIVERSITY PRESS
1967

Published by the Syndics of the Cambridge University Press
Bentley House, 200 Euston Road, London, N.W. 1
American Branch: 32 East 57th Street, New York, N.Y. 10022

Printed in Great Britain
at the University Printing House, Cambridge
(Brooke Crutchley, University Printer)

CONTRIBUTORS

ANDERSON, J. D., The Medical School, University of Bristol.

BRUCH, C. W., National Aeronautics and Space Administration, Washington, D.C.

CHAMBERLAIN, A. C., Health Physics and Medical Division, Atomic Energy Research Establishment, Harwell, Berkshire.

COX, C. S., Microbiological Research Establishment, Porton, Salisbury, Wiltshire.

DAWS, L. F., Building Research Station, Watford, Hertfordshire.

DRUETT, H. A., Microbiological Research Establishment, Porton, Salisbury, Wiltshire.

GREGORY, P. H., Rothamsted Experimental Station, Harpenden, Herts.

HALL, D. H., Department of Plant Pathology, University of California, Davis, California.

HIRST, J. M., Rothamsted Experimental Station, Harpenden, Herts.

HURST, G. W., Meteorological Office, Bracknell, Berks.

INGOLD, C. T., Department of Botany, Birkbeck College, Malet Street, London, W.C. 1.

KOEPSELL, P. A., Department of Plant Pathology, University of California, Davis, California.

LIDWELL, O. M., Cross-Infection Reference Laboratory, Central Public Health Laboratory, Colindale Avenue, London, N.W. 9.

LUDLAM, F. H., Department of Meteorology, Imperial College of Science and Technology, Exhibition Road, London, S.W. 7.

MAY, K. R., Microbiological Research Establishment, Porton, Salisbury, Wiltshire.

MONTEITH, J. L., Rothamsted Experimental Station, Harpenden, Herts.

NOBLE, W. C., Institute of Dermatology, St John's Hospital for Diseases of the Skin, Lisle Street, London, W.C. 2.

OGAWA, J. M., Department of Plant Pathology, University of California, Davis, California.

TYLDESLEY, J. B., Meteorology Research Division, Chemical Defence Experimental Establishment, Porton Down, Salisbury, Wiltshire.

TYRRELL, D. A. J., The Common Cold Research Unit, Harvard Hospital, Salisbury, Wiltshire.

VAN DER PLANK, J. E., Plant Protection Research Institute, Pretoria.

WILLIAMS, R. E. O., Department of Bacteriology, Wright-Fleming Institute, St Mary's Hospital Medical School, Norfolk Place, London, W. 2.

CONTENTS

MICROBIAL TRANSPORT IN THE ATMOSPHERE AND SPACE

EDITORS' PREFACE

The earth's atmosphere swarms with micro-organisms: many are killed by exposure to the elements; some survive and are harmless to higher forms of life; some spread disease among plants from field to field, or across the continents; others spread disease among animals and man. Suspended in the air, microbes are peculiarly difficult to study so that information about their dispersal and behaviour has been slow to accumulate. Problems of sampling, measurement and interpretation have challenged the ingenuity of workers in several disciplines—engineers and physicists as well as microbiologists and pathologists—and the time is opportune for a Symposium providing them with a common platform on which they all can review progress, compare tactics, and plan the strategy of attack.

Ulterior motives abound for the study of airborne microbes, but all studies are united by technical needs imposed by the air as a medium and by the minuteness of the objects of study. Pathology of man, animals and plants has obviously provided the main stimulus, but other interests have much to give and gain. Analysis of pollen in peat, and difficulties in decontaminating space vehicles spring to mind as part of the network of interests making up aerobiology today.

The contributors to the Symposium are concerned mainly with *viable* microbes, but the distribution of all small particles in the atmosphere is governed by physical factors irrespective of their viability and several papers describing these factors should excite the interest of palynologists for whom viability is unimportant. In respiratory allergy a pollen grain or spore can start a reaction whether it is alive or dead but, except for a passing reference, allergy has been deliberately excluded from this volume: the subject is sufficiently important to merit a symposium on its own.

The atmosphere is an effective medium for distributing microbes because of its continuous movement and mixing on many scales. Beginning with the global scale, F. H. Ludlam describes how the atmosphere works as a giant heat engine whose circulation in the great wind systems of the world is ultimately responsible for nearly all forms of microbial transport out of doors. Changing to a scale of tens or hundreds of metres, swirling eddies in the atmospheric boundary layer are responsible for the diffusion of suspended airborne microbes in a pattern that tempts quantitative analysis. J. B. Tyldesley describes the difficulties of such analysis and presents a new attempt, using a computer to calculate the effects of eddy diffusion for short distances. On a smaller scale still, the circulation of air in buildings is difficult to analyse quantitatively but the set of photographs discussed by L. F. Daws shows that illuminated tracer particles may be distributed by air currents in a room in the same way as microbes.

In any study of microbial aerosols, or suspensions of dust, the first step is sampling. Physical principles of sampling, and some of the pitfalls, are examined by K. R. May who describes existing equipment and foreshadows new developments. Once trapped, microbes are much more difficult to handle than inert dusts, posing another set of problems solved by a set of techniques described by W. C. Noble.

To become airborne a microbe needs enough momentum to detach it from its parents and substrate, and the organization of this momentum for the process of release may control the concentration of a particular micro-organism in the air. In the course of their evolution, the fungi have probably exploited the wind for dispersal more thoroughly than any other group of organisms and consequently dominate the airspora outdoors. C. T. Ingold describes the specialized processes by which fungi get the momentum to make them airborne. By contrast, O. M. Lidwell deals with the processes, mainly adventitious but still effective, which project bacteria and viruses into the air.

Launched into the air, a microbial cloud is subject to the process of transport and diffusion described in the first three papers of the Symposium. The next significant event is a return to the surface where the microbe can continue to grow if it is still viable. Complementing and extending May's discussion of sampling on artificial surfaces, A. C. Chamberlain analyses the various ways in which particles are deposited on natural surfaces outside the body; and H. A. Druett describes in detail a microbial trap of great complexity and interest—the respiratory tract. Transport as an aerosol is a serious threat to the viability of many microbes. J. D. Anderson and C. S. Cox describe how viability is affected by pretreatment, conditions in the aerosol phase, and the techniques of handling afterwards.

Although crop pathogens are often airborne, their hosts are fixed and seldom acquire immunity. Hence the spread of a plant pathogen described by J. E. van der Plank is somewhat simpler than the development of an epidemic of measles. However, J. M. Ogawa, D. H. Hall and P. A. Koepsell show that the often complex annual life cycle of plant-host and fungus-pathogen sometimes favours control of disease by attack at a weak point. By contrast, airborne bacterial pathogens are spread mainly indoors, often by the air currents described by Daws, and two types are examined in detail: *Mycobacterium tuberculosis* and other bacterial infections by R. E. O. Williams; and viruses of the respiratory tract, such as the common cold, by D. A. J. Tyrrell.

Both indoors and in the open, concentrations of micro-organisms decrease rapidly with distance from the source and with time after release, making their transport over long distances extremely difficult to detect. However, some fungus spores, readily identifiable under the light microscope, have been trapped from aircraft by J. M. Hirst and G. W. Hurst. Over the North Sea they have found spore clouds that originated in Britain as a succession of diurnal 'puffs', downwind of a large discontinuous source. Moving beyond the troposphere, through the stratosphere to space, Carl W. Bruch shows that the Symposium is relevant to the distribution of life on other planets and to problems of decontaminating space vehicles destined for planetary landing.

In a symposium of this kind, it is impossible to achieve complete consistency of language and particularly of units. In some papers we have tried to standardize units, but where this would have created more problems than it solved conversion factors are given. We were specially concerned to get a convention for the term 'boundary layer' which different authors have used in four clearly distinguished senses: (1) the skin of air in contact with a leaf, twig or artificial sampling surface, about a millimetre deep and usually free from turbulence so that processes of transport are governed by rates of molecular diffusion (Tyldesley, Chamberlain); (2) a corresponding skin of turbulent air in contact with the earth's surface, about 10 m. thick. Within this layer, the vertical transport of very small particles is proportional to their vertical gradient of concentration and to a transport coefficient often increasing linearly with height; (3) a frictional boundary layer, about 0·5–1 km. deep within which the effects of surface friction are manifest in vertical changes of wind speed and direction and in the pattern of atmospheric turbulence. Above this layer, turbulence generally decreases with height, and parcels of warm, buoyant air rising from the surface are the main vehicles of microbial transport. Transport and mixing by buoyancy are important up to the top of (4) the planetary boundary layer as defined by Ludlam, usually 2–5 km. deep.

The air we breathe is free, but we treat it like a sewer for disposing of waste products. Both industry and agriculture add to the unseen and dilute microbial aerosol in which man, his herds, crops and possessions are all immersed. Fortunately, many of these microbes are innocuous but the dangerous potential of airborne micro-organisms demands farsighted research. Borrowing from the language of microbiology, we hope that through the reading and discussion of these papers many fresh ideas will get airborne, will stay viable, and will spread by cross-infection to breed new ideas and to stimulate progress.

P. H. GREGORY
J. L. MONTEITH

Rothamsted Experimental Station,
Harpenden,
Hertfordshire

THE CIRCULATION OF AIR, WATER AND PARTICLES IN THE TROPOSPHERE

F. H. LUDLAM

Department of Meteorology, Imperial College of Science and Technology, London, S.W.7

INTRODUCTION

The atmosphere is set in general motion by the differential heating imposed by the distribution of sunshine over the curved surface of the rotating earth, and on smaller scales by irregularities introduced by the very variable surface topography. Its own motions also influence the pattern of heating, for example by producing clouds in which the energy received as sunshine in one place is liberated as the latent heat of condensation in another place. The fluid atmosphere is so vast, and responds so flexibly to the variable and shifting external and internal agencies, that its behaviour has an almost limitless complication. The hard task of the meteorologist is to make sensible and useful simplifications—to find laws for the behaviour of the atmosphere. However, complication must remain an essential characteristic, and consequently there are exceptions and qualifications attached to any generalization about the atmosphere, whether or not they are explicitly stated. In the following description they will not usually be mentioned, since only broad features and magnitudes are to be introduced.

WATER VAPOUR AND ATMOSPHERIC CONVECTION

The teeming life on earth and the incessant commotion in our atmosphere both depend upon the combination of sunshine and water.

On the average nearly half of the sunshine which reaches the earth is lost by reflection, especially from clouds, but nearly all of the remainder is absorbed at the surface, and warms it. The energy received on a unit area, and hence the temperature attained, is greatest in low latitudes, where the surface most directly faces the beam. All the energy absorbed is returned through the atmosphere, and ultimately into space as invisible infra-red radiation. Water vapour in the concentrations possible at terrestrial temperatures strongly absorbs part of the infra-red radiation and hinders its passage into space. Radiant energy can flow upward through a layer of air containing a significant amount of vapour only if the temperature rather rapidly decreases upward. This is the state generally encountered in the lower atmosphere. However, the possible concentration of vapour is limited to that representing saturation, and becomes ever less as the temperature becomes lower. Proceeding upwards, a temperature is eventually reached (about $-80°$ C, at

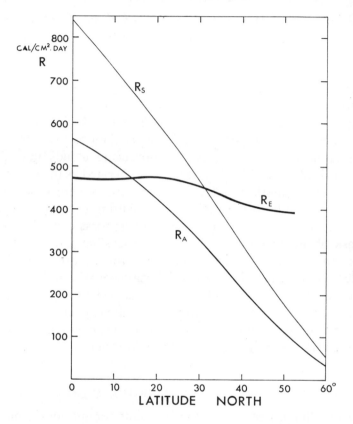

Fig. 1. Mid-winter average latitudinal radiation fluxes over the northern hemisphere: R_S, the solar radiation arriving in the outer atmosphere; R_A, the solar radiation absorbed within the atmosphere and at the earth's surface; R_E, the (infra-red) radiation into space from the atmosphere, from observations by the satellite TIROS II, between late November 1960 and early January 1961 (Winston and Rao, *Monthly Weather Review*, **91**, 1963, p. 641). The atmospheric water vapour makes R_E nearly uniform. The evident imbalance of the integrated values of absorbed and emitted radiation is associated with the winter efflux of heat from the cooling continents and oceans, and disappears in estimates of average *annual* values.

some 10–15 km. above the surface) at which the vapour remaining is insignificant. At greater heights, the radiation passes more freely, and the atmospheric temperature is more subtly controlled by the remaining vapour and other trace-gases, notably ozone.

Three circumstances of major interest arise:

First, viewed from outer space by eyes sensitive to the radiation strongly absorbed by water vapour, the atmosphere would seem transparent down to the highest layer containing a significant amount of vapour. To such eyes this layer would appear to be the earth's surface, of about the same temperature everywhere and therefore radiating energy everywhere at about the same rate. With eyes sensitive to another part of the radiation, hardly at all absorbed by water vapour, the true surface could be seen, radiating more strongly in low latitudes where temperatures are higher. Nevertheless, on the whole, the water vapour has the effect of making the rate at which energy is returned to space more nearly uniform than that at which sunshine is absorbed. This effect, long anticipated theoretically, can now be observed from artificial satellites (Fig. 1). Consequently, since on the average the total energy radiated into space equals that absorbed from sunshine, some energy must be passed from low to high latitudes within the lower humid part of the atmosphere. This is done by systems of warm currents directed poleward and cool currents directed towards the tropics (aided by corresponding ocean currents). These incessant but wavering currents are a form of convection which we may call 'deep', because it affects the whole of the humid part of the atmosphere (which is accordingly called the 'troposphere'). A similar but much less vigorous convection would occur if the atmosphere were perfectly dry. In the atmosphere we have, the radiative properties of water vapour play an important part in setting the temperature and speed of the winds in the troposphere. There is a very slow interchange of air between the troposphere and the dry 'stratosphere' which lies above it, and the stratosphere has its own characteristic slow circulations and sparse population of particles, but these will not be discussed in this review.

Secondly, a 'shallow convection' contributes to the local upward transport of energy by radiation, especially where the air is warmed most rapidly at the surface (over land during intense sunshine and over the oceans in strong winds towards warmer water). Such ordinary convection familiarly occurs in liquids, which are incompressible, when a warming below produces there a greater temperature (and therefore, by expansion, a lesser density) than in the layers above. In the atmosphere the lowest layer is always the most dense, having the greatest weight of air above to compress it; the condition for the onset of convection is that its 'potential density' shall be less than in the air above. Then as its air ascends and expands its actual density becomes less than the density of the air it replaces. This condition is met when the temperature diminishes with height at a rate (the 'lapse-rate') which exceeds a threshold value of 10° C/km., or rather less when cloud forms in the ascending air (to a degree depending on how much vapour condenses). Since in the lowest layers a greater lapse-rate would be required to transport energy upwards by radiation alone, the small-scale convection is continually called upon. Its efficiency is such that regardless of the proportion of the energy transport which it carries, it effectively holds lapse-rates in the lower troposphere close to the average threshold value of several degrees/km.

Thirdly, the temperature in the troposphere thus becomes directly related to the temperature at the earth's surface, and at the same level is on the average some 30–40° C higher in the tropics than near the poles. At any particular level the atmosphere is denser in high than in low latitudes, where the air is warmer. Consequently, the pressure (which is simply the weight of the atmosphere above) diminishes more rapidly with height in the high latitudes, and in the intermediate latitudes demands a *westerly* wind component strengthening with height, for in motion on this scale over a rotating globe a pressure gradient is associated with a wind nearly *along* the isobars (with low pressure on the left in the northern and on the right in the southern hemisphere), whose speed is proportional to the gradient. By the same effect, friction at the earth's surface, which reduces the wind speed near the ground to generally modest speeds, also exerts a control on the strong winds in the high troposphere. These are westerlies only on the average, being distorted by the deep convection into south-westerlies and north-westerlies, and here and there into weaker winds from other directions.

SHALLOW AND DEEP CONVECTION

The circulations of the shallow convection have horizontal and vertical dimensions of the same magnitude, and at least overland they increase in size and intensity with distance above the ground. Within the first metre or two they can, in quiet hot weather, be sensed as the small motions which cause shimmering; at heights of a few hundred metres, glider pilots find them exploitable, with updraughts 100 m. or more across and speeds of a few m./sec., and at 1 or 2 km. they ordinarily produce the small isolated 'cauliflower' clouds known as cumulus. Each circulation lasts not much longer than is needed to move air from its bottom to top: thus the duration of even the biggest, as indicated by the life of the individual cumulus, seldom exceeds about 20 min. Also, each circulation seems to have smaller ones within its flow: for example, individual cumulus are seen to have several domes or towers, whose surfaces have minor protrusions on scales which extend visibly down to metres and probably even to centimetres. The characteristically crenellated surfaces are indeed rather like those of cauliflowers.

There is a collaboration between the shallow and the deep convection: the former works to communicate energy from the surface to a lowermost layer, which then becomes a warm current of the deep convection.

Outside the tropics, this current flows poleward, encounters an ever colder and denser atmosphere, and ascends, producing extensive cloud

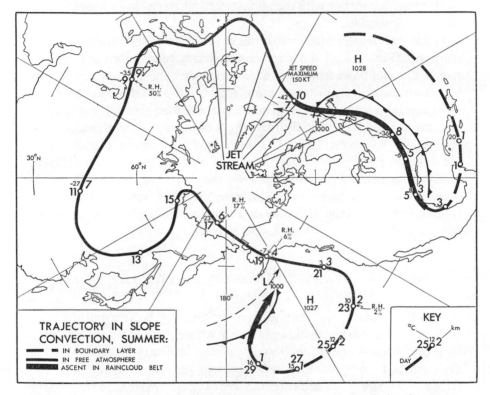

Fig. 2. Schematic path of air in the middle latitude slope convection during the summer season. Air in the boundary layer enters the Caribbean in the easterly trade wind, and ascends in a raincloud belt over the southern U.S.A. The typical position of the associated front and cyclone are shown in the conventional way. The air accelerates into a westerly jet-stream and emerges from the rainclouds into the free atmosphere with a speed of about 150 kt., at a height of about 10 km. During the following fortnight it meanders eastward around the hemisphere, slowly losing energy (kinetic and potential), but warming as it sinks. Ultimately it enters the boundary layer in the eastern Pacific and, after being warmed and moistened during a further four days, it again ascends in a frontal raincloud. Air which enters the raincloud belts in higher latitudes follows similar paths, but does not reach such great heights and speeds. The various paths are interwoven in a very complicated manner. As explained in the text, it may not be possible to identify a particular sample of air throughout the whole period between successive ascents.

and rain; after travelling 1,000 or more km. into higher latitudes it reaches a height of several km. Subsequently it meanders eastward around the hemisphere, slowly losing energy by radiation until eventually it sinks into a low latitude as a cool current (Figs. 2, 3). In this way the deep convection effects a heat transport not only poleward but also upward, so that generally the small-scale convection need work only in about the lowest 2 km. This form of deep convection, which produces the familiar cyclones and anticyclones, can be called 'slope convection', because its currents are tilted slightly but essentially away from the horizontal, in contrast with the almost vertical ascending currents of the shallow convection.

Inside the tropics there is little requirement for latitudinal heat transport (Fig. 1), and the slope convection is represented only by the feet of the cool flows from the higher latitudes. The shallow convection is widespread and its ordinary manifestation, the small cumulus, is the most common form of cloud. The deep convection which is required to effect a transport of heat through the whole troposphere (which here reaches up to about 15 km.) is seen in the towering thundercloud (cumulonimbus), into which the bigger cumulus here and there develop. There is no definite partition between the slope convection of middle latitudes and the more ordinary convection of low latitudes, and thunderclouds develop also outside the tropics, especially in the warm season, and combine with the slope convection.

THE 'PLANETARY BOUNDARY LAYER', THE 'FREE ATMOSPHERE', AND THE WATER CYCLE

Especially overland the shallow convection may be intermittent, but even in its absence we shall consider air whose state has been modified by recent shallow convection to compose a 'planetary boundary layer', distinguished from a deeper upper part of the troposphere called the 'free atmosphere'. Air can enter the free atmosphere from the boundary layer only through the cloud and rain systems in the ascending branches of the deep convection, and subsequently its state is not directly related to conditions at the earth's surface (Fig. 3). Water vapour is accumulated in the boundary layer, after evaporation from the surface, to reach an average concentration such that it would provide about 1 cm. of rainfall if shed. The average annual rainfall over the globe is about 100 cm., so that evidently air normally spends only a few days (about one-hundredth of a year) on each replenishing journey in the boundary layer before ascending into the free atmosphere and losing virtually all of its water as rain. The climb occupies little more than a day in the slope convection, and less than an hour in the thundercloud, but the subsequent descent proceeds everywhere at a slow rate dependent upon loss of energy by radiation, and it is some 10 to 20 days before the air sinks back into the boundary layer. Accordingly, the rainclouds in the ascending currents cover only a small fraction of the earth's surface: about one-thousandth inside the tropics and less than one-tenth elsewhere. At any one time there are 1,000 or more thunderstorms within the tropics,

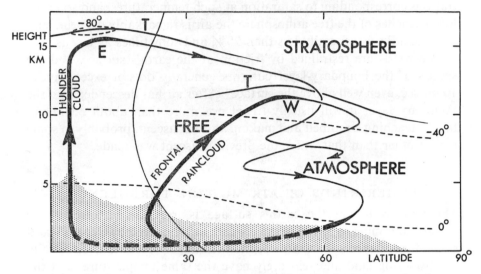

Fig. 3. Some schematic air paths in the general hemispheric circulation, projected on a vertical plane. The tropopauses T, T divide the stratosphere from the troposphere, and the boundary layer is shown by stippling. The thin line near latitude 30° divides tropical regions of mainly easterly winds (of maximum speed near E) from middle-latitude westerlies (of maximum speed near W). Three isotherms, labelled in °C., indicate the temperature distribution in the troposphere. The thick broken lines represent journeys of a few days in the boundary layer, followed by ascents (thick continuous lines) through rainclouds into the high troposphere. The ascents occupy less than an hour in thunderclouds (predominantly in the tropics), and about a day in the middle-latitude frontal clouds. Subsequently the air follows meandering paths (thin lines) during about a fortnight, before sinking back into the boundary layer. The thunderclouds are irregularly distributed in low latitudes; during summer they occur also over the continents in middle latitudes, where the boundary layer may be thicker than shown. Further, ascent in the frontal rainclouds occurs also in higher latitudes than shown, but then does not reach such high levels.

mainly over sunlit land, and several major rainbelts in middle latitudes corresponding to distinguishable individual slope-convection systems. In the air aloft moving away from the rainbelts the little cloud water remaining soon evaporates so that away from them the daytime hours in the free atmosphere are everywhere sunny.

The rather narrow currents which enter the free atmosphere in the slope convection accelerate and appear in the high troposphere of middle latitudes in the westerly or south-westerly 'jet-streams', which reach speeds of up to about 100 m./sec. In these streams air is soon carried far from the region of ascent, and it is likely to have circumnavigated the hemisphere before it is ready to return into the boundary layer.

Throughout most of the free atmosphere the air is icy cold, with temperatures as low as -50 to $-80°$ C near its top. Air which is settling back from high levels has water vapour in only the very small concentrations corresponding to saturation at such temperatures, and so in the lower reaches of the free atmosphere the air is remarkably dry: the relative humidity is generally less than 20% and sometimes as low as 2%.

The winds are restrained by friction at the earth's surface, and the speeds of the boundary-layer currents generally do not exceed about 10 m./sec. even well above the surface. After air has descended into the boundary layer it will usually travel not more than about 3,000 km. before reaching a rainbelt and making another ascent, probably in some region other than that where the previous ascent was made.

OTHER KINDS OF AIR MOTION. TURBULENCE

The temperature at the earth's surface is irregular because of the variable thermal properties of the ground, as influenced by elevation and slope, the soil type and moistness, and the kind of vegetation. Especially neighbouring land and sea rarely have the same temperature, and the shallow convection from the surface warms the lower atmosphere more effectively sometimes over the sea (especially in winter and in high latitudes) and sometimes over the land (especially in summer and in low latitudes). Consequently the over-all poleward fall of atmospheric temperature responsible for the deep slope convection is not smoothly distributed: apart from latitudinal and seasonal variations there are superimposed upon it many local and temporary temperature gradients (communicated to the boundary layer by the shallow convection) which produce within it small-scale slope convection. The most familiar manifestation of such convection is the sea-breeze, but another equally prevalent is the up-slope mountain breeze due to the more effective solar heating which occurs over high ground, especially if it is arid. The circulations of which these breezes are part have an extent determined by that of the responsible geographical feature, and are, for example, limited to a few kilometres near tiny islands, but may be hundreds of kilometres across, near and over broad mountain ranges, and even of continental scale, as in the summer monsoon of southern Asia, a kind of giant sea-breeze provoked by the strong inland warming. We can describe such circulations as convection of *intermediate-scale*, since they are mainly within the boundary layer and have a horizontal extent generally between the largest found in the shallow convection on the one hand and that of the deep slope-convection on the other. Whenever the shallow convection is active overland the intermediate-scale convection has the important effect of producing breezes near the surface which are directed towards warmer or higher ground, and of enhancing and deepening the convection over such places. It often happens that air modified by convection over high ground arrives over the plain downwind well above the limit of the local convection (Fig. 4).

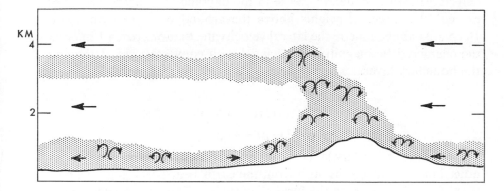

Fig. 4. A common effect upon the boundary layer (stippled) of an intermediate scale circulation over high ground. The shallow convection reaches a higher level over the hills, and a plume of modified air extends downwind above the top of the local boundary layer. The general wind direction is shown by horizontal arrows.

Some kinds of motion in the atmosphere are not directly due to convection. For example, air forced to rise in a stream which crosses a mountain barrier may oscillate markedly up and down several times before eventually settling down at or near its original level, and the pattern of motion is described as a train of 'lee waves'. A more important class of motions arises wherever there is a rapid change of wind with height; it consists of waves which develop, distort and 'break', producing a complicated and apparently chaotic intermingling of air from different levels. They tend to make the wind speeds more uniform, acting as a kind of internal friction. Because it is virtually impossible to follow their details, such motions are usually described as 'turbulence' and studied in terms of the statistics of the average flow and its fluctuations. Turbulence in the free atmosphere is encountered only in clouds and in the vicinity of the strong jet-streams. It is more important in the boundary layer, for the reduction in the wind speed virtually to zero at the earth's surface produces conditions which excite it in every air stream and ensure the stirring and mixing of at least its lowest few hundred metres, even in the absence of shallow convection. Accordingly, the wind we experience is always unsteady, containing an irregular succession of gusts and lulls which are accompanied by fluctuating up- and down-draughts. Near the ground the vertical velocities and fluctuations of horizontal speed are roughly proportional at each level to the average wind speed, and are about 5 times greater when convection is present than when the surface is colder than the air (during clear nights over land, when the wind falls light, the turbulence becomes hardly detectable). In a moderate breeze in the daytime the vertical velocities exceed 10 cm./sec. at heights above the ground of more than about 10 cm. At about a metre the lateral velocity fluctuations reach 1 m./sec., the characteristic magnitude associated with convective circulations in the boundary layer.

PARTICLES IN THE ATMOSPHERE

Provision of particles

The planetary boundary layer acquires not only water vapour but many other kinds of trace substance from the earth's surface, a high proportion of which appears in the form of particles. The particles may enter directly as fragments of surface material thrown into the air, or may be produced by the condensation of vapours. Natural and artificial fires are especially prolific sources, because the rather rapid quenching of the vapours which rise from them causes a condensation into very numerous (and therefore very small) smoke particles which, in the course of time, are aggregated by collisions due to Brownian motion into the size range 0·01 to 1 micron.

Other particles originate as dust, produced in arid lands, and as sea-spray. These are predominantly larger than 10^{-5} cm., and have an upper size limit of about 50 microns, corresponding to a settling speed of several cm./sec. In fresh winds over an irregular surface, such as ridged ground or the sea with waves, such large particles are thrown up to heights of 10 cm. or more where turbulent upward speeds in the air have the same magnitude as the settling speed and carry a proportion still farther aloft. Considerably larger particles have settling speeds which ensure their quick return to the surface.

Trace gases, particularly H_2S and NH_3 (from organic decay) and SO_2 (from combustion), condense and react upon particles. In this way, and by aggregation, solid particles acquire coats of water-soluble substances, so that virtually all particles are hygroscopic and at the rather high relative humidities characteristic of the boundary layer are watery or exist as droplets of solution containing solid motes.

Transport and dispersal of particles in the planetary boundary layer

The fate of particles injected into the atmosphere depends upon their size and the kind of air motion which they encounter. The effectiveness of gravity in recalling them to the surface can be represented by their fall-speed in still air, which is about 1 cm./sec. for a radius of 10 microns and is proportional to the square of the radius. If this fall-speed is greater than any frequently recurrent upward air speed at the time and level of injection, the particles return to the surface within a distance not many times the height at which they are injected, so that they can hardly be said to become 'airborne'. This is especially likely on calm nights. On the other hand, a fresh wind near the surface is the most favourable circumstance for *becoming* airborne. The presence of shallow convection at the time of injection (demanding sunshine overland and winds directed towards lower latitudes over the oceans) favours particles *remaining* airborne. To simplify the discussion we can consider particles introduced into the middle-latitude atmosphere at a height of 10 cm. above the surface, during shallow convection in an air stream whose average speed V in the boundary layer at heights of more than a few metres has the typical average value of several (say 8) m./sec., such as for example is prevalent in the trade winds.

In these conditions the turbulent upward speeds at a height of 10 cm. amount to about 10 cm./sec., the magnitude of the fall-speed in still air of a particle of radius about 30 microns. Accordingly, particles larger than this are unlikely to travel more than a few metres before settling upon the surface. But a proportion of smaller particles are lifted above the level of injection, encounter enhanced turbulent air velocities, and become diffused throughout the entire boundary layer by the turbulence and the circulations of the shallow convection. From a particular source they are spread out not only downwind, that is to say, in the direction recognized as that of the average wind, but also upwards and sideways to form a broadening plume. The edge of the plume rises and widens at rates corresponding to the upward and horizontal velocities characteristic of the turbulence or convection, for as the particles become involved in a succession of disturbances in the general air flow, a diminishing proportion happen to suffer displacements persistently in the same direction. In the convective circulations the vertical and

horizontal speeds reach a few (say 2) m./sec., so that the plume is likely
to occupy the whole depth D of the boundary layer at a distance L of
about $4D$ from the source, where the plume width W has become $2D$.
At first the small-scale and the intermediate-scale convection complicate
the pattern of diffusion; for example, particles leaving the surface on the
right of Fig. 4 are carried aloft over the higher ground by the intermediate-scale circulation to a level which may barely or not at all be
reached by the small-scale convection downwind. The particles may
then re-appear near the surface only a great distance downwind, after
diffusing slowly downwards by ordinary turbulence until they again
enter the layer occupied by convection. However, by the end of the day
the particles can be considered to have become spread throughout the
boundary layer and to have an average concentration $N(m^{-3})$ determined by the source flux, the rate of deposition at the ground, and the
flux $VNDW$ or $8NDL/2$ through the section of the boundary layer
across the plume.

The turbulence and the convection, containing vertical velocities
considerably greater than the fall-speeds of the particles in still air,
produce after some time a concentration of particles which is nearly
uniform with height above a level within a few centimetres of the surface.
Closer to the surface, particles of fall-speed of as much as 1 cm./sec.
settle out under gravity at a rate which leads to a considerable fraction
of the total source flux reaching the ground in one day. By night the
suppressed turbulence may severely limit the deposition rate by restrict-
ing the replenishing turbulent flux into the layer very close to the surface.
Travel continues by night throughout the remainder of the planetary
boundary layer, to distances beyond 300 km., and the plume may continue to widen at nearly the same rate in the circulations of the deep
convection, within whose generally diverging flow the wind velocities
differ appreciably at places more than about 100 km. apart.

Removal by rain and entry into the free atmosphere

After 3 days the plume has lengthened to over 2,000 km. and the air in
the boundary layer approaches an ascending branch of the deep convection. By this time nearly all particles of radius more than several
microns (fall-speed of about 1 cm./sec. or more) have been deposited
at the surface, but the flux of those which are smaller has been only
fractionally depleted in this way, and they enter the raincloud system of
the deep convection.

Rain falling through the air may remove some particles before the air
has ascended into the clouds. However, it is only those with a radius of

more than about 1 micron which have sufficient inertia to be captured by a raindrop: smaller particles lying ahead of the drop are swept aside with the air and escape collision.

Inside the clouds water vapour condenses upon the particles, except in the rare circumstance that their surfaces are hydrophobic. Perhaps half of those whose radius is as little as 0·1 micron, and practically all of those considerably larger, become the nuclei of cloud droplets whose average radius is about 10 microns. The larger settle amongst and collide with the smaller, so that the cloud droplets become aggregated into raindrops and precipitated: in this way, virtually all particles of radius more than about 0·1 micron are deposited in the rain, arriving at a rate probably two orders of magnitude greater than the daytime deposition rate under the plume before it reaches the rain area.

Particles of radius less than about 0·1 micron are collected by a different mechanism. All have a vigorous Brownian motion with a mean kinetic energy corresponding to speeds of more than 30 cm./sec. Those lying within a fraction of a millimetre of the droplets are occasionally knocked against them and trapped by surface forces. During the course of a day a high proportion of the very small particles may be collected in this way, and eventually incorporated into raindrops, or into snowflakes which finally melt into raindrops.

Accordingly, the air is efficiently cleansed in the rainclouds of the deep convection. Of all the particles which enter the clouds only about one-tenth of the smallest (radius 0·1 micron or less) make the passage through the rainbelt and enter the free atmosphere. Since it is implied that the bulk of the trace substance in the atmosphere, consisting of particles of radius a few microns or less, is removed in rain, the observed average concentrations in the boundary layer of trace substance and water vapour (about 20 μg./m.^{3} and 5 g./m.^{3} respectively) are related to their average injection- or deposition-rates (of order 10^9 tons/year of trace substance and about 100 cm./year of rainfall) by similar 'deposition speeds' (of a fraction of a centimetre per second—much less than the fall-speed of raindrops, because only a small fraction of the earth's surface is covered by rainclouds). The composition of rainwater is also consistent with the view that particles are removed from the atmosphere more effectively by rain than by settling out in dry weather. For example, the radioactivity of rainwater is greater than that of the air in the boundary layer by a factor of about 200, corresponding to the proportion there of water (vapour) to air: about 5 g./m.^{3} or 5 g./kg.

Transport and diffusion in the free atmosphere

It is interesting to consider the fate of the few very small particles which pass through the rainbelt into the free atmosphere. They lose much of their absorbed water as the air dries, and mostly have a radius of less than 0·1 micron, so that they cause little scattering of light. Accordingly, the air in the free atmosphere is characteristically dry, clean and clear, in great contrast with the moist, polluted and hazy air of the boundary layer. Only where air sinks into the boundary layer away from the surface sources of particulates, in quiet weather in high latitudes, is the transparency of the boundary layer air comparable with that which can be enjoyed on isolated mountain peaks which reach into the free atmosphere.

Since particles which enter the free atmosphere have settling speeds negligible by comparison with the vertical speeds of the descending branches of the deep convective circulations, they may remain in the rather strong winds of the high troposphere long enough to circumnavigate the hemisphere, even in summer, as suggested by the trajectory in Fig. 2. However, a trajectory entered upon a diagram is an artificial construction, whose implication about the travel of particles (or air molecules) may be acceptably definite only over a space and time less than the dimension and duration of the circulations which effect the transport. This is most obvious in the boundary layer, where there are circulations of all dimensions below about 1 km., and is illustrated by the rapid disappearance of a small cloud of smoke. In the free atmosphere the currents of air which enter the ascending branches of the deep slope-convection from the boundary layer have a vertical dimension of 1 or 2 km. and a horizontal extent of about 200 km. A trajectory in the free atmosphere which is at first representative of the flow of air in such a current has an increasingly indefinite meaning as it is extended beyond a period of about 3 days. A plume of the quoted dimensions widens at such a rate during flow through successive circulations that after a period as long as 20 days it may have spread in the horizontal and vertical to occupy a large fraction of the entire free atmosphere within the one hemisphere. Accordingly, the fraction of about a tenth of the very small particles of the original plume which travel through the free atmosphere may re-enter the boundary layer and subsequently return to the surface anywhere in the hemisphere. Their average deposition rate is about four orders of magnitude less than that in the rain belt and two orders less than that from the plume before it entered the rainbelt.

Table 1. *Dispersal of particles injected into the atmosphere from a middle latitude source at a height of 10 cm. above the surface, during shallow convection in a general wind of about 8 m. sec.*$^{-1}$

Radius (microns)	Transport in and settling from boundary layer	FATE Incorporation into rainwater	Prolonged return through free atmosphere into boundary layer
10^2	All fall within about 100 m.: not effectively airborne		
30	largest within a few km. Mostly deposited (by gravity). smallest within 3,000 km.		
10			
3		Remainder enter rainbelt within 3,000 km., become incorporated into cloud-water by condensation and reach surface in rain	
1			
0·3	Fractionally deposited within 3,000 km. (by turbulent and Brownian diffusion, overland mainly during daytime).		Small fraction enter free atmosphere, diffuse over hemisphere, and after about 20 days carried into boundary layer. Then subject to aggregation with boundary-layer particles, and to further deposition in dry and wet weather.
0·1		Mostly incorporated into rainwater (largest partly by condensation, otherwise by Brownian diffusion into cloud-water) and reach surface in rain.	
0·03			
0·01			

CONCLUSIONS

Table 1 summarizes the previous discussion. The conditions during the injection of the envisaged particles are about the most favourable for their dispersal, and in others the partitions in the table would need some displacement to reduce the magnitudes of the travel distances. In tropical regions where the deep convection appears in the form of cumulonimbus clouds, there is a much more variable distance of travel before precipitation in rain, for the cumulonimbus are irregularly scattered. It has to be considered that overland in the daytime, even outside the tropics in the summer, the boundary layer commonly extends up to 5 or 6 km., so that some large particles (radius up to 10 to 20 microns) may be found at such levels, but they are unlikely to reach greater heights, since they could only do so in the deep convection clouds which would almost certainly precipitate them in rain.

In principle, particles introduced into the atmosphere at one place may be taken away by its circulations and deposited on the surface anywhere on the globe. A dramatic illustration is given by the diffusion of the debris from atomic bomb explosions. However, particles larger than about a micron which leave the earth's surface other than in explosions, eruptions or conflagrations, are effectively confined within the boundary layer, and to travel limited to the typical distance of about 3,000 km. between neighbouring rainbelts. Transcontinental journeys in appreciable concentration over such a distance may be common. They are occasionally strikingly exemplified by the discoloration of rains in Mediterranean and southern European countries by Saharan dusts, and similarly dusts from the arid south-west appear in the rains over the north-east of the U.S.A. Spores have radii greater than about 1 micron, are therefore very efficiently precipitated in rainclouds and so have very little opportunity for inter-continental travel. The very few which escape precipitation and enter the free atmosphere must, for at least one and perhaps three weeks, undergo low temperatures, desiccation and prolonged exposure to intense sunshine, before they can return into the more congenial boundary layer, so that for them inter-continental air travel is not only very unlikely, but also hazardous.

BIBLIOGRAPHY

Atmospheric circulations

Theory

EADY, E. T. (1957). 'Climate' and 'The general circulation of the atmosphere and oceans'. Chapters 8 and 9 in *The Planet Earth* (ed. D. R. Bates). Oxford: Pergamon Press.

Description

KENDREW, W. G. (1953). *The Climates of the Continents.* Oxford: Clarendon Press.

Dispersion of wind-borne material

PASQUILL, F. (1962). *Atmospheric Diffusion.* London: D. van Nostrand Co. Ltd.

Physics of dusts, smokes, and mists; deposition of wind-borne material

JUNGE, C. E. (1963). *Air Chemistry and Radio-activity.* London: Academic Press.
GREEN, H. L. & LANE, W. R. (1964). *Particulate Clouds,* 2nd edn. E. & F. N. Spon Ltd.

MOVEMENT OF PARTICLES IN THE LOWER ATMOSPHERE

J. B. TYLDESLEY

Meteorology Research Division, Chemical Defence Experimental Establishment, Porton Down, Salisbury, Wiltshire

INTRODUCTION

For many years it was obscure to biologists how pollen and spores, with fall speeds of several centimetres per second in still air, could travel in the atmosphere even in the absence of organized vertical air-currents. In 1945, Gregory made the essential step of recognizing in this context that the wind in the lower atmosphere does not flow smoothly over the ground, but has chaotic motions induced by the drag of the ground on the air. Surface friction generates turbulence in the air to a height of 500–1,000 m., forming a 'frictional layer' (Sutton, 1953) within which typical vertical fluctuations are of order 10 cm./sec. Such fluctuations are at least as great as the fall-speed of large pollen so that the disorganized vertical motion of the air effectively inhibits settling. As well as suspending microbial particles, the vertical wind fluctuations spread them vertically. Similarly, particles from a source of limited extent are spread out horizontally by fluctuations in the wind. Thus the air spora of the atmospheric friction layer is essentially in suspension.

Above the friction layer, turbulence decreases, but is generally still sufficient to suspend the air spora, and to diffuse it at a reduced rate. In this region, organized large-scale currents (Ludlam, p. 6) control the dispersion. At the other extreme, the air movement very close to the ground is not turbulent but flows in smooth streamlines nearly parallel to the surface forming a laminar boundary layer which may be only a millimetre or so thick round a blade of grass on a windy day. Ingold (p. 102) describes how particles take off, and Chamberlain (p. 138) how they return to earth through this layer, without the aid of vertical wind fluctuations. The frictional layer should not be thought of as having fixed boundaries, either above or below. In particular, the laminar boundary layer will often be disrupted as gusts of air force their way to the surface from the turbulent layer above. On clear nights with light winds, a boundary layer several metres deep may develop, quasi-laminar in character because the smooth flow is interrupted by sporadic bursts of turbulent activity. The resulting rates of diffusion, averaged over a time long enough to include a number of these bursts, are an order of magnitude greater than in true laminar flow, although they are much smaller than rates of diffusion during the day.

The turbulence in the boundary layer, so far described as mechanical in origin and due to the drag of the wind on the ground, is profoundly modified by buoyancy. Wind fluctuations are increased by heating of the ground below (sunny days, thermally unstable conditions) and decreased by cooling from below (clear nights, thermally stable conditions). Buoyancy effects are not merely a matter of vertical gradients of temperature. There is a conflict between frictional turbulence tending to generate random swirling motion and buoyancy tending to encourage organized vertical motion. Consequently strong winds inhibit the development of buoyancy effects both in stable and in unstable conditions. The direct action of buoyancy is on the vertical motion, but the horizontal fluctuations are similarly affected by thermal stability. This coupling of the horizontal and vertical components is effected through the random swirling motion of the frictional turbulence. In Britain, thermally neutral conditions are very common because the weather is often either cloudy or windy or both. Nevertheless, thermal stability is particularly important for organisms that are released preferentially in certain conditions (e.g. some pollens on sunny days, some spores on calm nights). The condition of air temperature increasing with height is known as a temperature *inversion*, often formed by cooling at the ground on clear nights. Inversions may also form at heights of hundreds or thousands of metres, by large-scale motion of the atmosphere or by radiation from cloud or haze. Such inversions are very effective barriers to diffusion, either from above or below.

RELATION OF THE TURBULENCE TO THE MEAN PROPERTIES OF THE FLOW

Recognizing that dispersion in the atmosphere is a result of turbulent fluctuations in the wind, it seems natural to attempt to estimate rates of dispersion by measuring these fluctuations. Despite pioneer work in the 1930's, this is still difficult in practice, and requires sophisticated apparatus and techniques. Until quite recently, most methods of estimating dispersion depended on relating diffusion by the fluctuations to properties of the mean flow, especially the mean wind profile in the vertical. Before going into these methods in detail, mention must be made of a factor which affects all methods of estimation.

It is clear that dispersion is related to the magnitude of the wind fluctuations but their frequency is also very important. Every-day instruments will not respond to the highest frequencies present, and the length of the experiment determines to what extent the low frequencies are recorded. There seems to be an insuperable difficulty in measuring the low-frequency contribution satisfactorily, because conditions always change during the course of a long recording. Generally, if wind fluctuations are estimated (say by the root-mean-square deviations from a mean), the estimate will increase both with the frequency response of the instrument and with the length of the record. These considerations for the fluctuations have their counterparts for the resulting dispersion. Consider the smoke-plume downwind of a continuously emitting chimney and a sampling arc at some distance downwind. At any instant the intersect of the plume by the arc will have a certain width, and for an extended sampling period a mean of such widths can be found. During the sampling period the plume will meander horizontally, due to the low-frequency fluctuations, so that by the end of the period the width it has covered will be greater than its instantaneous width. Consequently, for a constant rate of emission, the peak concentration will be higher than the mean concentration. Most theories of turbulence do not attempt to predict the instantaneous concentration at any time or place, nor even the mean peak concentration. Instead they give the average concentration over a period long enough to embrace most of the low-frequency components of the turbulence. This should be borne in mind in what follows.

If the source of diffusing material is not continuous, but is emitted rapidly in a more or less instantaneous puff, the situation is more complicated. Only turbulent eddies of size comparable to that of the puff will effect its dispersion. Larger eddies will shift it bodily, and smaller ones will merely stir up its inside without extending its boundaries. The fluctuations of interest will be at lower and lower frequencies as the puff expands. Consequently we have a difficult circular situation where we do not know which frequencies to look at until we know the size of the cloud, which is just what we are trying to predict. Only limited progress has been made towards solving this problem.

Aware of the importance of the frequency of the turbulent fluctuations, we can now ask how their magnitude is related to average properties of the flow and to diffusion. The turbulence transports not only pollutants occurring irregularly, such as smoke and pollen, but other entities such as water vapour, heat and momentum, which may be regarded as native to the atmosphere. Over extensive uniform surfaces, steady vertical fluxes of these entities develop. Corresponding mean vertical distributions (profiles) of vapour concentration, temperature, and wind speed also develop. Neither the fluxes nor the gradients should be regarded as externally imposed because they are mutually self-adjusting to meet the requirements of the synoptic situation, the surface energy balance, and the nature of the ground surface itself. Much study has gone into the relation of fluxes and gradients, with the object of predicting the one by measuring the other. The ratio of flux to gradient is usually denoted by the symbol K, a diffusion coefficient; and the type of theory built around it, of which Sutton's is the most notable, is often referred to as K-theory. The theory is most fully developed for wind profiles and the corresponding momentum flux. Assuming that the same eddies are responsible for the transport of microbes and of momentum, values of K derived from the wind profile may be applied to the diffusion of the air spora.

The mean wind near the ground in thermally neutral conditions increases with the logarithm of the height: the most rapid change of wind with height occurs near the surface, and higher up the change is more gradual. This relation applies up to heights of 10 or 20 m. It is modified in unstable conditions when the most rapid change of wind is concentrated near the ground even more, and conversely in stable conditions. It can be shown theoretically that the logarithmic wind variation implies a constant vertical flux of momentum, and that the corresponding diffusion coefficient for momentum can then be derived from the flux-gradient relationship. The diffusion coefficient increases linearly with height in this case. Mathematically, these relations (mean wind increasing as the logarithm of the height, diffusion coefficient increasing linearly with height) are very intractable, so that the wind is often considered to increase as a power of the height. By choosing the power suitably, quite a good fit can be obtained, except for the region of rapid change very close to the ground. The power is about one-seventh in neutral conditions, increases in stable conditions and decreases in unstable conditions.

PREDICTION OF DIFFUSION FROM THE MEAN PROPERTIES OF THE FLOW

Turning now to Sutton's statistical theory of turbulence and its application to diffusion, considerations of the statistics of a particle moving in the turbulent flow lead to three similar expressions for the diffusion coefficients in the three dimensions; vertically upwards, along the mean wind, and across it. Each contains: (i) the mean-square value of the wind fluctuations in the appropriate dimension; (ii) the viscosity of the air; (iii) an index n derived from the wind profile, assuming a constant vertical flux of momentum. These diffusion coefficients may now be inserted into a diffusion equation which expresses the conservation of diffusing material. When this equation is combined with information on the nature of the source and the boundary conditions, solutions can be obtained which give the concentration of material downwind. Sutton's solutions deal with material which is not falling under gravity, and which is not deposited on the ground. The theory gives good agreement with observation in neutral conditions up to ranges of 1 km. or so, but only after some empirical adjustment. Returning to the three constituents of the diffusion coefficients listed above, it is evident from what has gone before that the wind fluctuations must be measured in an appropriate range of frequencies. In fact, Sutton had to use what measurements were available to him—recordings only a few minutes in length—and to take peak values rather than mean values. No provision was made for a variation of the fluctuations with height. Because the viscosity of the air was found irrelevant for the fully-rough type of flow in the atmosphere, it was replaced by a factor called the macro-viscosity, involving the roughness of the underlying surface. Finally, the derivation of the index n from the wind profile is only valid in the region of constant momentum flux. For mathematical reasons, the wind speed is considered constant with height. Consequently clouds diffusing above a height of a few tens of metres should not be expected to obey the solutions. Generally, the picture is of a theory starting from a rigorous theoretical basis, and then undergoing more and more empirical modification to cope with mathematical difficulties, and to secure agreement with the increasing body of diffusion data as it became available.

The above should not be taken as critical of Sutton's theory within its limits of applicability—diffusion up to ranges of 1 km. or so, in near-neutral conditions of stability. It is the extension to stable and unstable conditions, and particularly to longer distances of travel, which is more doubtful. Bearing in mind these limitations, we can consider how theories such as Sutton's may be adapted to deal with material settling under gravity.

Adaption of diffusion calculations to take account of settling

In considering the diffusion of heavy particles, three questions arise. First, do the particles respond immediately to the continual changes of the turbulent wind, or is the response reduced by their inertia? Fortunately, calculations for the turbulent frequencies important for dispersion in the atmosphere show that inertia is unlikely to be important, even for the largest constituents of the air spora. Secondly, are the diffusion coefficients (or whatever other measures of the diffusion are used) affected by the particles continually falling out of the sample of eddies affecting it at any instant? Generally, this is likely to be significant only for the largest particles, and then only when the diffusing cloud itself is quite small. For most purposes, and particularly at some distance from sustained sources, this loss of correlation can be neglected. Thirdly, how can the simultaneous processes of diffusion and settling be properly incorporated in the calculations?

The quantities used to measure deposition to the ground and the relations between them are:

(1) *Concentration*

C = amount of material per unit volume, above the ground.

(2) *Deposition*

D = amount of material deposited per unit area of ground, per unit time.

v_g = deposition velocity, defined as D/C.

p = deposition coefficient, defined as D/uC, where $\bar{u}$ is an average wind speed near the surface.

Gregory circumvented the third difficulty listed above in an ingenious way. We go back to the idea that the air spora is a suspension, because fall-speeds are small in comparison with vertical turbulent velocities. Deposition velocities are sometimes greater than fall speeds, but as the discrepancy is most marked for the slowly falling particles, deposition velocities also will be small in comparison with turbulent vertical velocities. The argument is that the deposition of material will not alter the *shape* of the vertical concentration profile of the diffusing particles, because deposition at the surface will rapidly be made good by diffusion from above. Only the *scale* of the concentration profile will be altered, to an extent determined by the surface concentration and the deposition velocity. Using the deposition coefficient p defined above, and Sutton's equations for the concentration, Gregory found the fraction of the original emission still airborne as a function of distance of travel. The concentrations given by Sutton's equations are then multiplied by this fraction, to give the concentrations in the presence of deposition. In his book, Gregory uses Chamberlain's modifications of the theory to include elevated sources, and the modern values of Sutton's diffusion coefficients.

In effect, Gregory's assumption is that the depletion at the ground is immediately spread through the whole depth of the diffusing cloud. This is reasonable with a shallow cloud and vigorous vertical mixing. It is more doubtful in stable conditions when the vertical velocities are small and at long ranges when the cloud will be deep. It also has to be borne in mind that Sutton's theory begins to break down at long ranges and in extreme conditions of stability. Gregory's curves are likely to be useful up to ranges of about 1 km. in near-neutral conditions, but otherwise should be treated with some reserve.

RECENT EXPERIMENTAL WORK ON TURBULENCE AND DIFFUSION

In recent years, knowledge of diffusion to long ranges (say 10–100 km.) has increased greatly. Previously, when diffusion was estimated at these distances, formulae such as Sutton's were extrapolated to ranges beyond those for which they were designed. There was no possibility of checking the results experimentally, because at these ranges the concentrations of the tracers then in use were too small to detect. This situation was completely changed with the advent of zinc cadmium sulphide as a tracer. This material is available in the form of small and uniformly sized particles. The material fluoresces violet in ultraviolet light, enabling single particles to be seen under the microscope in the presence of considerable amounts of background material. Its use makes diffusion experiments to 100 km. and beyond practicable. It has been found that at long ranges the spread of material is less, and the concentrations correspondingly greater, than is predicted by Sutton's type of equation.

Concurrently with the improvements in tracer technique, there have been improvements in instruments for measuring turbulence, and methods of using them at heights well above the ground. These measurements have shown relatively small turbulence above a shallow surface boundary layer in which the frictional drag is constant, i.e. above about 10 m. It follows that diffusion is slower above the surface boundary layer. Aircraft, tethered balloons and instrumented towers have been used not only to support turbulence-measuring instruments, but also to sample the vertical distribution of tracers. Such measurements have confirmed that high-level temperature inversions reduce turbulence and effectively put a 'lid' on vertical diffusion. Our three-dimensional picture of turbulence and diffusion, although sketchy in detail, begins to have a firm outline.

As a result of these developments it is now possible to predict diffusion more directly. First, if measurements of turbulent fluctuations are available, they may be used to estimate the dimensions of a diffusing cloud directly. The principle is that the angle swept out by a sensitive wind vane (arranged to register either horizontal or vertical fluctuations) is similar to the angle of the cone embracing a cloud emitted at the level of the vane. In selecting the range of vane frequencies to be recorded, proper account must be taken of the times of emission, travel, and sampling of the cloud. The method in its simple form does not allow for large changes of turbulence with height. Secondly, when specialized measurements of turbulence are not available, we can draw on accumulated experience of diffusion experiments in various stability conditions to estimate the horizontal and vertical dimensions of diffusing clouds at different ranges. Reasonable assumptions on the shape of the clouds then give the concentrations directly. Pasquill has given a practical drill for both methods, and he gives tentative estimates of the likely horizontal and vertical spreads at ranges up to 100 km. In one way this second method is really a natural extension of the successive empirical adjustments of the coefficients of Sutton's theory, but Sutton's theoretical basis is abandoned and empiricism is embraced more openly. These methods have not yet been fully adapted to include gravitational settling and deposition, but some progress already made is described in the next section.

Numerical calculations of diffusion

Techniques have recently been developed at Porton for calculating diffusion numerically, using both analogue and digital computers. Only the digital techniques will be described here, because they are more readily adaptable to take account of settling and deposition than the analogue methods.

The method employs conventional diffusion coefficients, but neither the coefficients nor the wind components are bound to a particular variation with height and they may have any desired values. With this freedom of specification goes the responsibility for finding realistic values. They may be derived from fluctuation measurements at different heights, from observed or idealized wind profiles, or they may be adjusted empirically to fit diffusion data. The atmospheric model has thirty equal layers in the vertical, in each of which wind components and diffusion coefficients are specified. The differential equation for diffusion is expressed in finite difference form, and a suitable computing step in the down-wind direction is chosen. The computer then performs alternately operations corresponding to a small amount of diffusion, and to a small horizontal movement under the influence of the wind. The process continues step-by-step until the required downwind distance is reached, and the resulting concentrations are then printed out. It is not difficult to incorporate vertical movement in this cycle of operations, and thus to achieve what has long been desired—a way of treating diffusion and settling as concurrent processes. However, the vertical velocity for transfer from the lowest layer to the ground need not be the same as that for transfer between the other layers. In this way, the fact that deposition velocities often exceed terminal velocities under gravity may be allowed for in a realistic way.

Specimen results are now presented, for short-range diffusion, to a range of 100 m., showing the effect on the deposition of: (i) particle size, (ii) thermal stability in the atmosphere, (iii) deposition velocity at the ground different from fall speed in the atmosphere above. The wind profiles used follow modern ideas on the variation of wind speed with height in different stabilities. The profiles of diffusion coefficient are derived from the wind profiles, assuming a constant vertical flux of momentum. This assumption is justified by the short ranges involved. The thermal stability is described qualitatively by means of Pasquill's categories, ranging from A (very unstable) through D (neutral) to F (stable). The categories are specified by wind speed, solar heating, and state of the sky. The profiles are related quantitatively to the stability categories, by adjusting the stability parameter contained in the profiles, so that for a non-settling material the computed cloud heights agree with Pasquill's average values. The computations are now repeated, with vertical velocities appropriate to particles of various diameters and unit density. First the settling velocity is used at all heights. Then the rate of transfer from the lowest layer to the surface is altered to allow for a deposition velocity greater than the settling velocity. All the computations are made with layers 2 m. deep. The source material may be considered spread uniformly through the bottom layer, but to find concentrations some distance downwind the source may be considered as half way up the bottom layer at a height of 1 m. The calculations are two-dimensional, so that they refer to a continuously emitting cross-wind line source. Alternatively, for a source of limited extent in the cross-wind direction, the results refer to the concentrations integrated across-wind. All these computations refer to open downland sites with rough grass. It is emphasized that the results, particularly as regards the enhanced vertical velocity at the surface, do not necessarily apply to any other conditions.

The results are shown in Fig. 1. On the left, terminal velocities under gravity have been used throughout the diffusion régime. On the right,

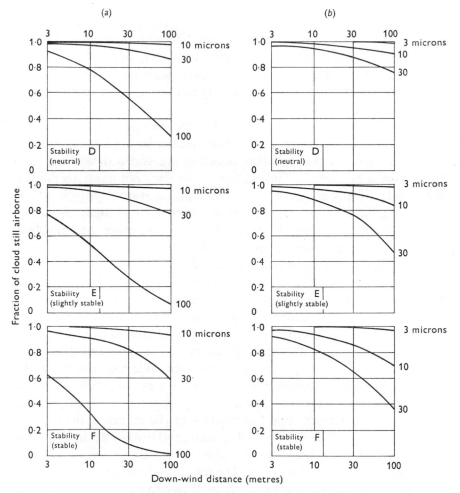

Fig. 1. Results of numerical calculations of deposition on grassland. Each graph shows the fraction of the cloud still airborne at a given down-wind distance. On the left, column (a) is for deposition under the gravitational fall speed. On the right, column (b), the rate of transfer to the surface is increased in accordance with the results of Chamberlain. Each graph is for one category of thermal stability, shown in the bottom left corner. Results for the unstable categories are substantially the same as for the neutral category D. Each curve is for particles of the diameter shown. For 100 micron particles, there is no enhancement of deposition velocity at the surface, and the curves are not repeated in column (a). For 3 micron particles, the deposition is too small to be shown in column (a). The source is a continuously emitting cross-wind line, and initially concentration is uniform in the first 2 m. above the ground. All the results refer to open downland with rough grass. They do not necessarily apply to any other conditions.

the deposition velocities given on p. 154 (fig. 6) have been introduced at the surface. Each graph refers to one category of thermal stability. The results for the unstable categories A to C were substantially the same as for the neutral category D, and are therefore not repeated. The ordinates are the fraction of the cloud remaining airborne and the abscissae are the corresponding downwind distances. The curves show the expected increase of deposition for larger particles, and with increasing distance. Deposition also increases as stability increases, as a result of the decrease in turbulent vertical velocities. At first sight it is surprising that deposition does not decrease in unstable conditions. The reason is that mean wind speeds are highest in neutral conditions, while very stable and unstable conditions are both associated with light winds. In unstable conditions, although the turbulent velocities are large relative to the mean wind, all the turbulent velocities are scaled down to a relatively slow mean speed. This scaling down does not apply to the terminal velocity under gravity. Similar considerations apply in stable conditions, but now the low mean speed, combined with slight turbulence relative to this mean speed, makes the fall-speed more, and not less, important relative to the turbulent vertical velocities.

For particles of 100 microns diameter, deposition velocity is less than terminal velocity, so no curves are given in the right-hand column. For all the other particle sizes, deposition increases as a result of turbulence, the most noticeable feature being that a curve for particles of 3 microns diameter appears in the right-hand column. Expressed in terms of the fraction of cloud still airborne, the effect of the enhanced deposition velocity at the surface is perhaps not very noticeable, but in terms of the actual deposition it is much more striking. An example will make this clear. Consider the case of neutral stability (category D), and particles of 10 microns diameter. Fig. 1 shows that at 100 m. range, the fraction still airborne is 0·98 under terminal velocity, and 0·90 when the increased deposition velocity at the surface is allowed for. Expressed in this way, the difference seems rather small. The fractions deposited, however, are 0·02 and 0·10 respectively, an increase of five to one. The increase in deposition depends little on stability or range (up to 100 m. at least), but does change with particle size. At 100 microns diameter, there is no increase. At 30 microns the increase is twofold, and at 10 microns fivefold. At 3 microns diameter, the enhanced velocity makes all the difference between deposition and no deposition.

'DOSAGE' AND 'CONCENTRATION'

As the expressions 'dosage' and 'concentration' are often found in the literature on diffusion, it is important to distinguish them clearly. Concentration is the amount of material per unit volume, without reference to how long the material remains in the volume. Dosage is the time-integral of concentration and is often the most useful measure of the degree of exposure to an infection. For example, when an animal breathes infected air, dosage gives the total amount of pathogen inhaled. The calculations described in the previous section all refer primarily to more or less continuous emission of material, so that the time-history is not described in detail. In such cases, dosage at any point is simply the product of time of exposure and the constant concentration. When the time of emission is relatively short, then we have to consider how the cloud is drawn out in the along-wind direction. Two important mechanisms operate. First, there is diffusion due to along-wind turbulent fluctuations. The same considerations on the significant range of frequencies of fluctuation apply in this case as for vertical or cross-wind spread. Secondly, a systematic increase of mean wind with height (which is nearly always present) will shear the cloud, and then vertical diffusion will act to spread the material again through the full depth of the cloud. The importance of the second mechanism has only recently been appreciated. The writer believes that, at ranges of 1 km. or more, it can dominate the diffusion process, but its importance is still a matter of controversy. As a result of the shear mechanism, clouds are more extended than would otherwise be expected, and concentrations correspondingly less. As there is no effect on the height of the cloud, dosages are not affected, the small concentrations being compensated by the longer time of exposure. The smaller concentrations are, however, important when it is desired to detect a cloud by air sampling, in order to take evasive action. There are cases where concentrations difficult to detect may accumulate to give significant dosages. The matter can be summed up by saying that concentrations are significant for detection, and dosages for infection.

SOME UNSOLVED PROBLEMS

We now have a framework for calculating atmospheric diffusion for heavy particles, but we still need to know a great deal more about the parameters to put into this framework, particularly diffusion coefficients to the greater heights appropriate to the longer distances of travel.

Such knowledge will come both from diffusion experiments, and from measurements of wind fluctuations at greater heights. More needs to be known too of deposition on different types of surfaces.

The behaviour of clusters of particles, for the part of their expansion when the size of the puff is growing through the significant range of atmospheric eddy sizes, has not yet been described in a way that makes calculations straightforward. This is particularly the case when the turbulence changes in the vertical, which of course it usually does.

The most important limitations of current methods, not explicitly stated but obvious throughout, are their restriction to conditions which are constant both in the horizontal and in time. These restrictions are so at variance with what we know, both of the surface of the earth and of the atmosphere, that we should perhaps be pleased that our idealized models work as well as they do. No doubt methods of computation involving non-uniform surfaces and changing turbulence parameters will be evolved, but progress may not be rapid.

ACKNOWLEDGEMENTS

The data on deposition velocities for particles of different sizes, used in the numerical diffusion calculations, are drawn from Fig. 6 of Mr A. C. Chamberlain's contribution to this volume. Mr Chamberlain kindly allowed the author to see his manuscript, and gave his permission for the use of the data. The digital computer programs described were developed by Mr C. E. Wallington.

This paper is published by permission of the Director-General of the Meteorological Office.

BIBLIOGRAPHY

GREGORY, P. H. (1961). *The Microbiology of the Atmosphere*. London: Leonard Hill. Written primarily from the biologist's point of view, but with a sound appreciation of the problems of the atmosphere. The best starting-point for the newcomer to the subject.

LUMLEY, J. L. & PANOFSKY, H. A. (1964). *The Structure of Atmospheric Turbulence*. New York: Interscience Publishers. Up-to-date information on measurements of both mean profiles and turbulent fluctuations.

PASQUILL, F. (1962). *Atmospheric Diffusion*. London: Van Nostrand. Takes up the subject where Sutton (1953) leaves off, and comprehensively describes modern methods of estimating diffusion.

SUTTON, O. G. (1949). *Atmospheric Turbulence*. London: Methuen. A small book more accessible to the general reader than the following, but slightly less up-to-date.

SUTTON, O. G. (1953). *Micro-meteorology*. London: McGraw-Hill. Basic reference for diffusion coefficient theories of diffusion.

MOVEMENT OF AIR STREAMS INDOORS

L. F. DAWS

Building Research Station, Watford, Hertfordshire

INTRODUCTION

The aim of this paper is to try to engender a 'feel' for the character of air flow indoors and to provide information which it is hoped may be of use to those engaged in the study of airborne infection. Air flow in rooms varies widely according to the design and manner of operation of the heating and ventilation systems, the size and shape of the room, its furnishings and the activities of occupants. Changes in weather influence the movement particularly where the thermal insulation of the building is poor and where the control of natural ventilation is lacking. Some variations therefore occur by chance, others are the result of satisfying the functional requirements of the building. Even the arrangement of the system of heating and ventilation, which can affect the pattern of air movement significantly, may be fixed by functional needs. Moreover, like larger-scale weather movements, air flows indoors are turbulent; so that, in the absence of a satisfactory general theory of turbulence, a semi-empirical approach is necessary to gain understanding of how particular patterns develop. Many of the contributory movements have been studied only qualitatively at present.

CAUSES OF MOTION

The more persistent movements of air through and within rooms are due to ventilation, and heating or cooling. Ventilation produces air currents across a room in directions initially determined by the shape of the air inlets; heating or cooling cause convection currents which affect the vertical distribution of heat and fresh air. Convection cannot be entirely prevented even in sealed unoccupied rooms, where, together with other natural processes of energy transfer, it serves to maintain thermodynamic equilibrium between inside and outside climates. The presence of concentrated heat sources produces convection currents which are comparable in strength with those due to ventilation. Each occupant contributes, because some of the heat of the body is removed by convection.

To appreciate the character of the movements it is necessary therefore to appreciate the requirements of heating and ventilation and to note how these are interrelated and how they are satisfied.

Heating and ventilation

Heating and ventilation are discussed in detail by Bedford (1964). The body mechanism can, with the aid of clothing, adjust to extremes of climate and to variations of climate, but not without some restriction on activity. A controllable thermal environment removes this restriction. Body heat should be supplemented when the environment is too cool because of heat loss by ventilation and conduction through the building fabric, and conversely heat should be extracted from the occupied space when conditions would otherwise be too warm.

The nature of the ventilation requirement is not so clear-cut, for fresh air to breathe is not in general the determining factor. It has been shown (Haldane & Priestley, 1905) that quite small air flows of about 30 ft.^{3}/hr. per person, can provide adequate oxygen. But body odour can become objectionable with such a small fresh air supply and there is evidence (Winslow & Palmer, 1915) of loss of appetite with prolonged exposure to such atmospheres. Present ventilation standards are therefore usually based on results of subjective studies made by Yaglou, Riley & Coggins (1936) in which the absence of disagreeable odour was used as the criterion of satisfactory ventilation. These indicated much larger requirements approaching 1,500 ft.^{3}/hr. per person. They also observed that, for a fixed ventilation volume flow rate, odour strength diminished as the cubic space available per person was increased; and that the efficiency of odour removal decreased as the fresh air supply was increased beyond 300 ft.^{3}/hr. per person. These results suggest that the concentration of odoriferous substances does not depend only on the rate of fresh air supply; and this may be of significance in the context of airborne infection.

Where natural ventilation is needed to cool an occupied space in warm weather, or where conditioned air is supplied to satisfy the heating or cooling requirement, there may be need to exceed the requirement for suppressing odour. Similarly, where it is necessary to extract contaminants before they mix with air in the occupied zones, efficient removal usually entails the extraction and thus also the supply of large quantities of air. Thus, the heating and ventilation requirements must be chosen to suit the particular situation, and air movement requirements have to be achieved in this framework.

The need for certain *types* of air movement derives from the nature of the metabolism and of the distribution of blood supply to the body. For comfort, the head requires a somewhat cooler environment than the feet. In extreme conditions with the air temperature above 80° F., air speeds of 100 ft./min., may provide welcome relief, whereas with a temperature of 50° F. air speeds of 40 ft./min. on the back of the neck or at foot level may be felt as cold draughts. At room temperatures of 65–70° F., air speeds of 15–35 ft./min. are regarded as satisfactory. Lower speeds can cause the sensations of lack of freshness and stuffiness, although these terms are difficult to define. The thermal sense responds to a number of factors including air temperature and radiant temperature, air speed and humidity, and it follows that a suitable distribution of the magnitudes of these factors is desirable for comfort. Discomfort may arise from the tendency for the warmer lighter air to gather near the ceiling and for the cooler heavier air to collect near the floor. This tendency is accentuated by the preference for low air speeds in the occupied zone, because convection currents are then strong enough to dominate the vertical distribution of heat, despite the action of ventilation flows.

Means of ventilation

Ventilation involves the movement of air into and out of the ventilated space and the distribution of the air during its passage through the space. Openings are required to provide access for flow and force is needed, both to move the air, and to overcome resistance to motion due to friction at the openings and in the space itself. The forces acting in natural ventilation are provided by wind and by differences between the buoyancy of air inside and outside the building; in mechanical ventilation, the flow is maintained by fan power.

The action of wind

Measurements of wind force on buildings are difficult to make and to interpret because of changes in weather during the period of measurement and because of turbulence of the wind. The few measurements that have been made are in broad agreement with the results of model studies in wind tunnels. They show that air flow around a building exerts a pressure (in excess of atmospheric pressure in the free wind stream) on the predominantly windward faces diminishing with the angle of impingement. The faces of buildings in line with the wind direction experience a suction with respect to the atmospheric pressure in the free wind. Faces to leeward experience a suction somewhat less than this. The pressures and suctions are proportional to a velocity head of the free wind, P_w, where

$$P_w = 0{\cdot}00051 \; v^2 \text{ (in. water gauge)} \dagger$$
and $\qquad\qquad v = \text{free wind speed (miles/hr.)}$ (1)

There are variations of pressure and suction over the faces in steady wind. Suction is greatest near sharp corners where the air flow breaks away from a face. The pitch of the roof, re-entrant corners and features such as balconies, which project beyond the face of the building, modify the pressure distribution, and the increase of wind velocity with height causes a vertical pressure gradient on the windward faces. Some of these effects are illustrated by the results of two model studies (Fig. 1 a,b).

Knowledge of the pressure distribution is important when choosing the position of ventilation openings; for example, roof shape cannot be ignored when designing the termination of a vertical ventilation shaft. But the main action of wind is to develop pressure differences between windward and the other faces of a building, and these pressure differences act to cause a flow of air into the building through any available openings in the windward faces, and a corresponding flow out of the building through available openings in the remaining faces.

The pressure differences are of the same order of magnitude as a velocity head of the free wind. Equation (1) shows that the pressure difference can be large in high winds (1 in. w.g. at 45 mi./hr.; 4 in. w.g. at 90 mi./hr.) but can of course be virtually zero in light winds. In built-up areas there is a shielding effect, wind speeds at street level being a third of corresponding free wind speeds (Bedford, Warner & Chrenko, 1943). Wind also changes direction, so that a ventilation opening may act as an inlet one day and as an outlet the next. Even in steady wind, turbulence causes fluctuations of wind speed from 50 to 150% or more of the mean, and fluctuations of wind direction of 30° on either side of the mean on a typical record (Shellard, 1963). So the function of an opening, as inlet or outlet, may change from one moment to the next. The intensity of wind gustiness does not vary much with height, nor is it reduced much in built-up areas.

Three characteristics of wind which affect natural ventilation are: (i) wind pressure acts *across* the building, so that air enters at one face and leaves from another; (ii) the magnitude of the pressure difference is extremely variable, requiring the adjustment of openings to control the flow; (iii) wind direction may alter from one minute to the next so that

† 1 in. w.g. = 1·87 mm.Hg = 2·5 mb.

the direction of the air flow cannot be controlled. Where openings are available in one face of the building only, cross-flow is prevented. Pressure gradients along the face may however still cause an air flow between openings, and wind turbulence may cause pulsating movements of air through the openings but these actions have not been studied.

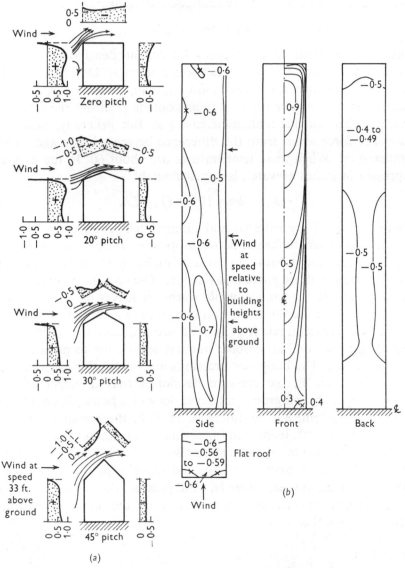

Fig. 1. (*a*) Pressure effect of a wind normal to the face of low buildings; (*b*) pressure effect of a wind normal to a tall building. The fractions shown in both (*a*) and (*b*) are those of the velocity head of the free wind upstream. (*a*, Irminger & Nøkkentved, 1936; *b*, W. D. Baines, 1963).

The action of buoyancy

The force due to the difference between densities of air inside and outside the building acts in a different way from wind force. The buoyancy force is developed over the vertical distance separating the ventilation inlet and outlet, and the pressure acting across the openings, P_s, is given by

$$P_s = (\rho_e - \rho_i)gh,\qquad(2)$$

where ρ_e = external air density, ρ_i = internal air density, g = acceleration due to gravity, h = height between openings. Differences in density may sometimes arise from differing composition of internal and external air—a greater water vapour content reducing the density, a greater carbon dioxide content increasing it. But, generally, most of the buoyancy force arises from the difference between inside and outside temperature. When these temperatures are about 60° F. the pressure, expressed in inches of water, is approximately

$$P_s = 2\cdot8 \times 10^{-5} h\,(T_i - T_e),\qquad(3)$$

where T_e and T_i are external and internal temperatures in °F. This pressure acts over the height between openings (rather than across the building with wind pressure) to cause an exchange of cool and warm air between the ventilated space and outside. The cool air enters or leaves through the lower openings, while warm air leaves or enters through the higher ones; the flow direction depending on the sign of the temperature difference in relation (3). The size and direction of flow varies according to season but seasonal fluctuations are not as great as when wind is acting. The buoyancy pressures are small. For a temperature difference of 20° F. the pressure developed over a height of 15 ft. (between openings on ground and first floor of a house) is about 0·010 in. w.g.; for a temperature difference of 5° F. the pressure developed over a height of 2 ft. (across an open window in summer) is only about 0·0003 in. w.g. From relation (1) a pressure of 0·010 in. w.g. is exerted by a wind speed of about 4 mi./hr. and experiments in houses (Dick, 1950) show that, at greater speeds, wind pressure dominates the process of ventilation. Small buoyancy pressures are the only ones acting in calm warm weather.

Fan action

Fans used in ventilation are of two types. Axial fans are used in situations where the resistance to flow is small; for example, where the fan can be positioned in the roof to extract air, ensuring that wind does not oppose the action. Replacement air then enters through suitably designed openings, or quite often through any available openings such as windows and doors. Centrifugal fans require more power but are able to overcome considerable resistance to flow. The pressure head exerted across the ventilation system may amount to many times the velocity head of wind, so that quantities of air delivered are largely independent of wind and the flow direction is fixed. A single centrifugal fan can provide the fresh air supply for all the spaces in a building by means of a network of ducts. By using two fans, one for supply the other for extraction, the air pressure in each space can be controlled with respect to those in surrounding spaces. This is useful in controlling the passage of contaminated air from one room to another. It is important with such mechanical systems to ensure that the outer fabric of the building is well-sealed against infiltration of air either to or from outside.

Table 1 summarizes orders of magnitude of acting pressures produced by wind, buoyancy and fans.

Table 1. *Typical acting pressures*

Agency		Pressure head (in. w.g.)	Assumptions
Wind.	Gale force	2·5	Velocity head at 70 mi./hr.
	Exposed area	0·04	Velocity head at 8·5 mi/hr.
	Built-up area	0·004	Effective wind speed reduced by factor of 3
Buoyancy.	Winter	0·01	Height 15 ft. Temperature difference 20° F.
	Summer	0·0003	Height 2 ft. Temperature difference 5° F.
	Heated flue	0·07	Flue 26 ft. high. Temperature difference 100° F.
Fan.	Axial	< 0·5	—
	Centrifugal	0·5–8	—

RELATIONSHIPS DETERMINING AIR FLOW THROUGH A BUILDING

The relationships for flow in air circuits, as set out by Shaw (1907), give a convenient picture. Because acting pressure heads are small compared with atmospheric pressure, and because temperature differences are small, changes in air density can be neglected to the first order. The law of continuity for steady flow in an air circuit then requires that the volume flow-rates of air entering and leaving the ventilated space are equal. The areas of inlets and outlets are usually small compared with the area of the surfaces enclosing the space, and measurements show that static pressure differences in the space may be neglected in comparison with those across the openings. Tests show that the static pressure loss across a ventilation opening is proportional to the square of the volume flow-rate of air. The factor of proportionality depends on the type of opening and to some extent on the volume flow, but the form of relationship applies equally to cracks around windows (Thomas & Dick, 1953) doors, and to ducts; it also applies to flow through a thin plate orifice, which for a coefficient of discharge of 0·65 is given by

$$V = 1{,}070\alpha p^{\frac{1}{2}}, \tag{4}$$

where V = volume flow-rate (ft.^{3}/hr.), p = pressure loss (in. w.g.), α = orifice area (in.^{2}).

Shaw suggested that each opening in a ventilation circuit could be regarded as a thin plate orifice of suitable area. The equivalent orifice concept is useful, since it provides a means of representing the network of flow paths in a building and enables the significance of individual openings to be assessed.

Applying the relationship to the situation where the same pressure head, p, acts across several openings in parallel, for example the openings in one wall of a room, the total air flow, V, is given by

$$\begin{aligned} V &= 1{,}070\alpha_1 p^{\frac{1}{2}} + 1{,}070\alpha_2 p^{\frac{1}{2}} + \ldots \\ &= 1{,}070\,(\alpha_1 + \alpha_2 + \ldots)p^{\frac{1}{2}}, \end{aligned} \tag{5}$$

where α_1, α_2, ... = equivalent orifice areas of individual openings. With openings in parallel, their combined equivalent orifice area is therefore the sum of the individual equivalent areas.

With equivalent openings α_1, α_2, ..., in series, and assuming the law of continuity is satisfied, the volume flow-rate through each opening is given by

$$V = 1{,}070\alpha_1 p_1^{\frac{1}{2}} = 1{,}070\alpha_2 p_2^{\frac{1}{2}} = \text{etc.}$$

where $p_1 + p_2 + \ldots = p$; p_1, p_2, ... = pressure losses across the individual openings, p = pressure head across the circuit. It follows that the equivalent orifice area, α, of openings, α_1, α_2, ... in series is given by

$$\frac{1}{\alpha^2} = \frac{1}{\alpha_1^2} + \frac{1}{\alpha_2^2} + \ldots . \tag{6}$$

The equivalent area of inlet and outlet is therefore always less than either area taken separately. If the two areas are equal the effective area is 70% of that of each and if one area is larger than the other the combined area is approximately that of the smaller. Examples of equivalent orifice areas of natural ventilation openings are given in Table 2, and these can be used to obtain estimates of volume flow-rates of fresh air in various situations.

For a room having a closed window and a closed door (neither draught proofed) in the windward and leeward faces respectively, the effective orifice area of the openings in series is (from Table 2 and relation (6)) $13/\sqrt{2}$ in.^{2}. With a pressure head acting across the circuit of 0·04 in. w.g., equivalent to that exerted by a wind speed of 8·5 mi./hr. (relation 1), it is seen from relation (4) that the fresh air flow is about

Table 2. *Typical equivalent orifice areas*

Component		Equivalent orifice area (in.^{2})	Description
Windows.	Not weatherstripped	13⎫	25 ft. of crack—Building Research
	Weather-stripped	3⎭	Station (B.R.S.) data
Doors.	Not weather-stripped	13⎫	18 ft. of crack—American Society
	Weather-stripped	7⎭	of Heating and Ventilating Engineers
Air-bricks		10–50	—
Floors.	Solid	0	—
	tongued and grooved boards	35⎫	$\frac{1}{16}$ in. gap at skirting,
	Square boards	200⎭	floor 12 × 12 ft.
	Ventilators	40–90	—
Flues.	Open fire	10–25	—
	Boiler	2–15	—
Ventilators.	Fixed louvres	24	12 × 3 in. (B.R.S.)
	Constant flow	13·5	At 2 mi./hr. wind speed
		3·5	At 20 mi./hr. wind speed

2,000 ft.^{3}/hr. With both door and window weather-stripped, the effective orifice area is reduced to 2·8 in.^{2} (Table 2, relation 4) and the flow to 600 ft.^{3}/hr., other things remaining equal. With the window weather-stripped but not the door, the equivalent orifice area is very nearly that of the window alone. Opening the door in this situation would not alter the ventilation through the room very much, but there might well be an exchange of warm and cool air through the doorway, under the influence of a buoyancy force. In estimating the effect of a small buoyancy pressure head of 0·0003 in. w.g. acting across a window opening 4 ft. high × 2½ ft. wide, it is sufficiently accurate to take the equivalent areas of inlet and outlet as half the area of the opening, 5 ft.^{2}. The equivalent area of inlet and outlet in series is then $5 \times 144/\sqrt{2}$ in.^{2} (relation 6) and the flow-rate through each half of the window opening is found to be nearly 9,000 ft.^{3}/hr. (relation 4). Evidently, even with small temperature differences, buoyancy forces are capable of providing a large ventilation flow through openings of several square feet positioned one above the other. This emphasizes the need for such openings in naturally ventilated spaces.

Means for heating or cooling

Naturally ventilated buildings. Here cooling is achieved mainly by increasing the ventilation rate—by opening available inlets and outlets to the extent necessary. Increasing air circulation and air speeds by means of a portable fan also improves comfort. Methods of heating such buildings are various.

Room heating. Most forms of room heating require manual control. Open-fires, burning gas or solid-fuel are being gradually replaced by openable appliances which are more efficient and create fewer draughts. But whereas the open fire radiates most of the heat supply, heat from an openable appliance is distributed to a large extent by convection. There is a variety of electric room heaters, some mainly radiant, others convective; a thermostat is sometimes provided with these to control room temperature.

Warm air heating. In the several forms of this system, air is heated by a central appliance and distributed under fan power through ducts to several rooms. Room temperature is thermostatically controlled, the fan switching on and off, and convection plays an important part in heat distribution within the rooms.

Low-temperature radiant panels. Panel heaters installed in the ceiling radiate to occupants and room surfaces but little heat is transferred by convection, because air warmed directly by the panels cannot rise. With floor heating, distribution is by convection and radiation but convection currents rise above the major portion of the floor area. With both systems, vertical air temperature gradients are small in the occupied zones.

Central heating. Distribution is by the flow of hot water, steam or some other agent in pipes to radiators, which are generally situated around the room perimeter at floor level. Heat distribution throughout the space is by convection and radiation, in nearly equal amounts. Thermostatic control is provided but the thermal inertia of the system is large.

Air-conditioned buildings. Heating or cooling requirements are met by tempering the air supply—temperature and flow-rate may be varied automatically according to these requirements. The air supply may be entirely fresh where cleanliness is at a premium, but otherwise part may consist of recirculated air. The aim is to obtain an even distribution of factors affecting comfort in the room and by efficient mixing of supply and room air to avoid undesirable convection effects. To this end, air is usually supplied at high velocity approaching 800 ft./min. and is directed so as to avoid high speeds in the occupied zone, but convection above heat sources or against cool or warm surfaces is difficult to suppress completely.

Heating systems therefore fall into several categories and there is a wide choice of components, and of their arrangement. The choice determines the location of convection streams and thus influences the resulting air movement pattern.

TRANSPARENT ROOM ILLUSTRATIONS

Some of the characteristic air movements to be found in rooms are illustrated by means of photographs (Pls. 2–14) of the motion of particle tracers in the 'Transparent Room' at the Building Research Station, constructed to study air-mixing processes. The room, situated in a controlled temperature laboratory, has a maximum size of $16 \times 12 \times 9$ ft. high and both shape and size can be altered within these limits. A frame construction is used and transparent plastic panels are fitted to provide a flush seal at the internal surface. Methods of ventilating and heating the room are flexible.

Tracer particles are produced by heating tablets of metaldehyde. The substance sublimes and then reverts to the solid phase to form light-weight particles (Pl. 1) somewhat like miniature dandelion seeds. The particles have a large range of sizes, but those below 0·2 in. diameter remain suspended in still air for upwards of 15 min.; and it is reasonable to assume that these trace air movement closely.

The particles are illuminated by collimated light sources and their movement is recorded by time-exposure photography. During the exposure, flash tubes are fired in rapid succession at a predetermined rate and the path of each particle is shown on the film as a line having five bright dots superimposed. Measurement of the separation of the images allows an estimate to be made of the resolved components of the particle velocity in the illuminated plane, and the direction of motion is indicated by the tail, produced by continuous lighting, at one end of the track. The technique is described by Daws, Penwarden & Waters (1965).

Plate 2 shows a natural ventilation flow due to buoyancy force acting across a window opening 4 ft. high by 2 ft. wide (the flow entering from right to left through the lower half and leaving left to right through the upper half). The air temperature difference across the window was

6·5° F. so that from relation (3) the buoyancy pressure was $3·6 \times 10^{-4}$ in. w.g. and from (4) and (6) the air flow entering or leaving is estimated to be 8,300 ft.³/hr. The mean speed of entry of particles in the photograph was 38 ft./min., giving an estimated volume flow-rate of 9,200 ft.³/hr. Particle speeds in this illustration and in succeeding ones can be estimated from the distance separating the first and fifth images using the scales provided.

AIR MOVEMENT IN ROOMS

Although there is no reason to doubt that equations of fluid motion, based on Newton's laws, give a correct representation of flow, these are extremely difficult to solve except in a few special cases, and the solutions are often subject to serious limitations. The greatest single limitation is that solutions representing steady motion may not be valid since in practice the motion becomes unstable, proceeding in a series of eddies. The velocity measured at a point is then quasi-periodic and the flow is described as turbulent. This is a characteristic of air movement in rooms, in general.

Ideas put forward by Prandtl (1952), and Taylor (1960), and others have increased understanding of flow close to surfaces. The 'boundary-layer' concept and 'mixing length' concept, in which eddies are assumed to have properties somewhat like molecules in the kinetic theory of gases, are useful in describing qualitative features; this applies particularly in the present context to the turbulent mixing of a stream of air with surrounding slower-moving air. But in any one flow there exists a spectrum of eddy size and an appeal to probability theory still appears to offer the best approach towards a complete description. An account of developments in the theory of fluid motion and applications up to the beginning of the last war is given by Goldstein (1943). Since then, advances along the same lines have been made in describing convection above heat sources (Schmidt, 1941); these have been variously applied, for instance, to the problem of fog dispersal above air strips, to describe the development of the plume in an atomic bomb explosion and, more recently, to the problem of atmospheric pollution. There have been many improvements to the approach in detail but, for description of particular turbulent motions in rooms, reliance has still to be placed on observation and measurement. To make progress, some idealization is necessary as described in the next section.

The effect of air leaving the room

If, as is usual, the outlet is small compared with the room surface area, air approaches the opening from all directions in quantity equal to the rate of air supply. The approach speed, u, is larger nearer the opening and there is a corresponding reduction in static pressure, p, given by the Bernoulli relation

$$p + \tfrac{1}{2}\rho u^2 = \text{constant}, \tag{7}$$

where ρ is air density. Approach speeds are inversely proportional to a power of the distance away from the opening (the power, lying somewhere between 1 and 2, depending on outlet shape).

Even at a few inches into the room the speeds are usually very small and, in the absence of other disturbances, an estimate of resulting speeds in the body of the room could be obtained by dividing the rate of air supply by the area of cross-section of the room. The flow in Pl. 2 illustrates the relative effects of inlet and outlet (being the lower and upper portions of the window opening). At 9,200 ft.³/hr. the estimated mean speed over the cross-sectional area of the room (108 ft.²) would be about 1·5 ft./min.

The influence of air leaving the room is confined in practice to the immediate vicinity of the outlet, and the pattern elsewhere is dominated by the actions of air entry and of convection. The position of the outlet is therefore important when contaminants have to be extracted. For it follows that, however powerful the suction may be, the opening should be placed as close as possible to the source of contamination. This ensures that the contaminants are removed in the outgoing air stream, rather than drawn towards other stronger currents. It is sometimes possible to position the opening in the path of an air stream containing contaminants, for example the convection streams rising above appliances in kitchens. It is then necessary to surround the opening with a canopy or extract hood of suitable size, for otherwise the stream would certainly be strong enough to flow past the opening, allowing much of the contaminant to escape into the body of the room. The flow pattern within such devices is similar to that due to convection in the upper portion of a room (see p. 48) and the action is to restrict the movement of the stream to the vicinity of the extract opening. Care is needed to ensure that other air currents do not deflect the rising stream past the extract device.

Isothermal motion of entering air

Consider the action of a ventilating air stream which is directed into a room well away from the surfaces at the same temperature as room air.

Then near the entry, the outer parts of the stream begin to exchange momentum with the neighbouring room air due to viscous action. The room air is given momentum in the direction of the stream, a process referred to as 'entrainment', and outer parts of the stream are correspondingly slowed. Room air, farther away, flows towards the stream to replace the air which has entrained, and this action is a continuous one along the length of the stream, which becomes progressively wider as the forward volume flow increases. Thus a pattern of movement is developed in the room.

Near the ventilation inlet, only the outer layers of the stream mix with room air, but beyond a distance about five times the inlet size, turbulent eddies have had time to penetrate throughout the stream cross-section and the forward velocity profile becomes fixed in shape. Measurements show it is then closely represented by a normal distribution curve, except near the outer edges. These edges are not clearly defined because of the presence of innumerable eddying motions.

Measurements indicate that there is a very small negative pressure gradient along the stream and that the pressure within the stream is slightly less than atmospheric pressure in the room, this difference being about 0·05% of the momentum flux per unit area along the stream axis (the product of the air density and the square of the axial velocity). The pressure difference is in general negligible compared with losses at ventilation openings but entrainment could be regarded as a sucking action.

Depending on the strength of the motion, a point is reached downstream where velocities are comparable with those in the room so that entrainment ceases and the stream spreads out in all directions, and becomes indistinguishable from the general pattern of flow in the body of the room. Plate 3 illustrates a stream issuing from cracks around a closed casement window. Owing to the shape of the crack the stream was directed inwards along the glass from the perimeter and was then projected into the room. The ventilation flow was about 1,000 ft.³/hr.

If the stream is strong enough, it reaches a room surface and spreads out in all directions (Pl. 4), clinging to the surface by virtue of its slight sucking action (known as the 'Coanda' effect). The surface stream, a few inches thick, persists until entrainment ceases and then breaks away from the surface and joins the movements induced by entrainment elsewhere.

Orders of magnitude of isothermal motions

The shear stresses at the outer edges of the stream may have some effect in reducing the total forward thrust, M (Nottage, Slaby & Gojsza, 1952) but to the first order the thrust can be assumed to have the constant value

$$M = \tfrac{1}{2}\rho\int_A u^2\,dA, \tag{8}$$

where ρ = air density, u = forward velocity, A = area of stream cross-section. For a given volume flow of entering air, V, and area of the inlet, α, the thrust depends on the velocity profile at entry. For a profile with uniform velocity, the thrust is given approximately by

$$M = \tfrac{1}{2}\rho V^2/\alpha.$$

The thrust of air from a sharp-edged orifice can be calculated for two special cases:

(i) For a circular orifice area α, radius R

$$V = 2\alpha\int_0^1 u_0 \exp(-a\eta^2)\eta\,d\eta = \alpha\,u_0/a,$$

$$M = \rho\alpha\int_0^1 u_0^2 \exp(-2a\eta^2)\eta\,d\eta = \rho\alpha u_0^2/4a,$$

where $\eta = r/R$, r = distance from the stream axis, u_0 = peak velocity at $r = 0$, a = constant. By substitution,

$$M = a\rho V^2/4\alpha.$$

(ii) For a long slot area α width b

$$V = \alpha\int_0^1 u_0 \exp(-a\eta^2)d\eta = \sqrt{\pi\alpha u_0}/2\sqrt{a}$$

$$M = \tfrac{1}{2}\rho\alpha\int_0^1 u_0^2 \exp(-2a\eta^2)d\eta = \sqrt{\pi\rho\alpha u_0^2}/4\sqrt{(2a)},$$

where $\eta = 2y/b$, y = distance from stream axis, a = constant, u_0 = peak velocity at $y = 0$. By substitution,

$$M = \sqrt{a}\rho V^2/\sqrt{(2\pi)}\alpha.$$

Experimentally, the constant a is about 3 (Tuve, 1953) so that the thrust for a given volume flow through area α is somewhere between $0\cdot5\rho V^2/\alpha$ and $0\cdot75\rho V^2/\alpha$. It is also observed that in the extensive region of a stream where the shape of the velocity profile is similar to a normal distribution curve, the stream width increases linearly with distance x from the source spreading at an angle of about 22°. The stream appears to emanate from a virtual point source about $2\tfrac{1}{2}$ diameters upstream from a circular opening or $2\tfrac{1}{2}$ slot widths upstream from a line source. With these assumptions and taking the thrust as constant ($= 0\cdot7\rho V^2/\alpha$) estimates can be made of the forward velocities $u(x)$ on the stream axis, the total volume flow, $V(x)$, and the entrainment speeds $v(x)$, into the stream at distance x from the virtual source. Expressions for these and for the thrust per unit area of cross-section of the stream P, are given as follows, for $\rho = 0.075$ lb./ft.^{3}.

For a circular orifice area α ft.^{2} and a volume flow V ft.^{3}/hr.:

$$\left.\begin{aligned}
u(x) &= 0.14 \ V/\sqrt{(\alpha)}x \text{ ft./min.,} \\
V(x) &= 0.35 \ Vx/\sqrt{\alpha} \text{ ft.}^3/\text{hr.,} \\
v(x) &= 0.0047 \ V/\sqrt{(\alpha)}x \text{ ft./min. on the edge of the} \\
&\quad \text{stream,} \\
&= 0.00093 \ V/\sqrt{(\alpha)}r \text{ ft./min. at distance } r \text{ ft. from} \\
&\quad \text{the axis,} \\
P(x) &= 1.9 \times 10^{-10} \ V^2/\alpha x^2 \text{ in. w.g.}
\end{aligned}\right\} \quad (9)$$

For a slot area α ft.^{2}, width b ft. and volume flow V ft.^{3}/hr.:

$$\left.\begin{aligned}
u(x) &= 0.052 \ V\sqrt{b}/\alpha\sqrt{x} \text{ ft./min.} \\
V(x) &= 0.63 \ V\sqrt{x}/\sqrt{b} \text{ ft.}^3/\text{hr.} \\
v(x) &= 0.0026 \ V\sqrt{b}/\alpha\sqrt{x} \text{ ft./min.} \\
P(x) &= 6.1 \times 10^{-11} \ V^2 b/\alpha^2 x \text{ in. w.g.}
\end{aligned}\right\} \quad (10)$$

Values are given in Table 3 for $\alpha = 0.1$ ft.^{2}, $b = 0.0035$ ft. corresponding to the area of gaps around a window (Table 2).

Isothermal flow against surfaces

Theoretical studies (Glauert, 1956) suggest that isothermal streams issuing from a slot source along a surface or from a point source and spreading out radially across a surface, experience drag which progressively slows the stream. But the free edge entrains air and the thickness of flow increases nearly linearly with distance from the source. The velocity profile from the peak to the free edge is roughly similar to half a normal distribution curve, and this similarity is maintained along a large proportion of the stream. Eventually, as already discussed, the stream breaks away from the surface and spreads out into the room.

Information collected by Tuve (1953) indicates that the shape of a conical stream issuing from a circular opening is altered when the flow is along a surface. The angle of spread perpendicular to the surface is slightly less than one-half the angle of the corresponding free stream, while the spread along the surface is greater. Estimates show that the retarding influence of the surface is very small. Tuve concludes that it is sufficiently accurate, for the purpose of calculating orders of magnitude to neglect surface drag, and to treat the stream, discharging from an opening of area α, as equivalent to one-half of a free stream issuing from an outlet of area 2α, other things remaining equal.

Thus the axial velocities, volume flows, entrainment speeds and thrusts per unit area of surface streams issuing from point and slot sources may be estimated from relations (9) and (10) by writing, $2b$ for b, 2α for α, $2V$ for V, and halving $V(x)$. It is seen that surface streams are stronger than corresponding free ones, velocities being increased by a factor of $\sqrt{2}$ at large distances from the source; observation confirms this.

The corresponding approximate relations for a stream spreading radially over a surface from a source are

$$
\left.
\begin{aligned}
u(x) &= 0\cdot030 \; V/\sqrt{(\alpha)}x \text{ ft./min.,} \\
V(x) &= 1\cdot12 \; Vx/\sqrt{\alpha} \text{ ft.}^3/\text{hr.,} \\
v(x) &= 0\cdot0030 \; V/\sqrt{(\alpha)}x \text{ ft./min.,} \\
P(x) &= 1\cdot9 \times 10^{-11} \; V^2/\alpha x^2 \text{ in. w.g.}
\end{aligned}
\right\}
\tag{11}
$$

where α is the effective area of the inlet.

Plate 5 illustrates such a flow. The photograph shows a vertical plane cross-section (area 12×9 ft. high) of the room containing the inlet and outlets. The inlet is situated in the centre of the ceiling and is shaped to direct the ventilation supply outwards radially across this surface. The ceiling stream reaches and flows down the walls, breaking away several feet above floor level. The upward and sideways flows in the cross-section are due to the entraining action of the surface stream. The outlets are situated in the floor in the left-hand and right-hand corners of the photograph, and these have little effect on the flow pattern. This system of ventilation is to be used to cool the internal rooms of a new hospital; a large volume flow-rate of cool air can be delivered without causing high air speeds in the occupied zone. In the illustration the air was supplied at $V = 12,000$ ft.^{3}/hr., the area of the inlet was about $0\cdot5$ ft.^{2} and the peak velocity at entry was about 450 ft./min. Measured peak and entrainment speeds at 3 ft. radius from the opening were about 200 and 15 ft./min. compared with values of 170 and 17 ft./min. derived from relation (11).

Convection above heat sources

The air in contact with a heat source is warmed by conduction, becomes lighter than the surrounding air, and rises. It is replaced by surrounding air and this in turn is warmed and rises. The stream entrains air by viscous drag. The volume flow-rate increases but the upward velocity does not necessarily decrease; for, unlike the ventilation or forced air stream, the motion is an accelerating one, the air in the stream being warmer and therefore lighter than room air. Initially, the movement is laminar with the air moving in layers, but at a short distance above the heat-source, a few inches with room heaters, eddies begin to form and the laminar stream degenerates into a turbulent one. The rate of mixing and the rate of entrainment increase. The movement continues to accelerate and in another foot or so measurement shows that the profiles of mean temperature and mean upward velocity become fixed in shape and are closely represented, except near the edges of the stream, by a normal distribution curve. Plate 6 illustrates the pattern of movement above short electric heaters. As with isothermal flow, the convection stream exerts a slight suction on the surrounding air, the pressure within it being close to atmospheric pressure in the room, and decreasing with height.

If the stream is not deflected by cross-flows it eventually reaches the ceiling, where its thrust is a maximum. The stream then spreads out over the ceiling in all directions, and remains in contact with the surface, due in part to relative buoyancy and in part to the Coanda effect. It continues to entrain but there may be heat exchange with the surface and some effect due to drag. Approaching a wall, the stream avoids the corner, leaving an area of recirculation, and then flows downwards in contact with the wall surface. If heat is lost to the surface, then some portion of the stream near the surface may be at a lower temperature than room air, and the downward motion of this portion is accelerated. The rest of the stream is retarded by its relative buoyancy and eventually ceases to fall. It then breaks away from the wall (Pl. 7) and immediately proceeds to rise, reaches a stable level, and moves horizontally towards the rising heater stream. Approaching this stream, the flow begins to spread out, part moving downwards and being entrained at lower levels in the room, the rest being entrained at higher levels. Meanwhile, the cool flow down the wall has reached the floor along which it proceeds to be entrained near the heat source. The entrainment pattern into a heater convection stream rising in contact with a room wall is shown in Pl. 8. As a result of this pattern of movement, air speeds can be extremely slow in the lower half of the room and a large vertical temperature gradient develops. Plate 9 shows the pattern in a cross-section of the room due to the convection stream of Pl. 8. Air speeds in the nearly stagnant regions were below 5 ft./min.

Orders of magnitude of convection

Convection above heat sources has been investigated by Schmidt (1941), Taylor (1950), Rouse, Yih & Humphreys (1952), Sutton (1950), Railston (1954), Priestley & Ball (1955), Morton, Taylor & Turner (1956).

Where the effect of vertical temperature gradients in the surrounding air can be neglected, and where the surrounding atmosphere is relatively undisturbed, the plume of convection rising above an irregularly shaped source tends to be confined in a conical region at heights large compared with the source dimensions (just as in the case of forced jets). In this region the velocity and temperature profiles approximate to normal distribution curves except near the edges of the stream, and it is as though the turbulent stream originated at a virtual point-source at a distance below the real source of about three times its average width. Where the source is long and narrow there exists a region of the convection stream (at large heights compared with the source width) which is wedge-shaped, as though the stream originated at a virtual line-source below the real source at a distance of three source widths or so. The distributions of temperature and velocity again follow a normal curve but at greater heights the stream becomes conical in shape. Plates 6 and 10 illustrate the stream shape above heaters 3 ft. long and 2 in. wide. The plane of illumination is at right angles to the heater axis in Pl. 6 and includes the axis in Pl. 10.

Studies at the Building Research Station (Loudon, 1959) suggest that above conventional heaters (e.g. radiators placed away from the room walls), parameters describing the pattern of flow can be derived from the dimensions and strength of the heat source (Rouse *et al.* 1952). For a *line* source of heat it is convenient to define a quantity with the dimensions of velocity by

$$\sigma = (gH/\rho CTL)^{\frac{1}{3}},$$

where L = length of source (ft.),

H = strength of source (B.t.u./hr.),

ρ = air density = 0·075 lb./ft.^{3},

C = specific heat of air at constant pressure
= 0·24 B.t.u./lb. °F.,

T = absolute temperature of air taken as 540° F.,

g = acceleration of gravity = 4·15 × 10^8 ft./hr.^{2}.

Then it can be shown that at a distance x (ft.) above the source

$$u(x) = \text{axial velocity (ft./min.)}$$
$$= 1 \cdot 8\sigma = 10 \cdot 5\,(H/L)^{\frac{1}{3}},$$
$$V(x) = \text{volume flow rate (ft.}^3\text{/hr.)}$$
$$= 0 \cdot 57\sigma\,xL = 200\,(H/L)^{\frac{1}{3}}/xL$$
$$v(x) = \text{entrainment speed (ft./min.)}$$
$$= 0 \cdot 28\sigma = 1 \cdot 67\,(H/L)^{\frac{1}{3}}$$
$$\theta(x) = \text{difference between axial and room temperatures}$$
$$\text{(°F.)}$$
$$= 2 \cdot 6\sigma^2\,T/gx = 0 \cdot 42\,(H/L)^{\frac{2}{3}}x,$$
$$P(x) = \text{thrust per unit cross-section (in. w.g.),}$$
$$= 3 \cdot 8 \times 10^{-6}\,(H/L)^{\frac{2}{3}}.$$

$$(12)$$

Similarly, at x (ft.) above a *point* source and r (ft.) from the stream axis, the flow parameters are functions of

$$\sigma' = (gH/\rho CTx)^{\frac{1}{3}},$$

viz. $u(x) = 4 \cdot 7\sigma' = 27 \cdot 5\,(H/x)^{\frac{1}{3}},$

$$V(x) = 0 \cdot 153\sigma'x^2 = 53 \cdot 5\,(H/x)^{\frac{1}{3}}\,x^2,$$
$$v(x) = 0 \cdot 041\sigma'\,x/r = 0 \cdot 24\,(H/x)^{\frac{1}{3}}\,x/r,$$
$$\theta(x) = 11 \cdot 0\sigma'^2\,T/gx = 1 \cdot 76\,(H/x)^{\frac{2}{3}}/x,$$
$$P(x) = 0 \cdot 61 \times 10^{-5}\,(H/x)^{\frac{2}{3}}.$$

$$(13)$$

Examples are given in Table 4. The large volumes of air circulated by convection and the persistence of the velocities along the length of the stream can be compared with corresponding values for ventilating jets in Table 3. At entry, the thrusts per unit area of the ventilating jets are comparable with pressures exerted by wind, but are reduced to negligible proportions a few feet into the room. It has already been noted that the major portion of the flow in convection streams is recirculated in the upper part of the room. The difficulty of avoiding vertical temperature gradients in naturally ventilated spaces is therefore apparent.

Convection against surfaces

It might be supposed that in estimating orders of magnitudes of flows where a convection stream from a heater rises in contact with the wall of a room, it would be accurate enough to treat the stream as one-half of a free stream of twice the strength (as for ventilation streams), i.e. by writing $2H$ for H in relations (12) and (13) and halving the resulting $V(x)$. This is likely to be true where the surface is extremely well insulated thermally, but the temperature of most room surfaces is not very different from room temperature. Measurements of surface streams above line heat sources in the Transparent Room indicate that the contact with the surface results in increased surface drag and loss of buoyancy, to the extent that the volume flows are about one-quarter to one-third rather than one-half of those in the equivalent free stream (Table 5).

Where a wall surface is cooler or warmer than room air, a downward or upward laminar flow develops near the top or bottom against the surface and in 2 ft. or so the stream becomes turbulent and entrains at a higher rate. This is typical of the development of convection streams against cool or warm surfaces (Eckert & Soehnghen, 1951). The action of mixing such a cool downward stream (developed near a window, for example) with a nearby rising heater stream is complex. If the heater is much longer than the breadth of the surface, Transparent Room observations show there are several streams both upward and downward in a plane cross-section of flow parallel to the surface. With a heater output of 200 B.t.u./ft. length and a surface temperature 15° F. below room air, the cool downward streams did not penetrate into the room beyond the heater, and Pl. 9 shows the pattern of air movement in the room. Where the length of the heater is comparable with the surface breadth, the two streams go around one another, both being deflected sideways; and cool air enters the room.

Non-isothermal motion of entering air

When warm or cool air enters a room, the stream rises or falls and the trajectory depends on the stream thrust and on its buoyancy relative to room air. An approximate method for calculating the trajectory is given by Koestel (1955). The characteristics of the stream lie somewhere between those of isothermal and convection streams, but closer to the former because of the rapid mixing occurring near the entry. The entry of cool air, 19° F. below room temperature, through cracks around a closed casement window is illustrated in Pl. 11.

The stream impinges at an oblique angle on the ceiling or floor where it spreads out across the surface in all directions, but preferentially away from the entry since the component of the free stream velocity parallel to the surface is transmitted to the surface motion. The surface flow continues to entrain, surface heat transfer occurs, and eventually it reaches and flows across the walls. In a short distance the retarding influence of buoyancy causes breakaway and the stream spreads out into the room, much of it remaining high up or low down in the room (according to its relative buoyancy) and returning to be entrained by the free and surface streams.

Patterns of movement produced by warm and cool air streams in the upper and lower portions of a room can co-exist with little interaction, the air at intermediate levels remaining relatively undisturbed and slow-moving. Differences between air temperatures at foot and head heights may then cause considerable discomfort.

Forced warm and cool air jets

In mechanical ventilation and air-conditioning, the supply air is usually directed into the room with thrusts considerably greater than are obtainable in natural ventilation. The aim is to achieve rapid mixing by entrainment and thus to nullify the effects of convection. In order to avoid uncomfortably high air speeds in the occupied zone the stream is preferably directed, by suitable choice of opening, to flow along a room surface.

The opening is usually small and it is seen from relation (9) that the thrust per unit area of cross-section of the jet decreases rapidly away from the opening. On approaching another room surface, the stream spreads out across this surface, and the thrust is further dissipated. The decrease in stream and entrainment velocities is also fairly rapid and it is seen that considerable total thrust is required to give comfortable room air speeds in the range 15–35 ft./min. Comfort requirements of room speed coupled with the rapid dispersal of the supply air stream create conditions where convection can develop above any heat sources with little hindrance, and stagnant regions may still occur in the occupied zone. Plate 14 illustrates the extent to which convection can modify the pattern produced by a forced cool air stream. This has been introduced, at a temperature 15° F. below that of room air, as a surface stream through a ceiling diffuser (cf. Pl. 5). The convection currents rising above tubular heaters (lower left-hand and right-hand corners of the illuminated plane, Pl. 14) interact with the cool surface stream some 4 ft. above floor level, to cause a flow of air into the body of the room. As a result, speeds in the occupied zone are increased from 30 ft./min. (Pl. 5) to approaching 60 ft./min., thus partly defeating the aim of this particular method of ventilating.

Patterns of movement obtained under various conditions and with various designs of opening have been studied by Straub, Gilman & Konzo (1956). The qualitative features are similar to those described here. The particular problem of air movement in hospital operating theatres has been studied by Stanley, Shorter & Cousins (1964), and again convection*appears to have a dominating influence.

The effect of occupants

About one-third of the heat generated by a human body is lost by convection at a rate of about 100 B.t.u./hr. Although this is a weak heat source, the resulting convection stream is surprisingly strong. Plate 12 shows such a stream above a seated occupant in the Transparent Room. The fastest speeds of particles above the head are about 60 ft./min. This is the order of speed estimated from relation (13) for a point heat source of 100 B.t.u./hr. situated 6 ft. below head level.

Other disturbances are caused by opening and closing doors and by walking across the room. Plate 13 illustrates the effects of walking at about 2 mi./hr. (180 ft./min.): the maximum speed of the disturbed particles was also 180 ft./min. Such disturbances are of short duration, the pattern due to more continuous sources of motion being re-established in 15 sec. or so.

CONCLUDING REMARKS

It has been noted that the requirements for heating, cooling, ventilation and air movement determine to a large extent the character and strength of air streams indoors. These are consequently extremely variable from situation to situation and from time to time, and turbulence adds to the variability.

It is possible, by considering the actions of wind, air buoyancy and mechanical forces, to estimate the rates of air flow through the rooms of a building in given circumstances. The equivalent orifice concept, due to Shaw (1907), allows a simplified view to be taken, and the merits of particular sizes and arrangements of ventilation inlets and outlets can thus be compared.

Within rooms, the more persistent air streams and air movements induced by entrainment are due to the action of air entry and to convection above heat sources. Orders of magnitude of the velocities and volume flows of individual streams can be estimated from the relations given in the paper. The strength of convection streams, even those developed above occupants, is comparable with that of ventilation flows and, moreover, the strength is more persistent along the length of a convection stream. It is therefore difficult to suppress the tendency of convection to cause recirculation of air in the upper portions of a room, while air in the lower portions remains relatively undisturbed.

Another common characteristic is the tendency for air streams to cling to the room surfaces, once contact is made, by virtue of a slight sucking action. Orders of magnitude given in the paper show that surface streams are more persistent than equivalent free streams.

It is notable that the action of air leaving the room is confined to the immediate vicinity of the outlet; careful design and positioning of the outlet are required for efficient local extraction of contaminants.

Disturbances caused by the transitory action of occupants die away in a few seconds, but quite high air speeds (about 180 ft./min.) were observed when a man walked across a room for example, and such speeds may therefore occur fairly frequently.

Although the approximate strength of individual air streams indoors can be estimated it is not possible at present to deduce the effect of the interaction of two or more streams. More information is needed on this aspect and on the influences of the shape and size of room and of room furnishings.

ACKNOWLEDGEMENTS

The author acknowledges the contributions of his colleagues, Mr A. D. Penwarden and Mrs D. Sellick, who prepared the photographs and tables. This paper deals with work forming part of the programme of the Building Research Station and is published by permission of the Director.

REFERENCES

BAINES, W. D. (1963). Effect of velocity distribution on wind loads and flow patterns on buildings. *N.P.L. Symposium*, No. 16: *Wind Effects on Buildings and Structures*, **1**, paper 6. London: H.M.S.O.

BEDFORD, T. (1964). *Basic Principles of Ventilation and Heating*. London: H. K. Lewis and Co. Ltd.

BEDFORD, T., WARNER, C. G. & CHRENKO, F. A. (1943). Observation on the natural ventilation of dwellings. *Jl R. Inst. Br. Archit.* **51**, 7.

DAWS, L. F., PENWARDEN, A. D. & WATERS, G. T. (1965). A visualisation technique for the study of air movement in rooms. *J. Instn Heat. Vent. Engrs*, **33**, 24.

DICK, J. B. (1950). The fundamentals of natural ventilation of houses. *J. Instn Heat. Vent. Engrs*, **18**, 123.

ECKERT, E. R. G. & SOEHNGHEN, E. (1951). Proceedings of the general discussion on heat transfer. *Inst. Mech. Engrs Lond. and Am. Soc. Mech. Engrs, New York*, pp. 321–3, 381, 387–8.

GLAUERT, M. B. (1956). The wall jet. *J. Fluid Mech.* **1**, 625.

GOLDSTEIN, S. (1943). *Modern Developments in Fluid Dynamics*. Oxford: Clarendon Press.

HALDANE, J. S. & PRIESTLEY, J. G. (1905). The regulation of the lung ventilation. *J. Physiol.* **32**, 225.

IRMINGER, J. O. V. & NØKKENTVED, C. (1936). Wind pressure on buildings. Experimental researches (second series). *Inquidensk. Skr.* A, Nr. 42.

KOESTEL, A. (1955). Paths of horizontally projected heated and chilled jets. *Heat. Pip. Air Condit.* **27**, 1.

LOUDON, A. G. (1959). Private communication B.R.S.

MORTON, B. R., TAYLOR, G. I. & TURNER, J. S. (1956). Turbulent gravitational convection from maintained and instantaneous sources. *Proc. R. Soc.* A, **234**, 1.

NOTTAGE, H. B., SLABY, J. G. & GOJSZA, W. P. (1952). Isothermal-jet fundamentals. *Heat. Pip. Air Condit.* **24**, 165.

PRANDTL, L. (1952). *Essentials of Fluid Dynamics.* London: Blackie and Son Ltd.

PRIESTLEY, C. H. B. & BALL, F. K. (1955). Continuous convection from an isolated source of heat. *Q. Jl R. met. Soc.* **81**, 144.

RAILSTON, W. (1954). The temperature decay law of a naturally convected air stream. *Proc. phys. Soc.* B, **67**, 42.

ROUSE, H., YIH, C. S. & HUMPHREYS, H. W. (1952). Gravitational convection from a boundary source. *Tellus,* **4**, 201.

SCHMIDT, W. (1941). Turbulent spreading of a current of heated air. *Z. angew. Math. Mech.* **21**, 265, 351.

SHAW, W. N. (1907). *Air Currents and the Laws of Ventilation.* Cambridge University Press.

SHELLARD, H. C. (1963). The estimation of design wind speeds. *N.P.L. Symposium,* No. 16: *Wind Effects on Buildings and Structures,* VI, paper 1. London: H.M.S.O.

STANLEY, E. E., SHORTER, D. N. & COUSINS, P. J. (1964). A laboratory study of the downward displacement system of ventilation in operating theatres. *Heat & Vent. Res. Assn Lab. Rep.* No. 19.

STRAUB, H. E., GILMAN, S. F. & KONZO, S. (1956). Distribution of air within a room for year-round air conditioning, Part 1. *University of Illinois Engineering Experiment Station Bull.* No. 435.

SUTTON, O. G. (1950). Dispersal of hot gases in the atmosphere. *J. Met.* **7**, 307.

TAYLOR, G. I. (1945). Dynamics of a mass of hot gas rising in air. U.S. Atomic Energy Commission MDDC 919 LADC 276.

TAYLOR, G. I. (1960). In *The Scientific Papers of G. I. Taylor,* I–III. Ed. G. K. Batchelor. Cambridge University Press.

THOMAS, D. A. & DICK, J. B. (1953). Air infiltration through gaps around windows. *J. Instn Heat. Vent. Engrs,* **21**, 85.

TUVE, G. L. (1953). Air velocities in ventilating jets. *Heat. Pip. Air Condit.* **25**, 181.

WINSLOW, G. E. A. & PALMER, G. T. (1915). The effect upon appetite of the chemical constituents of the air of occupied rooms. *Proc. Soc. exp. Biol. Med.* **12**, 141.

YAGLOU, C. P., RILEY, E. C. & COGGINS, D. I. (1936). Ventilation requirements. *Heat Pip. Air Condit.* **8**, 65; *Trans. Am. Soc. Heat. Vent. Engrs,* **42**.

EXPLANATION OF PLATES

(Crown Copyright Reserved)

Plate 1. Metaldehyde particle.

Plate 2. Flow through open window caused by air buoyancy.

Plate 3. Isothermal jet from a closed casement window. Flow rate 1,000 ft.³/hr. due to pressure difference of 0·05 in. w.g. (equivalent to 10 mi./hr. wind).

Plate 4. Spread of an impinging jet.

Plate 5. Flow induced by ceiling diffuser ventilation. Isothermal flow, 12,000 ft.³/hr.

Plate 6. Convection stream above short heaters (heater axis perpendicular to plane of illumination—cf. Plate 10) 2,400 B.t.u./hr.

Plate 7. Break-away of downward wall-stream due to air buoyancy.

Plate 8. Convection stream above a long heater placed close to a wall. Heat input 420 B.t.u./ft.

Plate 9. General view of flow in room due to convection stream of Pl. 8.

Plate 10. Convection stream above short heaters (heater axis parallel to plane of illumination—cf. Pl. 6). 2,400 B.t.u./hr.

Plate 11. Cold air entry through a closed casement window. Temperature difference 19° F., flow rate 1,300 ft.³/hr. due to pressure difference of 0·07 in. w.g. (equivalent to 12 mi./hr. wind).

Plate 12. Convection above the occupant of a room.

Plate 13. Disturbance due to walking in a room.

Plate 14. Disturbance of pattern in Pl. 5 due to convection.

PLATE 1

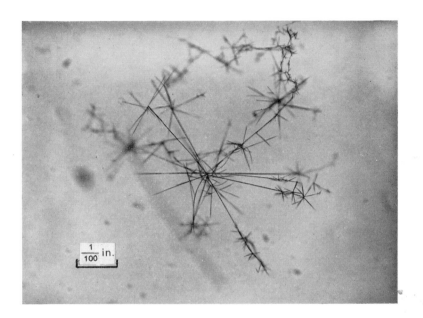

PLATE 2

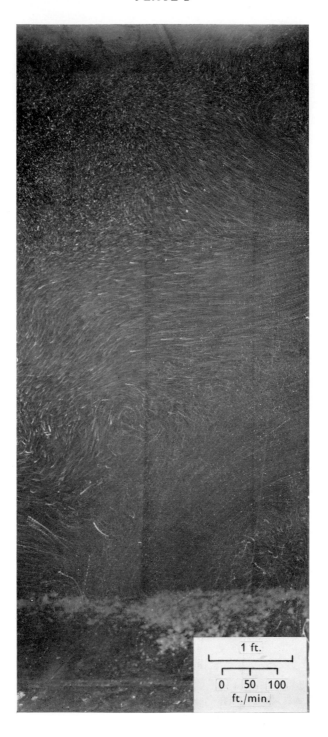

PLATE 3

PLATE 4

PLATE 5

PLATE 6

PLATE 7

1 ft.

| 0 | 50 | 100 |

ft./min.

PLATE 8

1 ft.

0   50   100
ft./min.

PLATE 9

PLATE 10

PLATE 11

PLATE 12

PLATE 13

PLATE 14

Table 3. Calculated values for isothermal jets

Volume flow at entry V (ft.³/hr.)	Distance from orifice (ft.)	Slot, area 13 in.², width = 0·0433 in.				Circular orifice area 13 in.²				Circular orifice area 72 in.²			
		u(x) (ft./min.)	V(x) (ft.³/hr.)	v(x) (ft./min.)	P(x) (10⁵in.w.g.)	u(x) (ft./min.)	V(x) (ft.³/hr.)	v(x) (ft./min.)	P(x) (10⁵in.w.g.)	u(x) (ft./min.)	V(x) (ft.³/hr.)	v(x) (ft./min.)	P(x) (10⁵in.w.g.)
1,000	0	360	1,000	—	300	560	1,000	—	300	100	1,000	—	9·7
	1·5	28	12,900	1·4	1·8	200	2,800	7	38	58	1,800	2·0	3·2
	2·5	22	16,600	1·1	1·1	140	4,000	5	19	45	2,300	1·5	1·9
	3·5	18	19,600	1·0	0·8	110	5,200	4	11	37	2,800	1·3	1·3
	4·5	16	22,300	0·8	0·6	90	6,400	3	7	31	3,300	1·1	0·9
	5·5	15	24,600	0·8	0·5	70	7,600	3	5	27	3,800	1·0	0·7
	6·5	14	26,700	0·7	0·4	60	8,800	2	4	24	4,300	0·8	0·5
	7·5	13	28,700	0·7	0·4	60	10,000	2	3	21	4,900	0·7	0·4
	8·5	12	30,600	0·6	0·3	50	11,200	2	2	19	5,300	0·7	0·4
3,000	0	1,100	3,000	—	2,700	1,700	3,000	—	2,700	300	3,000	—	87
	1·5	84	38,600	4·3	16	600	8,400	21	340	170	5,300	6·0	28
	2·5	65	49,800	3·4	10	420	12,000	14	170	135	6,800	4·5	17
	3·5	55	58,900	2·9	7	320	15,700	11	100	110	8,300	3·9	12
	4·5	49	66,800	2·5	5	260	19,200	9	66	92	9,900	3·2	8
	5·5	44	73,800	2·3	4	220	22,800	8	47	80	11,400	2·7	6
	6·5	41	80,200	2·1	4	190	26,400	7	36	71	13,000	2·4	5
	7·5	38	86,200	2·0	3	170	29,900	6	27	63	14,600	2·2	4
	8·5	35	91,800	1·8	3	150	33,600	5	22	57	16,000	2·0	3

Table 4. Calculated values for a line heat source

Distance above source (ft.)	H/L = 853 B.t.u./ft. hr.					H/L = 420 B.t.u./ft. hr.					H/L = 225 B.t.u./ft. hr.				
	$u(x)$ (ft./min.)	$V(x)/L$ (ft.²/hr.)	$v(x)$ (ft./min.)	$P(x)$ (10⁵ in. w.g.)	$\theta(x)$ (°F.)	$u(x)$ (ft./min.)	$V(x)/L$ (ft.²/hr.)	$v(x)$ (ft./min.)	$P(x)$ (10⁵ in. w.g.)	$\theta(x)$ (°F.)	$u(x)$ (ft./min.)	$V(x)/L$ (ft.²/hr.)	$v(x)$ (ft./min.)	$P(x)$ (10⁵ in. w.g.)	$\theta(x)$ (°F.)
1·5	94	2,800	16·0	34	25	78	2,200	13	21	16	64	1,800	10	14	10
2·5	94	4,700	16·0	34	15	78	3,700	13	21	9	64	3,000	10	14	6
3·5	94	6,600	16·0	34	11	78	5,200	13	21	7	64	4,300	10	14	4
4·5	94	8,500	16.0	34	8	78	6,700	13	21	5	64	5,500	10	14	3
5·5	94	10,400	16·0	34	7	78	8,200	13	21	4	64	6,700	10	14	3
6·5	94	12,300	16·0	34	6	78	9,700	13	21	4	64	7,900	10	14	2
7·5	94	14,200	16·0	34	5	78	11,200	13	21	3	64	9,100	10	14	2

Calculated values for a point heat source

Distance above source (ft.)	H = 3,000 B.t.u./hr.					H = 1,000 B.t.u./hr.					H = 100 B.t.u./hr.				
	$u(x)$ (ft./min.)	$V(x)$ (ft.³/hr.)	$v(x)$ (ft./min.)	$P(x)$ (10⁵ in. w.g.)	$\theta(x)$ (°F.)	$u(x)$ (ft./min.)	$V(x)$ (ft.³/hr.)	$v(x)$ (ft./min.)	$P(x)$ (10⁵ in. w.g.)	$\theta(x)$ (°F.)	$u(x)$ (ft./min.)	$V(x)$ (ft.³/hr.)	$v(x)$ (ft./min.)	$P(x)$ (10⁵ in. w.g.)	$\theta(x)$ (°F.)
1·5	350	1,500	15	97	215	240	1,100	10	47	89	110	490	5	10	19
2·5	290	3,500	13	68	92	203	2,500	9	33	38	94	1,100	4	7	8
3·5	260	6,500	11	55	50	181	4,500	8	27	21	84	2,100	4	6	5
4·5	240	9,400	10	47	35	167	6,600	7	23	14	77	3,000	3	5	3
5·5	220	13,200	10	41	25	156	9,200	7	20	10	72	4,200	3	4	2
6·5	210	17,500	9	36	19	147	12,100	6	18	8	68	5,600	3	4	2
7·5	200	22,200	9	33	15	140	15,400	6	16	6	65	7,200	3	3	0

Table 5. Experimental values for a line heat source against a wall

Distance above virtual source (ft.)	H/L = 614 B.t.u./ft. hr.					H/L = 420 B.t.u./ft. hr.					H/L = 225 B.t.u./ft. hr.				
	u(x) (ft./min.)	V(x)/L (ft.²/hr.)	v(x) (ft./min.)	P(x) (10⁵ in. w.g.)	θ(x) (°F.)	u(x) (ft./min.)	V(x)/L (ft.²/hr.)	v(x) (ft./min.)	P(x) (10⁵ in. w.g.)	θ(x) (°F.)	u(x) (ft./min.)	V(x)/L (ft.²/hr.)	v(x) (ft./min.)	P(x) (10⁵ in. w.g.)	θ(x) (°F.)
1·5	82	1,200	—	25	38	78	1,000	—	20	27	71	460	—	7	53
2	—	—	10	—	—	—	—	11	—	—	—	—	8	—	—
2·5	98	1,800	—	40	20	85	1,600	—	27	14	73	930	—	17	11
3	—	—	9	—	—	—	—	9	—	—	—	—	9	—	—
3·5	117	2,400	—	41	14	98	2,100	—	34	10	78	1,500	—	22	7
4	—	—	7	—	—	—	—	5	—	—	—	—	4	—	—
4·5	113	2,800	—	48	10	100	2,400	—	35	7	77	1,700	—	20	5
5	—	—	9	—	—	—	—	7	—	—	—	—	5	—	—
5·5	110	3,300	—	45	8	97	2,900	—	37	5	72	2,000	—	20	3
6	—	—	8	—	—	—	—	7	—	—	—	—	8	—	—
6·5	106	3,800	—	43	6	90	3,300	—	33	4	71	2,500	—	18	3
7	—	—	16	—	—	—	—	8	—	—	—	—	6	—	—
7·5	90	4,700	—	32	16	82	3,800	—	24	4	57	2,800	—	12	2

Calculated values for a line heat source against a wall

(Assuming equivalence with free line heat source of twice the strength.)

Distance above virtual source (ft.)	H/L = 614 B.t.u./ft. hr.					H/L = 420 B.t.u./ft. hr.					H/L = 225 B.t.u./ft. hr.				
	u(x) (ft./min.)	V(x)/L (ft.²/hr.)	v(x) (ft./min.)	P(x) (10⁵ in. w.g.)	θ(x) (°F.)	u(x) (ft./min.)	V(x)/L (ft.²/hr.)	v(x) (ft./min.)	P(x) (10⁵ in. w.g.)	θ(x) (°F.)	u(x) (ft./min.)	V(x)/L (ft.²/hr.)	v(x) (ft./min.)	P(x) (10⁵ in. w.g.)	θ(x) (°F.)
1·5	112	1,600	18	44	32	99	1,400	16	34	25	80	1,200	13	22	16
2·5	112	2,700	18	44	19	99	2,400	16	34	15	80	1,900	13	22	10
3·5	112	3,700	18	44	14	99	3,300	16	34	11	80	2,700	13	22	7
4·5	112	4,800	18	44	11	99	4,200	16	34	8	80	3,400	13	22	6
5·5	112	5,900	18	44	9	99	5,200	16	34	7	80	4,200	13	22	5
6·5	112	7,000	18	44	7	99	6,100	16	34	6	80	5,000	13	22	4
7·5	112	8,000	18	44	6	99	7,100	16	34	5	80	5,700	13	22	3

PHYSICAL ASPECTS OF SAMPLING AIRBORNE MICROBES

K. R. MAY

Microbiological Research Establishment, Porton, Salisbury, Wiltshire

INTRODUCTION

The term 'airborne microbes' includes particles varying in size from single virus units, which could be as small as 0·1 microns in diameter, to the larger fungal spores and pollens of say 50–100 microns. Small viable particles may also be attached to much larger rafts of other material, typically to dusts or fibres of many sorts. Viable airborne particles are known to occur in all air, unless it has been specially filtered or sterilized, up to an altitude of several miles. The problems of obtaining a representative sample of airborne material covering such a wide range of particle size and atmospheric conditions are such that no single instrument can cover them all, and sampling instruments tend to be specialized in fairly narrow fields.

Most microbial-aerosol sampling devices operate by suction from a pump. In this way air is easily accelerated to high velocities in jets which can be used to give both a high efficiency of particle deposition by inertial impingement and selective deposition according to size. Other methods of catching particles, such as filtration, centrifugal and electrostatic deposition, also require a pump or fan to draw a stream of particle-laden air from the environment.

In these types of apparatus the extraction of airborne particulate matter from suspension for assessment may be considered as two distinct steps. Step I is the process of drawing the stream of air into the sampling apparatus with as little change of concentration as possible. Step II is the process of depositing the airborne particles on or in a suitable medium for identification and counting. Step I poses purely physical problems so that published work on the sampling of dusts, mists, etc. is also applicable to viable material. On the other hand, in Step II the aerobiologist is often particularly concerned with avoiding loss of viability in the sample, so that it may be cultured, and this demands specially designed and somewhat bulky equipment. Simple weighing or optical measurement of the indrawn sample, commonly used with other particulate material, cannot be applied to microbial aerosols because their mass is so small.

In this paper the conditions militating for and against good sampling will be outlined and an attempt will be made to give the best estimates currently available for sampling efficiency. Emphasis will be given to practical aspects of sampling, which often outweigh pure theoretical considerations, particularly so for viable aerosols.

EFFICIENCIES OF SUCTION AND IMPACT SYSTEMS

Comprehensive reviews of papers on the physics of sampling and impaction of aerosols are given in the books by Fuchs (1964) and by Green & Lane (1964). The impaction performance of air-jets playing on flat surfaces and of cylinders across airstreams has received considerable attention and the literature shows a good measure of agreement. This is not the case for impaction on other geometrical forms or for Step I of sampling by a tube. Fuchs concludes: 'The problem of aerosol sampling has not been solved. The chief difficulty appears to be estimation of the true concentration in flowing, coarse aerosols.' This problem is very relevant to the assessment of wind-borne microbes. In this discussion, it will be convenient to group together Step I and the physical aspects of Step II, where impaction is employed to collect particles on a surface. This is because the same inertial properties of the particles govern the performance in both steps. The following symbols will be used:

C_0, C = the concentration of particles in the free air stream and in the sampling nozzle.

U_0, U = the speed of the free air stream and inside the sampling nozzle.

V_0 = the projected velocity of a particle relative to the air.

V_t = the free-falling speed of a particle through air (terminal velocity).

ρ_p, d = density and diameter of the (spherical) particle.

ρ_a, η = density and viscosity of the air.

$Re = Vd\rho_a/\eta$ = Reynolds number of the particle.

λ = the 'stop-distance' of the particle, which is the distance it will travel in still air before being brought to rest by air resistance, after being projected with a known velocity.

l = a characteristic length of a system such as the diameter of a sampling nozzle or impaction nozzle, or the width of an object such as a ribbon.

$P = \lambda/l$ = the inertial parameter of a particle, i.e. the distance a particle moves under its own inertia in units of l.

The accepted standard particle in this work is the unit-density sphere. Microbial particles often differ from the standard particle in shape and density but unless their form is extreme they will behave similarly, in dynamic systems, to the unit density sphere which has the same value of V_t. That is, they will be automatically classified by inertially selective

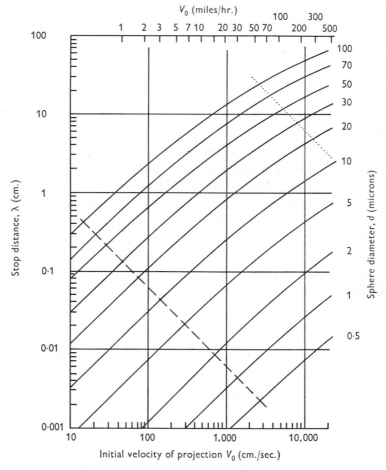

Fig. 1. Stop-distances of unit density spheres when projected into still air. To the left of the dashed line $Re < 1$ and Stokes' law holds. To the right of the dotted line where $Re > 150$ distortion of droplets due to aerodynamic forces is probable and the curves would then be flatter than shown. (Crown copyright reserved.)

apparatus (impingers, impactors, the respiratory system) according to their equivalent unit density sphere. For spheres in air between 1 and 50 microns, V_t is given directly by Stokes' law of motion through a viscous medium, $V_t = \rho_p d^2 g / 18 \eta$ in consistent units. At 70 microns V_t is 7 % below the Stoke value and at 100 microns, 16 % below. Where the physical characteristics of a particle are uncertain and important, their terminal velocity must be found by direct observation.

The stop-distance λ is of great importance in sampling work. When Re is less than about 1 (small particles, low relative speed) λ can be found from Stokes' law which gives $\lambda = \rho_p V_0 d^2/18\eta$ (or $V_0 V_t/g$). As Re increases above unity, deviations from Stokes' law appear, but by using the known relation between Re and the drag coefficient of spheres, corrected values of λ can be found, as described for example by Fuchs (1964). In Fig. 1 these corrected values of λ have been plotted over the

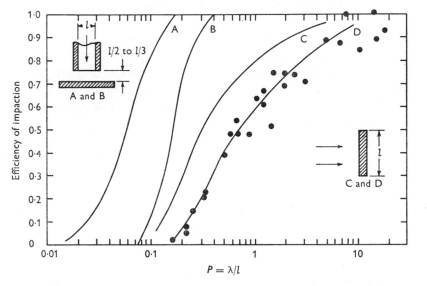

Fig. 2. Relation of the inertial impact parameter to efficiency of particle impaction for various systems. A, Round jets; B, rectangular jets; C, ribbons (theoretical curves from Langmuir & Blodgett (1946) and Ranz & Wong, 1952); D, ribbons (experimental points and curve from Clifford & May, unpublished). (Crown copyright reserved.)

range of particle size and speed likely to be of interest to the aero-biologist. The writer has been able to check the upper end of these curves at $Re = 130$ by measuring the projection distance in still air of droplets flung off the edge of a high-speed spinning disc and agreement was very good.

As described below, Fig. 1 can be used as a guide to the sampling efficiency of suction orifices in various situations. Also, with Fig. 2 it permits quick estimation of the collection efficiency of various impaction systems. These estimates are approximations, but in view of the uncertainties in the literature they are as good as we can hope for at present and are adequate for most purposes.

The efficiency of an impaction system or a nozzle intake at a given particle size is a function of the inertial parameter P. Efficiency is defined as follows: (i) For an impacting jet from a nozzle, the ratio of quantities of particles impacted to quantities emerging from the nozzle before impaction. (ii) For impaction on an obstacle such as a ribbon or disc, the ratio of quantities of particles caught to quantities that would pass through the area of the object if it were removed. (iii) For a nozzle intake, C/C_0. In Fig. 2 the relation of efficiency of impaction to P is shown for systems of principal interest here. Curves A and B for impacting jets apply to systems which are geometrically similar to that depicted on the left of the figure. Greater clearances between the end of the nozzle and the plate give less efficiency for equal values of P; smaller clearances give greater efficiency but increased flow resistance. Curve A, for round jets, is the mean of the experimental results of Stern, Zeller & Schekman (1962), Mitchell & Pilcher (1959) and May (1966) which are in good agreement over a wide range of variables. The curve of Mercer (1962) agrees well with the upper part of A, but is much steeper over the lower half. Curve B, for rectangular jets, is from the experimental results of Stern *et al.* (1962) which are the best available for systems where the clearance between jet and plate is about $l/3$. Their work at clearances of l and greater is in good agreement with that of Ranz & Wong (1952) and May (1945), embracing a very wide range of variables.

Curves A and B give a rather false impression of the relative impaction efficiencies of round and rectangular jets. For a given jet area, flow rate and pressure drop, the rectangular jet can be made into a long narrow slit with a very small value of l, giving a higher collection efficiency than the circular counterpart.

The curve C for 'ribbons' (e.g. the central portion of a microscope slide facing a wind) is the theoretical form given by Langmuir & Blodgett (1946) and by Ranz & Wong (1952) whose curves are almost identical. Experimental confirmation of this curve was attempted by Clifford and May of this laboratory in work which has not yet been published. In a specially designed wind-tunnel they studied the impaction efficiency of basic geometrical forms in ranges of 20–40 microns for drop diameter, 2–6·5 m./sec for wind speed and 1–20 mm. for object dimension (l). Their experimental results for a ribbon, calculated from the stop distances of Fig. 1, are shown at D in Fig. 2. Curve D is considerably lower than the theoretical curve C, a finding in accord with the experiments of Gregory & Stedman (1953) and Landahl & Hermann (1949). Weight is also given to Clifford and May's method by the fact that their curve for cylinders is in good agreement with the collective experimental points of Ranz & Wong (1952), Wong, Ranz & Johnstone (1955), Landahl & Hermann (1949) and Gregory (1951), also with the theoretical curves of Langmuir & Blodgett (1946). Curve D will therefore be used in computations in this paper. It must be very strongly emphasized that Fig. 2 applies only to smooth surfaces where adhesion of any particle or droplet touching the surface is 100 %. In practice, adhesion may be substantially less than this. On the other hand, rough, spiky or hairy surfaces could give greater collection efficiencies than indicated by Fig. 2.

The use of Figs. 1 and 2 in estimating impaction efficiency is best illustrated by examples:

(i) A sticky microscope slide, 2·5 cm. wide, faces into a 10 m./sec. (20 mi./hr.) wind. Assuming 100 % adhesion, what is the size above which more than 60 % of unit density spheres will be collected? From curve D (Fig. 2), at $E = 0·6$, $P = 1$, therefore $\lambda = 2·5$ cm. From Fig. 1 the particle having a stop-distance of 2·5 cm. at 10 m./sec. is 37 microns, which is the required figure.

(ii) An impaction system at the end of a probe from the nose of an aircraft consists of a cylindrical ram-jet tube impacting on a moist agar-gel surface. At 100 m./sec. (200 mi./hr.) it is required to collect all particles down to 4 microns. What should be the tube diameter? From Fig. 1, λ is found to be 0·25 cm.; from Fig. 2 curve A at $E = 1, P = 0·18$, therefore $l = 25/18 = 1·4$ cm. The same nozzle would collect 50 % of 2 micron particles. Because the high Reynolds number of flow through the tube is above the critical value for turbulent flow, the estimates might be a little optimistic in this case.

Rough estimates of the deposition efficiency of wind-borne plant-pathogen spores can also be obtained from Figs. 1 and 2 by equating l to the width of a leaf or stem of a host plant. The curve for deposition on a cylinder is quite close to curve D in Fig. 2.

Figure 2 shows a great difference in impact efficiency between an object such as a ribbon or disc (values of P for a disc are about half those for a ribbon (Ranz & Wong, 1952)) and a circular jet system when each has the same value of l. The reason for this is apparent in Pl. 1a, b, which are photographs of smoke-flow patterns. In Pl. 1a, the streamlines approaching the plane obstruction begin to diverge some distance upstream, there are no abrupt changes in direction and there is time for particles to be pushed sideways, giving a low collection efficiency. In Pl. 1b the very abrupt directional change just before the impact plate is clearly shown and the film of air through which particles must be forced in order to strike the plate is quite thin. If one measures this film

5

thickness in the photograph and equates it to the required stop-distance λ for the minimum size of particle certain to strike the plate, then $\lambda/l = 0.2$, which is close to the upper limit of P found experimentally and plotted in Fig. 2.

With regard to the efficiency of intake, C/C_0, at the front end of a sampling tube in Step I of the sampling process, several workers, notably Fairs (1944), Watson (1954), and Badzioch (1960) have attempted to obtain a useful relationship between C/C_0, U_0, U, λ, d, and the nozzle diameter, but a general solution is not yet apparent, nor is adequate experimental work available. A rigorous theoretical treatment is given by Vitols (1966) but his computations on heavy dusts at high velocities are unfortunately of limited interest in aerobiology. The physical effects having a bearing on tube sampling will therefore be considered separately here. As a general statement, if Fig. 1 shows that the ratio of λ to the nozzle radius is small, C/C_0 will be near to unity. Nozzles should be as large as possible. A large sample also allows more accurate assessment.

Isokinetic sampling

$C = C_0$ at any value of λ can be achieved by adopting the so-called 'isokinetic' condition demonstrated by the smoke flow photograph of Pl. 1c. Flow into the sampling orifice, which had thin walls and a sharp leading edge, was adjusted so that there was no change in velocity as air entered the orifice, which faced exactly upwind. The sampled streamlines thereby display no directional change which could cause inaccurate sampling. Large airborne particles with a relatively high free-falling speed will describe trajectories which slope downwards through the air streamlines, but as many particles fall into the orifice as fail to enter it on this account.

Anisokinetic sampling

With the exception of sampling from still air as discussed later, any state of flow other than the isokinetic will cause C to differ from C_0. When the velocity U in the tube is greater than that in the free air upstream U_0, then $C < C_0$. An extreme case of $U > U_0$ is shown by the photograph of Pl. 1d. The curvature of the streamlines in the vicinity of the orifice causes airborne particles to be projected, by reason of their inertia, out of the streamlines and beyond the orifice in a downstream direction, so that they fail to enter the orifice. The magnitude of the sampling error is a function of λ. In the reverse situation, when $U < U_0$, then $C > C_0$ because the streamlines diverge in front of the orifice and surplus particles, again with effects depending on λ, are projected into the orifice. Pl. 1*a* which shows the streamlines past a flat plate, resembles the extreme case of $U < U_0$ where U is vanishingly small. Particles are thrown on to the plate, although there is no flow through it, in the same way as they would be thrown into the cushion of air in an orifice which replaces the plate and samples very slowly.

Turbulence

It must now be emphasized that laminar flow conditions, such as those depicted in the plates, never occur except in a highly refined wind tunnel. The nearest approach to such ideal conditions is probably achieved by a probe some distance in front of an aircraft structure. In all other practical situations air is in a state of small-scale turbulence. For example, at a few feet above open ground in daylight, wind speed variations of $\pm 40 \%$ of the mean can be found in a short period while direction may vary $\pm 20°$ horizontally and $\pm 15°$ vertically. The question to be answered therefore is what effect has such turbulence on sampling and what can be done to minimize unfavourable effects.

Intake efficiency curves

The performance of the system composed of a thin-walled nozzle sampling at a steady rate and facing directly into an airstream of variable velocity is demonstrated by the curves of Fig. 3. This figure is a generalization of the work of Griffiths & Jones (1939), Fairs (1944), May & Druett (1953), Hirst (1952), Watson (1954), May (1956) and Badzioch (1959, 1960). The curves apply to a nozzle of about 1-2 cm. diam. sucking at a velocity of about 5 m./sec. in aerosols with droplets or spheres of unit density but because of the paucity of experimental and theoretical work on such a system they can only be taken as a rough guide to the situation.

The overall shape of the curves may be explained as follows: In stagnant air when $U_0 = 0$, lines of flow into the orifice are radial from all directions. Particles which are destined to be sampled have vertical free-fall trajectories initially; these are bent inwards as the particles fall into the rapidly increasing influence of the flow field. Eventually particles are entrained, with a small inertial lag, along the radial flow lines and the limiting sampled trajectory is J-shaped (H. A. Druett, quoted by Davies, 1947). In the steady state of particles of negligible inertia disappearing in a small orifice in this manner in a boundless aerosol of uniform concentration, there is no change of concentration at the orifice and a true sample is obtained (Walton, 1947). A practical bonus in this situation is that because of the inward radial velocity component at the nozzle, particles tend to concentrate along the axis of the nozzle and there is no internal wall loss near the leading edge.

As soon as U_0 assumes a small positive value and we move to the right in Fig. 3, a flow pattern similar to that in Pl. 1d develops. At the trough in the efficiency curves in Fig. 3 where $U_0/U \approx 0.4$ the combined effects of velocity and streamline curvature are at their maximum in projecting

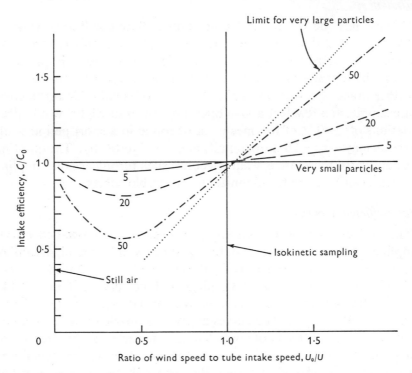

Fig. 3. Effect of changing wind speed past a horizontal sampling nozzle for particles of different diameters (in microns). The curves apply to a nozzle of 1–2 cm. diam. sampling at about 5 m./sec. (Crown copyright reserved.)

particles behind the orifice. As U_0 continues to approach U, the streamline curvature decreases, the flow régime approaches the isokinetic case of Pl. 1c, and the efficiency curves climb from the trough. They continue to climb after passing the isokinetic point, as particles begin to be projected into the orifice.

In Fig. 3 the possible range of sampling intake efficiency for various particle diameters lies between the limiting lines drawn for large and small particles. When similar curves have previously been published, for example, by Watson, all have been shown passing through the point

$C/C_0 = 1 = U_0/U$ because of the dogma that isokinetic sampling gives $C = C_0$. In Fig. 3 the curves are shown passing below and to the right of this point in recognition of the practical point that both the nozzle's leading edge and the particles have appreciable width. Therefore some of the particles, which in theory should be sampled, actually are lost by impact on the leading edge. This point is another reason for avoiding small nozzles, where the effect is proportionately greater. For example a 2 mm. diameter nozzle can lose about 10 % of 100 microns diameter particles in this way but a 1 cm. nozzle would only lose 2 %.

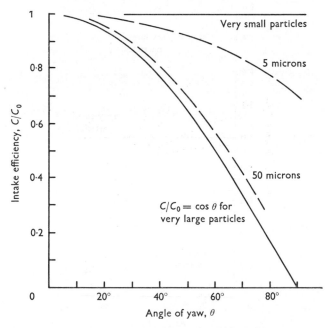

Fig. 4. Effect of yaw on a nozzle similar to that in Fig. 3, the speed in the nozzle being the same as the ambient wind. (Crown copyright reserved.)

In Fig. 3 the large particle limit has the slope of $C/C_0 = U_0/U$ (Watson, 1954). In this context the term 'large particle' means those which have sufficient inertia effectively to ignore bends in the streamlines in the vicinity of the orifice. At low wind speeds this may be taken as 100 microns and above, so is outside the range of normal interest to the aerobiologist. 'Very small' particles implies those of 1 micron and below, for which $C = C_0$ always. In the intermediate ranges we see that particles of 5 microns and below show little error over the whole range of Fig. 3. These are the particles which are capable of reaching the respiratory portion of the lung (Druett, p. 165). Therefore, unless the air velocity is exceptionally high, step I of sampling such particles presents no problem.

It will be seen that if a nozzle be aligned by means of a vane so that it always faces into the wind and has its flow-rate adjusted so that it is isokinetic at the mean wind speed, then sampling errors will cancel out as the wind fluctuates above and below the mean. Therefore there is no point in introducing the complication of a sensing device which adjusts

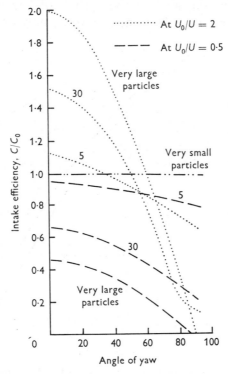

Fig. 5. Estimated curves of the effects of yaw on a nozzle as in Fig. 4, but with the ambient wind at one-half and twice the nozzle intake speed. Particle diameters in microns. (Crown copyright reserved.)

the sampling speed to match the short-period wind speed fluctuations. Manual adjustment of the sampling speed to equal the mean wind speed is usually quite sufficient in short-term experiments.

Effect of yaw

We now consider the errors arising from imperfect alignment of the nozzle with the wind direction. This again is a field which has been inadequately covered in published work. Some curves have been presented by Watson (1954) and an interpretation of these is given in

Fig. 4. As a nozzle yaws away from the wind, the acceptance curve for very large particles will be the curve of the cosine of the angle of the tube axis from the wind direction, while very small particles will be unaffected by the yaw. Intermediate particles will have intermediate values and even at yaw angles exceeding 90°, some of the smaller particles will be sampled. From Fig. 4 which applies to the case $U = U_0$ we see that for angles of yaw up to 30° no serious intake error is suggested for microbial particles. No data are available for $U \neq U_0$, but we can obtain the curves of Fig. 5 by applying the hypothesis that very large particles follow a cosine curve for intake efficiency, while very small ones always approximate to $C = C_0$, interpolating for intermediate particles, and giving due weight to the form of Watson's curves for $U = U_0$ and to May & Druett's (1953) curves for 45° of yaw. This figure gives the probable general form for the intake efficiency curves for several particle sizes in the two cases $U_0 = 2U$ and $= 0.5U$.

The foregoing applies to the sample recovered from nozzles where everything that passes the leading edge is assessed by some form of bulk estimation. In suction-operated microbial aerosol samples (with the sole exception perhaps of the 'tilting pre-impinger' (May, 1960)), particles must pass along some kind of tube before reaching the site of deposition (step II) and they can be very readily lost on the walls of this tube, particularly just inside the entrance. In reality therefore losses due to yaw will be greater than indicated by Figs. 4 and 5 and with large particles at large yaw angles, much greater. Even at zero angles of yaw, internal wall losses can occur when $U_0 > U$ because the outward component of the entering streamlines (cf. Pl. 1) tends to throw particles on to the walls. So does turbulence behind the leading edge.

Avoiding of yaw and turbulence effects

An instrument which avoids the errors just described is the 'ideal sampler' of May (1960). This is a universally pivoted knife-edge nozzle with a light-weight tail fin which follows all wind direction changes with rapid response. The collecting surface for the aerosol particles is a very fine fibreglass filter of low flow resistance set at the extreme front end of the nozzle so that internal wall losses are eliminated. The use of this device for sampling in microbial aerosols would be limited to robust particles such as spores which could be washed off the filter for assay, but it is invaluable for calibrating other devices in turbulent airstreams, as described by May (1960). Edwards (1966) described a servo-controlled, power-operated device which follows horizontal wind changes with small lag and could carry heavy apparatus. The cascade impactor

(May, 1945) and the spore trap of Hirst (1952) can be directed into the wind by a tail fin, but both these devices are only suited to the microscopic examination of samples on glass slides.

Sampling from still air and 'Stagnation-point' sampling

We now consider the sampling of aerosols in still air where the only motion is the free fall of the particles and the radial inflow of air at the nozzle. This is the situation at the left-hand side of Fig. 3 where it will be seen that particles of interest to the aerobiologist, which are those with small inertia, are sampled with high efficiency by a horizontal nozzle.

The high efficiency of sampling in still air contrasts with the variable errors of anisokinetic sampling in unsteady airstreams. This suggests that if moving aerosols could be brought nearly to rest around the sampling point, then high efficiency sampling over a wide range of air speed and direction might be achieved by an orifice sucking at a constant rate. This suggestion is particularly attractive for impingers, where large particles must be sampled into a liquid surface which must of necessity be horizontal, so that the impingement tube must be vertical. In a free air stream, if the intake tube is straight we then have 90° of yaw and sampling, as shown in Fig. 4, is very inefficient. A 90° bend in the intake tube does not improve matters as particles are lost by impaction at the bend.

By placing a baffle of suitable size and shape round the back of the orifice so that the orifice is at the stagnation point of the system, sampling from nearly still air is achieved. This is illustrated by the photograph of Pl. 1e, which shows the effect of a hemicylindrical baffle round an orifice. Air approaching the baffle is brought nearly to rest just in front of the nozzle by the cushion effect inside the baffle, as shown by the great broadening out of the smoke streamlines there. A wisp of smoke is seen moving towards the nozzle, the velocity inside which corresponds to $U_0 = 0.2U$. It is true that the general flow pattern resembles that of Pl. 1a and that the stagnation region will be enriched by large particles preferentially projected into it, but this may help to compensate for the preferential wall loss of large particles. With the baffle at 45° of yaw the flow pattern still looked satisfactory. It is obvious that the baffle should be large, if possible very large, so that the arresting of the airflow is effective and so that the dimensions of the system are large compared with the stop distance of large particles approaching at velocity U_0. Of course, some ventilation of the sampling region is essential so that the concentration at the baffle should follow that in the free air stream. Stagnation point sampling will require full experimentation before its value can be firmly stated. J. Edwards has obtained some figures in an application described by May (1966). An intake nozzle of 15 mm. bore sampled vertically down at 55 litres/min. and was exposed to an aerosol of 15 microns droplets in a 4·5 m./sec. wind. With no baffle C/C_0 was 0·09, with a 3×3 in. concave baffle just behind the orifice C/C_0 increased to 0·69 and to 0·99 with a 6×6 in. baffle, though there were rather serious internal losses on the walls of the nozzle. A large baffle would be expected to reduce these and it is hoped to extend the work.

Wind-tunnel sampling

Wind speed fluctuations in the open may be greatly damped and directional variations eliminated by the use of a small portable wind tunnel, as described in a fog-sampling study by May (1961). The tunnel was mounted on a trolley and was turned to face the general wind direction. It was made of plywood and thin sheet metal, had a flared out mouth and was 3 ft. long by 8 in. square in cross-section. A fan driven by a $\frac{1}{8}$ horse power electric motor could draw a steady flow of air at 5 m./sec. (10 mi./hr.) through the tunnel. Because the section of such a tunnel is very large compared with the stop distance of the largest particles of interest, the concentration of particles flowing along the axis of the tunnel must be the same as in the free air, and a sampling nozzle in the middle of the tunnel can be adjusted to function at nearly ideal isokinetic conditions.

This device, which is light in weight and readily portable, enables an absolute check on the concentration of coarse wind-borne aerosols to be obtained, or can be used on its own merits in a routine sampling programme.

Sampling by very thin wires or threads

When air flows past a very narrow cylinder, P is large and the collection efficiency is high. If the cylinder diameter decreases until it is comparable to or smaller than the particle, a process called interception takes place. The particles are scarcely deviated by the flow lines round the thread and, provided that there are adequate adhesion forces, the grazing particle will be captured, giving a collection efficiency practically equal to $1 + d/l$ (Fuchs, 1964). Thus the 'collection efficiency' for a very fine thread can greatly exceed 100 %. The system is not subject to the sources of error to which sampling tubes are liable.

The Russian authors Kordyum & Bobchenko (1959) used very fine glass threads to capture and hold airborne microbes and studied their growth on them. They concluded: 'The fine glass thread method of studying air microflora renders it possible to study the micro-organisms under conditions most closely approaching to natural ones.' The limit of fineness was achieved by Dessens (1949) who used the silk threads made by small spiders to capture atmospheric particles. A very convenient way of setting up such threads for use is to place a very young orb-spinning spider on a frame like a tuning fork. Tapping the frame causes the spider to drop on its safety-line which may be wound up to the required number of turns. The threads have a diameter of roughly 0·5 microns but some of the side threads, also ejected by the spider, are as small as 0·01 microns (Dessens, 1944). To capture airborne particles, the frame may be mounted on the end of a rotating arm or on a turntable and the threads can tolerate wind speeds of up to 10 m./sec. The threads are clean and sterile as generated and have no sticky film so that, unfortunately, particles like fungal spores and pollens, which have a very dry surface designed in nature to give easy disposal, will not adhere to them. To capture such particles it would be necessary to use somewhat thicker and stronger threads which could be dipped in an adhesive solution. Sampling by fine threads is independent of wind direction, turbulence and other sources of sampling error.

SAMPLING INSTRUMENTS

A strongly recommended review of techniques and instruments available for sampling airborne bacteria has been given by Wolf *et al.* (1959). Another good review of instruments suitable for airborne pollens, spores, plant disease microbes, etc., has been given by Gregory (1961). These works and Noble's paper in this Symposium cover the major part of current technique. In this paper we consider only items not covered by the above.

Electrostatic precipitators

Rather high cost, electrical complexity, and the need for pre-ionization to avoid uncertain collection efficiency have made electrostatic precipitators less popular than simple impingement and impaction devices for collecting airborne microbes. Their most important characteristic is that they can give a high collection efficiency for very small particles, with negligible pressure drop. Two recent developments may prove useful.

Morris, Darlow, Peel & Wright (1961) describe a cylindrical precipitator with an axial electrode operating at +5 to 10 kV. A fine disc at the front of the electrode emits a silent discharge and ionizes the indrawn particles which are then drawn to the walls of the cylinder. This is coated internally with a film of agar, or by rotation, a film of liquid. In the latter case a high concentration of cells per unit volume of fluid is possible. This sampler would seem to have much promise for virus aerosols, especially when particles too small to collect by impingement are suspected.

Gerone *et al.* (1966) describe a new high volume electrostatic sampler which is capable of collecting all the contents of 10,000 l. of air into 10 ml. of glycerin every minute. Air is drawn into the apparatus through a large horizontal hole which impacts the air on the centre of a large rotating metal disc over which a continuous film of glycerin is induced to flow at 10 ml./min. A ring of needles at high voltage round the underside of the inlet hole ionize the indrawn particles which are then attracted to the disc which is charged at opposite polarity. The film of liquid is continuously scraped off the rim for subsequent assay.

The very high concentration obtainable by this apparatus has obvious applications, though glycerin is not always the most suitable of collecting fluids for microbes and there is some difficulty in maintaining the integrity of the film. The apparatus is expensive and it may be that a smaller model of one-tenth the capacity, also commercially available, would be more generally useful (Litton Systems Inc., Minneapolis, Minnesota).

Cyclones

These are mechanically simple, very robust, can operate at high flow rates with quite high collection efficiency and have an unlimited holding capacity for the sample, which may be collected in a bottle. For these reasons they may be of value in collecting airborne pollens and spores over long periods.

As an example of performance which may be obtained, E. O. Powell (private communication) states that a cyclone based on the designs of Lapple (1950), with an internal cylinder diameter of 12·5 mm. and a 6 mm. square entry to the volute can retain all particles down to about 2 microns at a flow rate of 75 l./min. and a pressure drop of 75 mm. Hg.

Cascade centripeter

This device is described by Hounam & Sherwood (1965). It resembles the cascade impactor in that a series of jets of increasing velocity is used to give several stages of particle size discrimination. Particles are projected into the open apices of conical bins and the holding capacity is therefore great. Flow-rate is 30 l./min. and the final stage operates down to the 1–2 micron region. A backing filter is standard, giving complete collection of particles at an overall pressure drop of 65 mm. Hg. This device would seem to have the advantages of cyclones plus particle size discrimination, though internal wall losses, which can be as high as 40%, may often be unacceptable.

The instrument is commercially available in a unit complete with pump which is designed for continuous running over periods of days.

The Andersen sampler

In its standard commercial form (Andersen, 1958) this is a six-stage cascade impactor in which each stage consists of 400 jets impinging on an agar surface in a Petri dish. Particles containing at least one viable cell grow as colonies which are counted. A correction factor based on the probability of more than one viable particle passing through the same hole enables a rough estimate to be made of the total viable particles in each of the six size ranges. This sampler is in wide use because it is robust and simple to use and is useful in aerosols consisting of a single bacterial species of rather small particle size. Both May (1964) and Lidwell & Noble (1965) who were particularly interested in the larger particles find that it is less useful above 12 microns and suggest top-stage additions to solve this problem. Lidwell & Noble also point out the difficulties arising in aerosols of several species, where colonies grow in mutual competition unless they are very sparse.

There is no doubt that the Andersen sampler should be used without its standard intake cone, and, if it is used in a draught, it should have a large 'stagnation point' shield as described in this paper.

The liquid impinger

This is another very widely used device of established efficiency, as reported for example by Tyler & Shipe (1959), Tyler, Shipe & Painter (1959) and May & Harper (1957). It is commonly used with a pre-impinger (May & Druett, 1953) to simulate the upper and lower respiratory system. Unlike slit samplers and the Andersen sampler which impinge particles directly on agar for immediate incubation, impingers are intended to break up the particles into their component viable cells or units in the collecting fluid. This suspension is then diluted serially for plating out of aliquots, so that there is no upper limit to the concentration which may be handled and multi-species aerosols can be dealt with. In certain naturally occurring aerosols the break-up of clumps may not be fully effective (Noble, p. 87) and it may be important to make a microscope study of the sampled organisms to reduce uncertainties in the meaning of the final colony counts.

A recent development in impingers is the three-stage model of May (1966). The three stages are intended to match the principal sites of deposition in the human respiratory system and impingement is very gentle to minimize the loss of viability which is sometimes attributed to impact trauma (May & Harper, 1957). This device has shown that the survival time of *E. coli* cells in air, under conditions of stress, is directly related to the size of particle in which they are contained, a point which may be of considerable significance in the spread of airborne disease.

Sampling instruments operated from aircraft

As reviewed in detail by Gregory (1961) measurement of the microbial content of the lower atmosphere has been in progress since the end of the last century. A striking feature of this work is that most of the authors make no attempt to estimate or to state the collection efficiency of their equipment. In most cases this must have been very low and comparisons between the meaning of the results of different workers are difficult.

The simplest and most popular way of collecting aerosol particles from aircraft is to expose a sticky microscope slide or Petri dish normally to the slipstream, but fitting any form of fixed protrusion usually poses major problems in engineering and safety. Relatively slow aircraft have therefore been commonly used but impact collection is then inefficient. For example Figs. 1 and 2 show that a 1 in. wide microscope slide will only be useful for particles larger than about 15 microns at 200 mi./hr. To collect particles down to 2 microns at this speed would require an object width of less than 1 mm., yielding an inconveniently small sample. A 5 cm. diameter Petri dish normal to a 200 mi./hr. wind would have a performance similar to the microscope slide, but a 9 cm. dish would be of little value below 20–25 microns.

Several workers have used pump-operated slit impactors to obtain a high efficiency of collection of small particles. There are serious disadvantages to this. The pump itself is an undesirable complication and must have a high capacity in order to draw an adequate sample through an intake of reasonable size. The pumping speed must be adjusted with great accuracy to give isokinetic flow because at these high values of U_0 and λ, small deviations from isokinetic flow can cause large intake errors. Again, the nozzle must be developed into a slot of smaller cross-section which can cause wall loss. It would seem to be more practical to develop a straight-tube ram-jet impactor which, as derived earlier in this paper, would sample particles down to 2 microns via a tube of 1·4 cm. diameter at 200 mi./hr. Sampling would be at the usefully high rate of

800 l./min. for the dilute natural aerosol and would be automatically isokinetic.

As a circular deposit is inconvenient to scan microscopically it might be better in this work to employ a parallel sided jet tube in the form of a slot, say $2·5 \times 0·5$ cm. which would give a similar performance to the above and sample at 700 l./min. Flow lines through a section across such a slot in a suggested design are shown in Pl. 1*f*. It will be noted that the flow régime at the entry is nearly perfect so that the device should give a nearly absolute sample of all particles down to about 2 microns. It is envisaged as mounted at the tip of a probe from the nose of the aircraft so that operation would be in undisturbed air. It would be important to align the impactor exactly with the ambient air-stream direction because intake losses due to yaw and particles striking the internal walls could become important at these comparatively high speeds. The impact surface could be clear 35 mm. cine film, in the form of a long loop passing up and down inside the probe shaft and moved as required from within the aircraft. The film would need a suitable sticky surface and many successive samples of high volume could be taken. Noble (this Symposium) describes how such samples can be handled. Alternatively small dishes filled with nutrient agar could be pushed through the probe shaft to the impact point.

To avoid undesirable curves in the streamlines just in front of the entry in systems of this sort the frontal area must be kept to a minimum and smooth unobstructed channels for the exhaust air after impact must be provided. In a slit-sampler rotating-dish device, which would be essentially bulky, the intake nozzle should be more than one diameter of the main body upstream.

It is good practice to make an impaction system no more efficient than is necessary to collect the smallest particles of interest. Unwanted and confusing small particles of dust, etc., which are always relatively abundant, are thereby eliminated. If particles as small as 1 micron are of interest they would require a circular ram jet of only 3 mm. diameter for 60% collection at 200 mi./hr., according to Figs. 1 and 2, and this may be too small for effective operation. A pump-operated impactor or liquid impinger or an electrostatic precipitator may therefore be more practical for such particles.

The foregoing efficiency estimations apply to the first few kilometres of atmosphere, in which the majority of airborne microbes are confined and over which the curves of Fig. 1 do not greatly change. Impaction at greatly reduced pressures was studied by Stern *et al.* (1962), who found that the curves of Fig. 2 were unchanged when the appropriate

Cunningham–Millikan corrections for inter-molecular slip of their small particles were applied. At very low pressures the Fig. 1 curves will change substantially as λ increases, but methods of sampling at great altitudes are discussed by Bruch (p. 345).

REFERENCES

ANDERSEN, A. A. (1958). New sampler for the collection, sizing and enumeration of viable airborne particles. *J. Bact.* **76**, 471.

BADZIOCH, S. (1959). Collection of gas-borne dust particles by means of an aspirated sampling nozzle. *Br. J. appl. Phys.* **10**, 26.

BADZIOCH, S. (1960). Correction for anisokinetic sampling of dust particles. *J. Inst. Fuel*, **33**, 106.

DAVIES, C. N. (1947). *Symposium on Particle Size Analysis.* Suppl. to *Trans. Instn chem. Engrs*, **25**, 25.

DESSENS, H. (1949). The use of spider's threads in the study of condensation nuclei. *Q. Jl R. met. Soc.* **75**, 23.

EDWARDS, J. (1966). *Handbook of the Physics Exhibition*, p. 67. London: The Institute of Physics and the Physical Society.

FAIRS, G. L. (1944). Ed. *The Sampling and Sizing of Particles.* Imperial Chemical Industries Ltd., Birmingham: Kynoch Press.

FUCHS, N. A. (1964). *The Mechanics of Aerosols.* London: Pergamon Press.

GERONE, P. J., COUCH, R. B., KEEFER, G. V., DOUGLAS, R. G., DERRENBACHER, E. B. & KNIGHT, V. (1966). Assessment of experimental and natural vital aerosols. *Bact. Rev.* **30**, 576.

GREEN, H. L. & LANE, W. R. (1964). *Particulate Clouds, Dusts, Smokes and Mists*, 2nd edn. London: Spon.

GREGORY, P. H. (1951). Deposition of air-borne *Lycopodium* spores on cylinders. *Ann. appl. Biol.* **38**, 357.

GREGORY, P. H. (1961). *Microbiology of the Atmosphere.* London: Hill.

GREGORY, P. H. & STEDMAN, O. J. (1953). Deposition of air-borne *Lycopodium* spores on plane surfaces. *Ann. appl. Biol.* **40**, 651.

GRIFFITHS, J. H. & JONES, T. D. (1939). The determination of dust concentrations in mine atmospheres. *Trans. Instn Min. Engrs*, **99**, 150.

HIRST, J. M. (1952). An automatic volumetric spore trap. *Ann. appl. Biol.* **39**, 257.

HOUNAM, R. F. & SHERWOOD, R. J. (1965). The cascade centripeter. *Am. ind. Hyg. Ass. J.* **26**, 122.

KORDYUM, V. A. & BOBCHENKO, E. S. (1959). Air as a habitat for microorganisms. *Microbiology*, **28**, 215.

LANDAHL, H. D. & HERRMANN, R. G. (1949). Sampling of liquid aerosols by wires, cylinders and slides. *J. Colloid Sci.* **4**, 103.

LANGMUIR, I. & BLODGETT, K. B. (1946). A mathematical investigation of water droplet trajectories. *U.S. Army Air Forces Tech. Rep.* no. 5418. Washington, D.C.

LAPPLE, C. E. (1950). Dust and mist collection. In *Chemical Engineers' Handbook*, 3rd edn. Ed. J. M. Perry. New York: McGraw-Hill.

LIDWELL, O. M. & NOBLE, W. C. (1965). Modifications of the Andersen Sampler. *J. appl. Bact.* **28**, 280.

MAY, K. R. (1945). The cascade impactor, an instrument for sampling coarse aerosols. *J. sci. Instrum.* **22**, 187.

MAY, K. R. (1956). A cascade impactor with moving slides. *Archs. ind. Hyg.* **13**, 481.

MAY, K. R. (1960). A size-selective total aerosol sampler—the tilting pre-impinger. *Ann. occup. Hyg.* **2**, 93.

MAY, K. R. (1961). Fog-droplet sampling using a modified impactor technique. *Q. Jl R. met. Soc.* **87**, 535

MAY, K. R. (1964). Calibration of a modified Andersen sampler. *Appl. Microbiol.* **12**, 37.

MAY, K. R. (1966). A multi-stage liquid impinger. *Bact. Rev.* **30**, 559.

MAY, K. R. & DRUETT, H. A. (1953). The pre-impinger, a selective aerosol sampler. *Br. J. ind. Med.* **10**, 142.

MAY, K. R. & HARPER, G. J. (1957). The efficiency of various liquid impinger samplers in bacterial aerosols. *Br. J. ind. Med.* **14**, 287.

MERCER, T. T. (1962). A cascade impactor operating at low volumetric flow rates. Rep. LF-5. Contract No. AT(29-2)-1013. U.S. Atomic Energy Commission, Lovelace Foundation, Albuquerque N.M.

MITCHELL, R. I. & PILCHER, J. M. (1959). Improved cascade impactor for measuring aerosol particle size. *Ind. Engng Chem.* **51**, 1039.

MORRIS, E. J., DARLOW, H. M., PEEL, J. F. H. & WRIGHT, W. C. (1961). The quantitative assay of mono-dispersed aerosols of bacteria and bacteriophage by electrostatic precipitation. *J. Hyg., Camb.* **59**, 487.

RANZ, W. E. & WONG, J. B. (1952). Impaction of dust and smoke particles. *Ind. Engng Chem.* **44**, 1371.

STERN, S. C., ZELLER, H. W. & SCHEKMAN, A. I. (1962). Collection efficiency of jet impactors at reduced pressures. *Ind. Engng Chem. Fund.* **1**, 273.

TYLER, M. E. & SHIPE, E. L. (1959). Bacterial aerosol samplers. I. *Appl. Microbiol.* **7**, 337.

TYLER, M. E., SHIPE, E. L. & PAINTER, R. B. (1959). Bacterial aerosol samplers. III. *Appl. Microbiol.* **7**, 355.

VITOLS, V. (1966). Theoretical limits of errors due to anisokinetic sampling of aerosols. *J. Air Pollut. Control Ass.* **16**, 79.

WALTON, W. H. (1947). *Symposium on Particle Size Analysis.* Suppl. to *Trans. Instn chem. Engrs*, **25**, 136.

WATSON, H. H. (1954). Errors due to anisokinetic sampling of aerosols. *Am. ind. Hyg. Ass. Q.* **15**, 21.

WOLF, H. W., SKALIY, P., HALL, L. B., HARRIS, M. M., DECKER, H. M., BUCHANAN, L. M., DAHLGREN, C. M. (1959). *Sampling Microbiological Aerosols.* U.S. Public Health Monograph, no. 60. Washington D.C.: United States Government Printing Office.

WONG, J. B., RANZ, W. E. & JOHNSTONE, H. F. (1955). Inertial impaction of aerosol particles on cylinders. *J. appl. Phys.* **26**, 244.

EXPLANATION OF PLATE

PLATE 1

All photographs (except *b*) are of smoke filaments in a laminar flow wind tunnel, with air moving from left to right.

(*a*) Flow past a flat plate.

(*b*) Side view of circular air jet impacting on a flat plate ($Re = 2000$).

(*c*) Ideal isokinetic sampling.

(*d*) Flow into a nozzle sampling at a velocity greatly in excess of that of the ambient flow.

(*e*) Sampling at the stagnation point of a hemicylindrical baffle.

(*f*) Flow through and past a ram-jet impactor mounted on the tip of a probe. Hatching has been superimposed over the solid parts for the sake of clarity. The forward end of the probe, carrying the impact surface, is the large block on the right.

(Crown copyright reserved. Reproduced with the permission of the Controller, H.M.S.O.)

PLATE 1

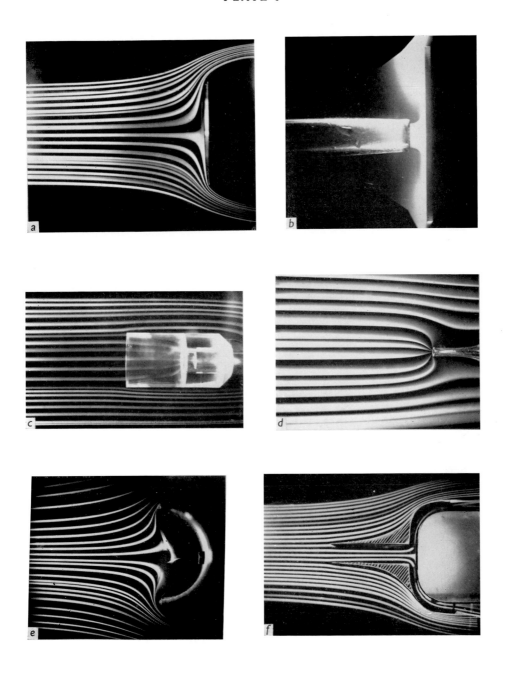

SAMPLING AIRBORNE MICROBES— HANDLING THE CATCH

W. C. NOBLE

Department of Bacteriology, Institute of Dermatology, University of London—British Postgraduate Medical Federation, St John's Hospital for Diseases of the Skin, London, W.C. 2

INTRODUCTION

This paper presents methods of isolating and identifying micro-organisms recovered from the air. Since many of the methods are simple extensions of those used in normal laboratory practice, it will be assumed that details of standard techniques, for example fluorescent antibody staining, may be consulted elsewhere.

It is useful to distinguish between 'naturally' generated clouds of organisms, such as those encountered out of doors or in a hospital ward, which have a diversity of species and a wide range of particle size, and 'artificially' generated aerosols, the composition and size distribution of which are known in advance. For example, the Andersen (1958) sampler, a multi-stage sieve sampler, deposits bacteria on the agar plate in a pattern determined by the position of the holes in a 'sieve' plate through which the air passes. Since the distribution of bacteria in a small volume of air is essentially random, some holes will deposit more than one cell on the agar whilst others will deposit none. To assess the number of bacteria in the air, therefore, the total number of holes yielding colony-forming bacteria is counted and a correction factor applied. This 'positive hole' method of counting and correcting for superimposition of colonies is satisfactory for artificial aerosols where the colonies formed are likely to be of the same size. In a normal environment, however, where a variety of colony types may be encountered, it is essential to limit the size of the sample so that the correction factor does not exceed 10 % (Lidwell & Noble, 1965).

Many aerosolized bacteria and viruses die before and during sampling, and it may therefore be difficult to distinguish between efficiency of sampling and efficiency of recovery from the sampler without a physical or chemical technique such as radio-active labelling (e.g. Harper, Hood & Morton, 1958). Such a method enables the total cells sampled to be counted, in addition to an assessment of viability. Various criteria, such as the ability to exclude dyes, have been proposed for distinguishing

6

between 'live' and 'dead' cells (e.g. Hanks & Wallace, 1958) but in this paper a micro-organism will be considered 'viable' when it is capable of reproducing itself in a living host or on an appropriate culture medium.

Although it will be most convenient to discuss the methods of identification in relation to the broad taxonomic groups of organisms, many of the methods available may be applied to any group. Full discussion of a technique in relation to one group does not therefore imply that it is inapplicable to others.

IDENTIFYING FUNGI

Visual methods

Many genera of fungi, including representatives of the Phycomycetes, Basidiomycetes, Ascomycetes and Fungi Imperfecti, may be identified from the microscopic appearance of the spores alone. Some, which may fail to grow on artificial media, such as rusts and smuts infecting cereal crops, may be identified to the specific level by this method; others such as the Aspergilli, Paecilomyces and Penicillia cannot be identified even to the generic level and must be recorded as a conglomerate group (Gregory & Hirst, 1957; Hamilton, 1959). Since fungi appear to be dispersed mainly as spores, although fragments of mycelium are also seen, the most useful method is to impact the airborne particles on a slide coated with an adhesive and to scan the slide under a microscope. The slides may be exposed in either the Cascade Impactor (May, 1945) which contains four slides in series, to obtain a size distribution, or the Hirst Spore Trap (Hirst, 1952), which contains one moving slide, to obtain a time distribution. Although glycerine jelly is the best adhesive optically, it is hygroscopic and may dissolve in wet weather; petroleum jelly is satisfactory and may even be used in the tropics provided that paraffin wax is added to harden it (Cammack, 1955); silicone grease is another valuable adhesive (Pady & Kelly, 1949). Although this method yields accurate quantitative counts and enables dispersion units to be studied, it does not distinguish between live and dead spores. However, since Davies (1957) has shown that the majority of spores of at least one fungus, *Cladosporium*, are viable, this may not be important. Further, for studies on allergy, a count of total spores may be more relevant than one of live spores only, since dead spores or their extracts may produce an allergic response. In studies on plant pathogens, however, a knowledge of live, infective particles is more important. If the viability of a small fraction of the total catch is of interest, individual spores may be removed from the slide by micro-pipette (e.g. Martin, 1943) or, if the spores have been sampled on an agar-coated surface, by a device of the biscuit-cutter type (e.g. Leach, 1955). Sampling on pectic jelly has also been used in a study of the viability of airborne organisms, the jelly being dissolved in distilled water and mixed with molten agar in a Petri dish (Baruah, 1961).

Reference pictures of fungus spores isolated from the atmosphere may be found in the monograph produced by Gregory (1961) but there is a lack of any reference work on this subject comparable with that on pollen grains by Hyde & Adams (1958); such a work would be of great value, for the spores produced on artificial growth media may not be typical of those produced naturally and care must be used in extrapolating from one source of material to another.

Cultural methods

Fluid samplers are much less satisfactory than solid-medium samplers for the isolation of fungi, since many spores are 'non-wettable' so that difficulty is experienced in manipulating the sampling fluid. This may be overcome by using wetting agents such as 'Tween' (Davies, 1960). Many studies on airborne fungus particles, especially on those species causing disease in man, have used 'settle plates' or solid-medium impaction-samplers (e.g. Thomas, 1943; Richards, 1954). Although some slightly selective media have been devised in order to retard the growth of contaminant 'moulds' (Littman, 1947), most studies have relied on techniques selective for one group or species of fungus. Dermatophytes have been isolated from air using media containing the antibiotic 'Actidione' to suppress mould growth (Georg, Ajello & Papageorge, 1954; Friedman, Derbes, Hodges & Sinski, 1960; Clayton & Noble, 1963); *Candida albicans* and *Aspergillus fumigatus* can be selected by incubating the media at 37° C (de Vries, 1960; Clayton & Noble, 1966), and certain Actinomycetes may be isolated by incubation at temperatures as high as 60° C (Gregory & Lacey, 1962), or by using an alkaline medium (de Vries, 1960).

It may be necessary to subculture and grow the fungus on some natural host or another laboratory growth medium for complete species identification. Plant pathogens may be inoculated into the leaves of host plants by rubbing in the organisms mixed with carborundum (Nour & Nour, 1958); fungi responsible for 'damping off' of seedlings will infect host plants if an agar culture is placed adjacent to the seedling (Rathbun-Gravatt, 1925); selective 'media' in the form of freshly cut pine stems may be used to identify fungi such as *Fomes annosus* and *Peniophora gigantea* (Rishbeth & Meredith, 1957). The many 'mould'

6-2

fungi and those causing disease in man, such as the dermatophytes, are best identified by their appearance on laboratory growth media, whilst the *Allescheria*, *Cryptococcus* and *Histoplasma* groups may be selected by animal inoculation (Ibach, Larsh & Furcolow, 1954; McDonough, Ajello, Ausherman, Balows, McClellan & Brinkmans, 1961) or the use of specific media (Shields & Ajello, 1966). Sterilized hair has been used as a 'bait' for the isolation of keratinophilic fungi (Vanbreuseghem, 1952).

When the total composition of the airborne flora is to be studied, it is most satisfactory to use a variety of media and incubation temperatures, for there is evidence that even the normal laboratory media may be slightly selective. Sabouraud's agar, composed of peptone and sugar, has been found to give a greater recovery of *Aspergillus* species than either the synthetic Czapek-Dox agar or Malt agar (Noble & Clayton, 1963). When incubation is likely to be prolonged, as during the isolation of dermatophytes, care must be taken that the medium does not become too dry. Plates may be incubated in plastic bags provided that condensed water does not flood over the surface of the agar, but it is often satisfactory merely to pour a thick layer of agar initially. It is important to bear in mind the size of the particles sought when making a comparison between the fungal floras of different environments. Many of the airborne fungus particles have a mean equivalent diameter (see p. 141) close to that of a single spore (Noble, Lidwell & Kingston, 1963) and since particles of different equivalent diameters settle at different rates, inefficient samplers such as settle plates may discriminate against the recovery of some species (Richards, 1954).

Animals have been used to detect airborne fungi by allowing them to inhale the particles and thus act as primary samplers; dermatophytes have been recovered from the air of caves (Lurie & Way, 1957), and *Cryptococcus neoformans* has been isolated, presumably airborne, from infected soils by this method (Smith, Ritter, Larsh & Furcolow, 1964). This technique is obviously limited in that the volume of air breathed by the animals is small and that not all inhaled particles may give rise to disease, but in terms of infective particles it probably gives more meaningful results than other techniques. The final identification of the fungus is made by inoculating material from the viscera of the infected animals on to laboratory growth media.

Serological tests

Where cultural studies cannot be performed, as with suspected human disease due to *Histoplasma capsulatum*, skin tests and serological reactions may be used. The most useful of these are precipitin and agar diffusion techniques; complement-fixation tests may also be used. Because the minimal infecting dose of *Histoplasma* is very small— Furcolow (1961) has shown that for guinea-pigs three viable particles may suffice to produce a positive skin reaction—it is possible to use positive skin reactions in a population as a measure of exposure to airborne *H. capsulatum*. Care must be exercised in applying this method to a study of other fungi, however, since exposure to *Aspergillus fumigatus*, for example, apparently does not result in serological changes unless the person is continually exposed to exceptionally high concentrations of fungus particles, as in a farming community. Positive serological reactions to *A. fumigatus* products are normally indicative of hypersensitivity or clinical infection due to the organism.

IDENTIFYING BACTERIA
Visual methods

Most studies on airborne bacteria have used cultural methods to assess the qualitative and quantitative properties of the aerosols. Attempts have been made, however, to use purely mechanical methods, such as the Coulter Counter, for both counting and sizing bacteria in fluids, and Kubitschek (1958) was able to obtain a satisfactory differentiation between *Bacillus megaterium* spores and vegetative *Escherichia coli* by this method. Where a specific staining method is available, as with *Mycobacterium tuberculosis*, it is possible to assess the number of cells present in artificial aerosols by impacting the aerosol on to a glass slide and examining the stained deposit under the microscope (Glover, 1948).

Direct fluorescent staining can be used to differentiate between bacteria and inorganic debris (Pital, Janovitz, Hudak & Lewis, 1966) but direct examination under the microscope of material sampled from natural clouds of bacteria is normally of little value because of the difficulty of distinguishing single bacterial cells from other organic material.

Cultural methods
Micro-techniques

Incubation of trapped material on agar growth medium for 3 or 4 hr. yields micro-colonies which, although more easily recognized than single organisms, still cannot normally be identified even to the generic level. However, such micro-colonies may be subcultured using the micro-pipette technique of de Fonbrune, and the normal processes of identification carried on from this point. This technique proved particularly useful when the nature of the rafts on which the bacteria were carried was investigated (Davies & Noble, 1962). Rapid identification of micro-colonies can be obtained using fluorescent antibody techniques, and *Pasteurella* and *Brucella* species recovered from artificial aerosols have been identified in pure and mixed cultures in this way (Chadwick & Slade, 1960). With aerosols impacted on glass, Jaeger, Spertzel & Kuehne (1961) were able to detect one particle bearing *Pasteurella tularensis* in up to 5 l. of air by fluorescent antibody staining. When aerosols containing more than one bacterial species were sampled, difficulty was experienced in obtaining specific fluorescent staining, unless the serum was absorbed with live organisms of the interfering species. For work on infectivity, however, this last method has the limitation that all bacteria, alive and dead, will stain, whereas interest in airborne bacteria is centred mainly on live organisms.

Chadwick (1959) was able to distinguish micro-colonies of *Bacillus anthracis* from those of *B. cereus* in pure culture by treating them with phage. Lysis was complete within a short period and identification could be accomplished within about 7 hr. The method was virtually specific in that, whilst all micro-colonies of *B. anthracis* were lysed by the phage, only two of fifty-six cultures of *B. cereus* gave false positive results. It would seem possible to extend this technique to the direct identification of airborne material, if a selective medium is used to increase the probability that a micro-colony exposed to phage is of the type sought.

Fluid-medium samples

When handling aerosols with an unknown density of microbes, or mixed clouds of organisms with very different nutrient requirements, there is much to be gained by using a fluid impinger (e.g. Tyler & Shipe, 1959) although some types of impinger kill a large proportion of vege-tative bacteria during sampling, presumably as a result of the violent impact, and may discriminate against certain size particles (Tyler, Shipe & Painter, 1959). Known volumes of fluid from the impinger may be inoculated on solid media and quantitative counts are then obtained. The organisms must have no opportunity for multiplication in the sampling fluid, however, and when there is any delay between collection and manipulation refrigeration of the sample is desirable. When sampling aerosols of one bacterial species only, and where either a total cell count will suffice or where the proportion of live and dead cells is known, the catch can be estimated with some precision by counting the organisms in a haemocytometer chamber. This technique can be applied even when the bacteria are in chains or clumps (Williams, 1952), and provided that no non-microbial particles are present, it might be mechanized using the Coulter Counter as described previously.

It has been suggested that because of the turbulent sampling conditions in bubbler samplers, some of the clumps of organisms are broken up to give a larger quantitative count than would have been obtained using, for example, a slit sampler. In 'natural' clouds of bacteria, however, the number of viable units per clump is probably not very large; Lidwell, Noble & Dolphin (1959) found that airborne particles carrying staphylococci have a mean of only about four viable units per clump, and so this factor may be relatively unimportant provided that quantitative comparisons between samplers are not needed.

If the bacteria in the sampling fluid are to be inoculated on to a solid medium for identification, it is important that a suitable medium be chosen. Work on the recovery of lyophilized bacteria has shown that a rich medium can yield a greater percentage recovery than a poor medium (e.g. Shaw, 1956; Baird-Parker & Davenport, 1965). Differences in the quality of growth media become more pronounced when 'aged' aerosols are sampled than when freshly aerosolized bacteria are sampled (Goldberg, Watkins, Boerke & Chatigny, 1958). When testing solid media designed to be selective for staphylococci, Innes (1960) found that media using tellurite and glycine as selective agents were markedly inhibitory to small inocula of staphylococci applied by the Miles & Misra (1938) technique. As pathogenic bacteria may be present in only very small numbers in natural clouds (Noble & Lidwell, 1963) the effect of any inhibition may be very important.

Solid-medium samples

The majority of studies on microbes airborne in normal environments have been carried out using solid medium samplers such as sieve or slit-samplers. One of the advantages of solid medium samplers is that the effects of contamination are less than with those using fluids. In a fluid medium there is always the possibility that a contaminant may reproduce and swamp the trapped organisms, whereas on a solid medium the contaminant is restricted to one colony; provided that sterile air is not being sampled, one extra colony on a plate will not markedly affect the result. If a knowledge of the mean contamination is desired, unexposed plates can be incubated and contaminant colonies counted.

A time differentiation as good as one second can be obtained using a slit sampler incorporating a marker (Bourdillon, Lidwell & Schuster, 1948). Since observer error in noting time may be of the order of

0·5 sec., this represents a very reasonable level. The Petri dishes used in solid medium samplers need no further manipulation after sampling, and no precautions are necessary to prevent growth of organisms as with fluid samplers. Samplers can therefore be devised which incorporate an incubation chamber so that the instrument is self-contained and automatic (Decker, Kuehne, Buchanan & Porter, 1958).

Choice of medium

The media most generally used in medical microbiology are those such as blood agar, that permit growth of most organisms or those that incorporate a non-selective indicator such as that designed to detect phosphatase production (Barber & Kuper, 1951). Counts of total organisms and of presumptive pathogens may easily be made on these media and colonies may be subcultured for further identification. Reference has already been made to the small numbers of pathogens present in the normal environment and some good selective media have been devised and used for air sampling, e.g. that for *Clostridium welchii* described by Lowbury & Lilly (1955). However, one devised for streptococci was known to inhibit some of the streptococci themselves, mouth streptococci being more sensitive to the inhibitors than enterococci (Williams & Hirch, 1950). It is, however, fair to point out that even an over-inhibitory medium, which suppresses the growth of a number of the organisms sought, may still result in an apparently larger 'catch' of the specific organism by reducing the growth of the competitors. This is particularly true of organisms such as streptococci, where the tiny colonies may be overgrown by micrococci or aerobic spore-bearing organisms normally present in the air.

Selective media have not proved to be entirely satisfactory in air-samplers, since many are inhibitory to small inocula even of the organisms for which they are 'selective'. An attempt was made to overcome this by sampling on to a non-selective nutrient medium such as serum agar and incubating until micro-colonies were formed (P. Jerram, personal communication). The micro-colonies were then subcultured by the replica-plating technique using velvet on to a medium selective for staphylococci. It was hoped that, by this method, the few colonies of *Staphylococcus aureus* present could be selected from amongst the hundreds of micrococci normally present in the air of hospital wards. The main difficulties encountered were that the primary plates had to be incubated for 3–4 hr. before subculture and that replica-plating tended to spread these colonies out to a large size. The initial incubation period was necessary to provide a large enough inoculum of staphylococci but, even so, less than half the colonies of *S. aureus* growing on the initial medium ever grew on the selective medium. The secondary plates had to be incubated for 48 hr. resulting in delay in recognizing the pathogens.

The design of a selective medium for air-sampling is complicated by many factors. For staphylococci, the major problem is not only that the organisms sought form only 1 % of the airborne bacteria, but that the remaining 99 % are taxonomically and physiologically closely related organisms. A medium which is satisfactory when tested by the Miles & Misra technique using fluid culture may not be so when exposed in an air-sampler, because drying out of the agar surface may result in a concentration of the inhibitors. In a slit sampler drawing 1 ft.³ of air per minute (30 l.) on to a 9 cm. Petri dish containing about 30 g. of medium, a sample of 10 ft.³ removed 4 % of the water and one of 60 ft.³ removed 18 % of the water (Noble & Lidwell, 1963). Experiments in which bacteria were sampled on agar using 10 ft.³ of air and then a further 40 ft.³ of filtered air passed over the plate showed that, whilst very few of the spores of *Bacillus subtilis* failed to germinate, as much as 30 % of an inoculum of micrococci failed to grow; the effect was even more pronounced when streptococci were sampled on to the selective medium of Williams & Hirch (1950). Similar results have been reported by Kuehne & Decker (1957).

Membrane filters

When seeking organisms that are rare in the air, it may be useful to sample large volumes of air through a number of fluid samplers and to concentrate the catch by filtering the sampling fluid through filter paper or a membrane filter (Ibach, Larsh & Furcolow, 1954). The value of the filter method is illustrated by Haas (1956) who showed that whereas inoculation of 1 ml. aliquots of a fluid on agar might yield only two to three colonies, filtering 100 ml. of the same fluid through a membrane filter could yield 200–300 colonies, giving a more accurate count and enabling any diversity of species to be detected.

As an alternative method of sampling, membrane filters can be used directly by drawing air through and incubating the membrane itself on a cotton pad (Torloni & Borzani, 1958), on agar growth medium (e.g. Muir & Milne, 1963), or by staining the organisms on the membrane (e.g. Haas, 1956). Growing fungi on the membranes may help to speed up diagnosis, perhaps because sporing takes place earlier (Funder & Johannessen, 1957). Membrane filters have the advantage over filter paper that the micro-organisms are retained on a smooth surface rather than being partially trapped in the interstices of the fibrous material.

Any tendency for the organisms to wash off during staining may be prevented by overlaying the membrane with an adhesive before staining (Gordon & Cupp, 1953). Permanent preparations can be made by fixing and mounting the membranes, and both membranes and glass filter 'paper' may be made transparent by application of cotton seed oil or immersion oil (Paulus, Talvitie, Fraser & Keenan, 1957). A comprehensive bibliography of membrane filter techniques may be found in the *Oxoid Manual* (2nd edition 1961).

A simple alternative to sampling through filter paper or a membrane is to use a cotton-wool or muslin pad. The pad may be shaken in water to release the catch (e.g. Rishbeth, 1958) but it seems likely that many organisms may remain trapped in the fibres. This can be overcome by using a soluble material such as alginate wool (Richards, 1955; Hammond, 1958) but for reliable results alginates must be dissolved in buffer solution or the release of positive ions on solution may result in marked changes in pH, destroying all or part of the catch. Long-period sampling through filter material may result in a proportion of the catch being destroyed by desiccation in the air stream (Splittstoesser & Foster, 1957).

Some special techniques have been devised for electrostatic samplers, although there appears to be no fundamental reason why they should not be adopted elsewhere. One especially applicable to sampling artificial aerosols of one organism only is the use of agar-impregnated filter paper. The paper can be premarked with a grid to facilitate counting of the colonies and after incubation may be dried down to form a permanent record. The exposed sheet can be sterilized with formaldehyde (Morris, Darlow, Peel & Wright, 1961).

Animals as samplers

When rats, mice, guinea-pigs, hamsters or rabbits inhale either human or bovine tubercle bacilli as single cells of small equivalent diameter, the number of initial tubercles is approximately equal to the number of bacilli inhaled (Wells, 1955; Ratcliffe & Palladrino, 1953). It is thus possible to use animals directly as a means of assessing airborne contamination, but quantitative studies are only possible with organisms which give an initial discrete lesion. With other organisms it may be necessary to use death of the animal as a criterion of infection (e.g. Druett, Robinson, Henderson, Packman & Peacock, 1956). Alternatively, exposure of humans or animals to a pathogen might be assessed in a purely qualitative fashion by seeking changes in antibody titres to the organism, or by the use of a skin test such as that for sensitivity to tubercle bacilli (Riley & O'Grady, 1961). When dealing with an organism which cannot be traced in this way it may be possible to recover the cells from the respiratory tract; with doses lower than 150 cells, however, inhaled organisms may be recovered from less than 20% of human subjects exposed (Meyers, James & Zippin, 1961), and a respiratory inoculum of 1,000 cells is the smallest that can be detected with certainty in all subjects (Ostrom, Wolochow & James, 1958).

Counting techniques

Assessment of the total number of airborne microbes in a sample collected on agar is most conveniently made by counting the colonies on an illuminated glass 'window', such as that described by Wilson (1935), with the aid of a lens and a tally-counter. Clear media, such as serum agar or Sabouraud's agar, are better for this purpose than opaque media, such as blood agar or malt agar. Up to 1,000 colonies of a single bacterial species from an aerosol may be counted on the surface of a 6 in. Petri dish, especially if the glass plate has been ruled off in radial sectors, but half this number is more convenient. Natural clouds composed of a variety of species of micro-organisms are more difficult to count and relatively few colonies of fungus or *Bacillus* species can be counted owing to their large size. With pure cultures, fungus colonies are best counted when very small, although it is possible that at this stage some may be missed owing to slow germination. Mycoplasma colonies recovered from artificial aerosols on enriched P.P.L.O. medium may be counted under the microscope. Recognition is made easier by staining the colonies *in situ* with dilute Dienes's stain (Kundsin, 1966).

Correction factors have been devised to allow for confluence and superimposition of colonies, but care must be taken that these are suitable for the material sampled (Bourdillon, Lidwell & Raymond, 1948). When making counts from fluid suspensions in roll tubes and surface plates, it must be recognized that the count is subject to 'Poisson error' due to the distribution of the organisms in the fluid (e.g. Wilson, 1922; Miles & Misra, 1938; Snyder, 1947; Crone, 1948). Mechanical methods for counting colonies have been devised (e.g. Malligo, 1965) but they suffer from the disadvantage that two nearly-confluent colonies may be read by the machine as either one colony or as two colonies, depending on the direction of scan. An excellent discussion of viable counting techniques is given by Meynell & Meynell (1965).

IDENTIFYING VIRUSES
Visual methods
In view of their small size, it seems a formidable task to identify virus particles visually, although since inclusion bodies may be demonstrated in the epidermal scales of persons suffering from a number of viral skin diseases, examination of airborne squames, perhaps by fluorescent antibody techniques, might reveal the presence of virus.

Cultural methods
Fluid-medium samplers
The majority of the cultural methods are modifications of those devised for bacteria, with the obvious proviso that the catch must be inoculated on to living cells for growth. For fluid samplers a variety of buffers and diluents have been used depending on the viruses sought. These are generally 'richer' than the sampling fluids used in studies on bacteria: for example, Hahon & McGavran (1961) used 10% skim-milk and olive oil in the study of the variola–vaccinia group. Culture systems include embryonated eggs, membrane pieces, suckling mice and tissue culture cells.

For samples drawn from artificial aerosols, methods have been devised for the recovery of vaccinia, influenza, Venezuelan equine encephalo-myelitis and poliomyelitis (Harper, 1961), foot-and-mouth disease, (Thorne & Burrows, 1960) and measles virus (Jong & Winkler, 1964).

Using fluid impingers, *para*-influenza virus has been recovered from a natural aerosol (Artenstein & Cadigan, 1964) and foot-and-mouth disease virus from boxes housing infected cattle (Hyslop, 1965). Because the concentration of virus was thought likely to be small, Hyslop absorbed the virus from the sampling fluid using a finely divided magnesium silicate clay (Attaclay) and inoculated the concentrate into animals and on to tissue culture. A common cold virus, Coxsackievirus A21, has been recovered from natural clouds of virus produced by infected volunteers (Buckland, Bynoe & Tyrrell, 1965).

Meiklejohn *et al.* (1961) sampled very large volumes of air in a small-pox hospital but were able to recover virus on one occasion only. This apparent paucity of small-pox virus in the air was curious: small-pox is highly contagious and presumably spread on particles of desquamated skin; and the sampler systems were shown to be efficient in the labora-tory. The authors suggested that if the virus were airborne it might have been intracellular in the squames and thus not available for infecting the tissue culture cells. Further studies using both 'settle' plates and impinger samplers revealed that the virus was present mainly as particles of large equivalent diameter and that it could be recovered from dust from the bedding as well as from aerosols of saliva (Downie *et al.* 1965).

Coxiella burneti has been recovered from the air of premises harbouring infected goats by sampling air into skim-milk and olive oil in an impinger. After separation the milk fraction was injected into guinea-pigs and complement-fixing antibodies to *C. burneti* demonstrated in the blood of the guinea-pigs 4–6 weeks after infection (Lennette & Welsh, 1951).

Solid-medium samplers

Various methods have been devised for sampling on to solid media, all of them requiring some further manipulation of the sample. It is not possible to sample directly on to tissue culture cells since the effect of air blowing over the cells would be to kill them and so render recognition of the virus impossible. Covering the cells with agar or gelatine is unsatisfactory as virus must diffuse through the·layer to reach the cells. Slit sampling directly on to a solid medium may result in adsorption of the virus on the agar (Vlodavets, Gaidamovich & Obukhova, 1960).

Using the Andersen sampler, Jensen (1964) found that covering agar with 20% skim-milk suspension recovered more virus than either agar or skim-milk alone. After sampling, the skim-milk was washed off the surface, diluted in Hanks solution and inoculated on to tissue culture. Guerin & Mitchell (1964), who used a medium based on gelatine which could be melted at 37° C and centrifuged to concentrate the virus, found that where high concentrations of influenza virus were available the presence of the virus, which included 'dead' virus particles, could be shown immediately after sampling by haemagglutination.

Recently it has been demonstrated that tissue culture cells can be shown to be infected with virus within 24 hr. of inoculation, using the fluorescent cell counting technique (Hahon, 1965, 1966) and this should make identification of virus aerosols swifter.

IDENTIFYING BACTERIOPHAGE PARTICLES

Airborne phage particles have been used as a model in virus studies and may be recovered from fluid samplers by mixing the sampling fluid with a suitable host culture in soft agar and flooding this on to the surface of a plate (Hemmes, Winkler & Kool, 1962; Harstad, 1965) or by mixing the sample with culture and passing both through a membrane filter which is incubated on the surface of a nutrient plate. The filter method is less satisfactory than the soft agar method, for not all phage will be adsorbed on to cells immediately, and unadsorbed phage will pass through the filter and be lost (Loehr & Schwegler, 1965). With a solid-medium sampler the phage may be sampled on to agar which is subsequently flooded with culture (Kewitsch, 1964) or on to gelatine which can be melted and mixed with culture, but this appears not to be as satisfactory as using a fluid sampler (Dahlgren, Decker & Harstad, 1961). Electrostatic precipitators have been reported as more efficient than slit samplers for sampling phage particles (Morris *et al.* 1961).

In all investigations on airborne phage or virus, the experimenter is faced with the problem that more than one phage or virus particle may be adsorbed on any host cell. This will, of course, result in fewer visible plaques than there were infective particles in the inoculum, but correction factors have been evaluated to overcome this problem (Armitage & Spicer, 1956; Larsen & Reinicke, 1956; Lorenz & Zoeth, 1966).

OTHER AIRBORNE PARTICLES

A large variety of other particles may be isolated from the air. Perhaps the most important of the organic particles are the pollen grains, which may be identified by their microscopic appearance; an excellent diagnostic book is the *Atlas* compiled by Hyde & Adams (1958). Microscopic fragments of lichen thallus, moss gemmae, liverwort spores, Myxomycete spores, algae and protozoa have been identified by visual or culture methods (e.g. Puschakarow, 1913; Pettersson, 1940; Gregory, Hamilton & Sreeramulu, 1955; Hamilton, 1959) and plant hairs and fragments of insects may also be identified visually. Textile fibres are often present in the air of occupied environments and the chemical nature of these—protein, cellulose or synthetic material—may be determined using the Pressley (1958) dye system. Desquamated fragments of human skin present in the air of hospital wards and homes must be identified by their appearance under the microscope, for there is no satisfactory staining method for keratin (Davies & Noble, 1962). It is normal to find large numbers of particles of soot, ash spheres and cenospheres (hollow bodies formed by combustion of pitch, coal or fuel oil) in samples from any atmosphere. In the air of cities they may be so numerous as to obscure the field completely and may be identified under the microscope from their appearance alone.

DISCUSSION

Few of the techniques described in this paper have been devised specifically for the identification of airborne micro-organisms. The visual techniques used in identifying airborne fungi and pollen grains are tedious and time-consuming, yet it is difficult to see how this work could be made easier or mechanized without losing precision in identification. Work on air pollution has shown that the concentration of gaseous matter in the air may be followed with ease (Baker & Doerr, 1959; American Conference of Industrial Hygienists, 1960; Welch & Terry, 1960; Bokhoven & Niessen, 1966) and samplers have been devised to run for periods up to a week unattended (Mitchell, 1965). Identification of particulate matter, however, remains an essentially visual process.

Natural clouds of bacteria have been studied mostly by collecting the organisms on growth medium, rather than impacting on to glass and identifying the organisms by techniques such as fluorescent antibody staining. There are two basic reasons why cultural techniques are the methods of choice for sampling natural clouds. The first is that unless it is known which organisms will be collected or unless only one species of organism is sought, fluorescent staining using a variety of sera would be a tedious method of identification. The second is that many species of pathogenic bacteria may be split into distinct types by methods such as serological typing, phage-typing or biochemical tests. Although more detailed identification of the organisms is often invaluable in epidemiological studies, it does require isolation of the organism in pure culture. Application of phage to micro-colonies as described by Chadwick (1959) is not practicable since, for example, up to thirty different phages may be used in typing staphylococci. When dealing with artificial aerosols of known composition these considerations do not apply, and it is in this field that most of the advances in technique have been made. Rapid identification of organisms in aerosols can be achieved by fluorescent antibody techniques even when other organisms are present, provided only that an anti-serum specific to the organism is available. Doubtless methods could be devised for mechanical scanning and counting of the fluorescent stained slides, although the gain in time might not be justified on a commercial basis.

The biggest challenge today lies in devising methods for recovering and identifying virus particles in the air. At present the most satisfactory methods appear to be those in which the virus is recovered in a fluid medium and inoculated on to tissue culture or embryonated eggs. The recent description of fluorescent cell-counting techniques, by which infected cells in tissue culture can be detected within 24 hr. of inoculation, should make identification of virus more rapid. Although it is not possible at the moment to foresee how natural clouds of virus containing different virus species could be investigated with the same ease as clouds of bacteria or fungi, aerosols containing more than one virus species can be assessed provided that, like vaccinia virus and poliomyelitis virus, the plaque types can be distinguished in tissue culture. Some success has already been reported in this field (Guerin & Mitchell, 1964; Gabrielson & Hsiung, 1965).

Finally one can speculate on the problems involved in identifying microbial particles in any studies of extra-terrestrial life, a prospect which seems less remote now than formerly. Before it can be decided whether a particular fungus spore or pollen grain is of 'earthly' origin or not, it will be necessary to have a very complete knowledge of the earth's microbial flora, for the chances of contamination of a space craft before it leaves the earth are very large. Pital *et al.* (1966) have suggested that matter of living origin might be distinguished from that of non-living origin by fluorescent staining of the protein by fluorescein isothiocyanate and suggest methods for carrying this out from a space probe. This assumes, however, that unusual chemical substances will not stain in the same way as protein and that they will not possess a green auto-fluorescence, which is relatively rare on earth. It is certain, however, that methods will be found, perhaps using techniques unknown to us today. Robert Hooke could not have known of techniques such as electron microscopy or fluorescent antibody staining when he wrote: 'Tis not unlikely, but that there may yet be invented several other helps to the eye, as much exceeding those already found, as those do the bare eye, such as by which we may perhaps be able to discover *living Creatures* in the Moon, or other Planets, the *figures* of the compounding Particles of matter and the particular *Schematisms* and *Textures* of Bodies.' (Robert Hooke, *Micrographia*, The Preface, 1665.)

REFERENCES

AMERICAN CONFERENCE OF INDUSTRIAL HYGIENISTS (1960). *Air Sampling Instruments for Evaluation of Atmospheric Contaminants.* Cincinnati.

ANDERSEN, A. A. (1958). New sampler for the collection, sizing, and enumeration of viable airborne particles. *J. Bact.* **76**, 471.

ARMITAGE, P. & SPICER, C. C. (1956). The detection of variations in host susceptibility in dilution counting experiments. *J. Hyg., Camb.* **54**, 401.

ARTENSTEIN, M. S. & CADIGAN, F. C. (1964). Air sampling in viral respiratory disease. *Archs envir. Hlth*, **9**, 58.

BAIRD-PARKER, A. C. & DAVENPORT, E. (1965). The effect of recovery medium on the isolation of *Staphylococcus aureus* after heat treatment and after the storage of frozen and dried cells. *J. appl. Bact.* **28**, 390.

BAKER, R. A. & DOOER, R. C. (1959). Methods of sampling and storage of air containing vapours and gases. *Int. J. Air Pollut.* **2**, 142.

BARAUH, H. K. (1961). The air spora of a cowshed. *J. gen. Microbiol.* **25**, 483.

BARBER, M. & KUPER, S. W. A. (1951). Identification of *Staphylococcus aureus* by the phosphatase reaction. *J. Path. Bact.* **63**, 65.

BOKHOVEN, C. & NIESSEN, H. L. J. (1966). The continuous monitoring of traces of SO_2 in air on the basis of discolouration of the starch iodine reagent with prior elimination of interfering compounds. *Int. J. Air Wat. Pollut.* **10**, 233.

BOURDILLON, R. B., LIDWELL, O. M. & RAYMOND, W. F. (1948). Overcrowding on culture plates. In 'Studies in air hygiene'. *Spec. Rep. Ser. med. Res. Counc.* no. 262, p. 48. London: H.M.S.O.

BOURDILLON, R. B., LIDWELL, O. M. & SCHUSTER, E. (1948). An improved slit sampler with accurate timing. In 'Studies in air hygiene'. *Spec. Rep. Ser. med. Res. Counc.* no. 262, p. 12. London: H.M.S.O.

BUCKLAND, F. E., BYNOE, M. L. & TYRRELL, D. A. J. (1965). Experiments on the spread of colds. II. Studies in volunteers with Coxsackievirus A21. *J. Hyg., Camb.* **63**, 327.

CAMMACK, R. H. (1955). Seasonal changes in three common constituents of the air-spora of Southern Nigeria. *Nature, Lond.* **176**, 1270.

CHADWICK, P. (1959). Rapid identification of *Bacillus anthracis* by microscopic observation of bacteriophage lysis. *J. gen. Microbiol.* **21**, 631.

CHADWICK, P. & SLADE, J. H. R. (1960). Identification of bacteria by specific antibody conjugated with fluorescein isothiocyanate. *J. Hyg., Camb.* **58**, 147.

CLAYTON, Y. M. & NOBLE, W. C. (1963). The airborne spread of Dermatophytes and *Candida albicans*. *Trans. a. Rep. St John's Hosp. derm. Soc., Lond.* **49**, 36.

CLAYTON, Y. M. & NOBLE, W. C. (1966). Observations on the epidemiology of *Candida albicans*. *J. clin. Path.* **19**, 76.

CRONE, P. B. (1948). The counting of surface colonies of bacteria. *J. Hyg., Camb.* **46**, 426.

DAHLGREN, C. M., DECKER, H. M. & HARSTAD, J. B. (1961). A slit sampler for collecting T_3 bacteriophage and Venezuelan equine encephalomyelitis virus. I. Studies with T_3 bacteriophage. *Appl. Microbiol.* **9**, 103.

DAVIES, R. R. (1957). A study of airborne *Cladosporium*. *Trans. Br. mycol. Soc.* **40**, 409.

DAVIES, R. R. (1960). Viable moulds in house dust. *Trans. Br. mycol. Soc.* **43**, 617.

DAVIES, R. R. & NOBLE, W. C. (1962). Dispersal of bacteria on desquamated skin. *Lancet*, **2**, 1295.

DECKER, H. M., KUEHNE, R. W., BUCHANAN, C. M. & PORTER, R. (1958). Design and evaluation of a slit incubator sampler. *Appl. Microbiol.* **6**, 398.

DOWNIE, A. W., MEIKLEJOHN, M., VINCENT, ST L., RAO, A. R., SUNDARABABO, B. V. & KEMPE, C. H. (1965). The recovery of small-pox virus from patients and their environment in a small-pox hospital. *Bull. Wld Hlth Org.* **33**, 615.

DRUETT, H. A., ROBINSON, J. M., HENDERSON, D. W., PACKMAN, L. & PEACOCK, S. (1956). Studies on respiratory infections. II. The influence of aerosol particle size on infection of the guinea pig with *Pasteurella pestis*. *J. Hyg., Camb.* **54**, 37.

FRIEDMAN, L., DERBES, V. J., HODGES, E. P. & SINSKI, J. T. (1960). The isolation of dermatophytes from the air. *J. invest. Derm.* **35**, 3.

FUNDER, S. & JOHANNESSEN, S. (1957). The membrane filter as an aid in the cultivation and identification of fungi. *J. gen. Microbiol.* **17**, 117.

FURCOLOW, M. L. (1961). Airborne histoplasmosis. *Bact. Rev.* **25**, 301.

GABRIELSON, M. O. & HSIUNG, G. D. (1965). Sensitivity of the agar overlay method for the recognition of enterovirus. *Appl. Microbiol.* **13**, 967.

GEORG, L. K., AJELLO, L. & PAPAGEORGE, C. (1954). Use of cycloheximide in the selective isolation of fungi pathogenic to man. *J. Lab. clin. Med.* **44**, 422.

GLOVER, R. E. (1948). Estimation of aerosols of *Mycobacterium tuberculosis* by a microslide slit sampler. In 'Studies in air hygiene'. *Spec. Rep. Ser. med. Res. Counc.* no. 262, p. 293. London: H.M.S.O.

GOLDBERG, L. J., WATKINS, H. M. S., BOERKE, E. E. & CHATIGNY, M. A. (1958). The use of a rotating drum for the study of aerosols over extended periods of time. *Am. J. Hyg.* **68**, 85.

GORDON, M. A. & CUPP, H. B. (1953). Detection of *Histoplasma capsulatum* and other fungus spores in the environment by means of a membrane filter. *Mycologia*, **45**, 241.

GREGORY, P. H. (1961). *The Microbiology of the Atmosphere.* London: Leonard Hill.

GREGORY, P. H., HAMILTON, E. D. & SREERAMULU, T. (1955). Occurrence of the alga *Gloeocapsa* in the air. *Nature, Lond.* **176**, 1270.

GREGORY, P. H. & HIRST, J. M. (1957). The summer air-spora at Rothamsted in 1952. *J. gen. Microbiol.* **17**, 135.

GREGORY, P. H. & LACEY, M. E. (1962). Isolation of thermophilic Actinomycetes. *Nature, Lond.* **195**, 95.

GUERIN, L. F. & MITCHELL, C. A. (1964). A method for determining the concentration of airborne virus and sizing droplet nuclei containing the agent. *Can. J. comp. Med.* **28**, 283.

HAAS, G. J. (1956). Use of the membrane filter in the brewing industry. *Wallerstein Labs. Commun.* **19**, 7.

HAHON, N. (1965). Assay of Variola virus by the fluorescent cell counting technique. *Appl. Microbiol.* **13**, 865.

HAHON, N. (1966). Fluorescent cell counting assay of yellow fever virus. *J. infect. Dis.* **116**, 33.

HAHON, N. & MCGAVRAN, M. H. (1961). Airborne infectivity of the variola–vaccinia group of pox viruses for the cygnomolgus monkey *Macaca irus. J. infect. Dis.* **109**, 294.

HAMILTON, E. D. (1959). Studies on the air-spora. *Acta allerg.* **13**, 143.

HAMMOND, E. C. (1958). Ammonium alginate wool as a filter for collecting microorganisms from large volumes of air. *J. gen. Microbiol.* **19**, 267.

HANKS, J. H. & WALLACE, J. H. (1958). Determination of cell viability. *Proc. Soc. exp. Biol. Med.* **98**, 188.

HARPER, G. J. (1961). Airborne micro-organisms: survival tests with four viruses. *J. Hyg., Camb.* **59**, 479.

HARPER, G. J., HOOD, A. M. & MORTON, J. D. (1958). Airborne micro-organisms: a technique for studying their survival. *J. Hyg., Camb.* **56**, 364.

HARSTAD, J. B. (1965). Sampling submicron T Bacteriophage aerosols. *Appl. Microbiol.* **13**, 899.

HEMMES, J. H., WINKLER, K. C. & KOOL, S. M. (1962). Virus survival as a seasonal factor in influenza and poliomyelitis. *Antonie van Leeuwenhoek*, **28**, 221.

HIRST, J. M. (1952). An automatic volumetric spore trap. *Ann. appl. Biol.* **39**, 257.

HYDE, H. A. & ADAMS, K. F. (1958). *An Atlas of Airborne Pollen.* London: MacMillan and Co. Ltd.

HYSLOP, N. ST G. (1965). Airborne infection with the virus of foot-and-mouth disease. *J. comp. Path. Ther.* **75**, 119.

IBACH, M. J., LARSH, H. W. & FURCOLOW, M. L. (1954). Epidemic histoplasmosis and airborne *Histoplasma capsulatum*. *Proc. Soc. exp. Biol. Med.* **85**, 72.

INNES, A. G. (1960). Tellurite-egg agar, a selective and differential medium for the isolation of coagulase-positive staphylococci. *J. appl. Bact.* **23**, 108.

JAEGER, R. F., SPERTZEL, R. O. & KUEHNE, R. W. (1961). Detection of air-borne *Pasteurella tularensis* using the fluorescent antibody technique. *Appl. Microbiol.* **9**, 585.

JENSEN, M. M. (1964). Inactivation of air-borne viruses by ultraviolet light. *Appl. Microbiol.* **12**, 418.

JONG DE, J. G. & WINKLER, K. C. (1964). Survival of measles virus in air. *Nature, Lond.* **201**, 1054.

KEWITSCH, VON, A. (1964). Experimenteller Beitrag zur Verminderung des Virushaltes der Luft durch Luftfiltration. *Z. ges. Hyg.* **10**, 11.

KUBITSCHEK, H. E. (1958). Electronic counting and sizing of bacteria. *Nature, Lond.* **182**, 234.

KUEHNE, R. W. & DECKER, H. M. (1957). Studies on continuous sampling of *Serratia marcescens* using a slit sampler. *Appl. Microbiol.* **5**, 321.

KUNDSIN, R. B. (1966). Characterisation of Mycoplasma aerosols as to viability, particle, size and lethality of ultra-violet radiation. *J. Bact.* **91**, 942.

LARSEN, S. O. & REINICKE, V. (1965). Some statistical problems in relation to the use of the Poisson distribution in virus plaque assays. *Acta Path. microbiol. scand.* **65**, 84.

LEACH, C. M. (1955). A simple device for single spore isolation. *Phytopathology*, **45**, 405.

LENNETTE, E. H. & WELSH, H. H. (1951). Q fever studies in California. X. Recovery of *Coxiella burneti* from the air of premises harbouring infected goats. *Am. J. Hyg.* **54**, 44.

LIDWELL, O. M. & NOBLE, W. C. (1965). A modification of the Andersen sampler for use in occupied environments. *J. appl. Bact.* **28**, 280.

LIDWELL, O. M., NOBLE, W. C. & DOLPHIN, G. W. (1959). The use of radiation to estimate the numbers of micro-organisms in airborne particles. *J. Hyg., Camb.* **57**, 299.

LITTMAN, M. L. (1947). A culture medium for the primary isolation of fungi. *Science, N.Y.* **106**, 109.

LOEHR, R. C. & SCHWEGLER, D. T. (1965). Filtration method for bacteriophage detection. *Appl. Microbiol.* **13**, 1005.

LORENZ, R. J. & ZOETH, B. (1966). An estimation of the overlap bias in plaque assay. *Virology*, **28**, 379.

LOWBURY, E. J. L. & LILLY, H. A. (1955). A selective plate medium for *Clostridium welchii*. *J. Path. Bact.* **70**, 195.

LURIE, H. I. & WAY, M. (1957). The isolation of dermatophytes from the atmosphere of caves. *Mycologia*, **49**, 178.

MALLIGO, J. E. (1965). Evaluation of an automatic electronic device for counting bacterial colonies. *Appl. Microbiol.* **13**, 931.

MARTIN, W. J. (1943). A simple technique for isolating spores of various fungi from exposed slides in aerobiological work. *Phytopathology*, **33**, 75.

MAY, K. R. (1945). The cascade impactor: an instrument for sampling coarse aerosols. *J. scient. Instrum.* **22**, 187.

MCDONOUGH, E. S., AJELLO, L., AUSHERMAN, R. J., BALOWS, A., MCCLELLAN, J. J. & BRINKMANS, S. (1961). Human pathogenic fungi recovered from soil in an area endemic for North American Blastomycosis. *Am. J. Hyg.* **73**, 75.

MEIKLEJOHN, G., KEMPE, C. H., DOWNIE, A. W., BERGE, T. O., VINCENT, ST L. & RAO, A. R. (1961). Air sampling to recover variola virus in the environment of a small-pox hospital. *Bull. Wld Hlth Org.* **25**, 63.

MEYERS, C. E., JAMES, H. A. & ZIPPIN, C. (1961). The recovery of aerosolized bacteria from humans. I. Effects of varying exposure, sampling times, and subject variability. *Archs envir. Hlth*, **2**, 384.

MEYNELL, G. G. & MEYNELL, E. (1965). *Theory and Practice in Experimental Bacteriology*, p. 15. Cambridge University Press.

MILES, A. A. & MISRA, S. S. (1938). Estimation of the bactericidal power of the blood. *J. Hyg., Camb.* **38**, 732.

MITCHELL, K. K. (1965). Continuous outdoor air sampler. *Am. ind. Hyg. Ass. J.* **26**, 285.

MORRIS, E. J., DARLOW, H. M., PEEL, J. F. H. & WRIGHT, W. C. (1961). The quantitative assay of mono-dispersed aerosols of bacteria and bacteriophage by electrostatic precipitation. *J. Hyg., Camb.* **59**, 487.

MUIR, W. & MILNE, G. R. (1963). The use of membrane filters for the detection of airborne contamination. *J. med. Lab. Technol.* **20**, 85.

NOBLE, W. C. & CLAYTON, Y. M. (1963). Fungi in the air of hospital wards. *J. gen. Microbiol.* **32**, 397.

NOBLE, W. C. & LIDWELL, O. M. (1963). Environmental contamination, in *Infection in Hospitals*, p. 87. Oxford: C.I.O.M.S. Blackwells.

NOBLE, W. C., LIDWELL, O. M. & KINGSTON, D. (1963). The size distribution of airborne particles carrying micro-organisms. *J. Hyg., Camb.* **61**, 385.

NOUR, M. A. & NOUR, J. J. (1958). A simple technique for inoculating pathogenic bacteria on susceptible plant leaves. *Nature, Lond.* **182**, 96.

OSTROM, C. A., WOLOCHOW, H. & JAMES, H. A. (1958). Studies on the experimental epidemiology of respiratory disease. IX. Recovery of airborne bacteria from the oral cavity of humans: the effect of dosage on recovery. *J. infect. Dis.* **102**, 251.

PADY, S. M. & KELLY, C. D. (1949). Use of silicones in aerobiology. *Science, N.Y.* **110**, 187.

PAULUS, H. J., TALVITIE, N. A., FRASER, D. A. & KEENAN, R. G. (1957). Use of membrane filters in air sampling. *Am. Ind. Hyg. Ass. Q.* **18**, 267.

PETTERSSON, B. (1940). Experimentelle Untersuchungen über die Euanemochore Verbreitung der Sporenpflanzen. *Acta bot. fenn.* **25**, 1.

PITAL, A., JANOWITZ, S. L., HUDAK, C. E. & LEWIS, E. E. (1966). Direct fluorescent labelling of micro-organisms as a possible life detection technique. *Appl. Microbiol.* **14**, 119.

PRESSLEY, T. A. (1958). The fibre composition of hospital dust. *Lancet*, **2**, 712.

PUSCHKAREW, B. M. (1913). Über die Verbreitung der Süsswasserprotisten durch die Luft. *Arch. Protistenk.* **28**, 323.

RATCLIFFE, H. L. & PALLADRINO, V. S. (1953). Tuberculosis induced by droplet nuclei infection. *J. exp. Med.* **97**, 61.

RATHBUN-GRAVATT, A. (1925). Direct inoculation of coniferous stems with damping-off fungi. *J. agric. Res.* **30**, 327.

RICHARDS, M. (1954). Atmospheric mold spores in and out of doors. *J. Allergy*, **25**, 429.

RICHARDS, M. (1955). A water soluble filter for trapping airborne micro-organisms. *Nature, Lond.* **176**, 559.

RILEY, R. L. & O'GRADY, F. (1961). *Airborne Infection*. New York: Macmillan.

RISHBETH, J. (1958). Detection of viable airborne spores in air. *Nature, Lond.* **181**, 1549.

RISHBETH, J. & MEREDITH, D. S. (1957). Surface microflora of pine needles. *Nature, Lond.* **179**, 682.

SHAW, C. (1956). Effect of blood on the viability of dried cultures of cholera vibrios. *Nature, Lond.* **178**, 1352.

SHIELDS, A. B. & AJELLO, L. (1966). Medium for selective isolation of *Cryptococcus neoformans*. *Science, N.Y.* **151**, 208.

SMITH, C. D., RITTER, R., LARSH, H. W. & FURCOLOW, M. L. (1964). Infection of white Swiss mice with airborne *Cryptococcus neoformans*. *J. Bact.* **87**, 1364.

SNYDER, T. L. (1947). The relative errors of bacteriological plate counting methods. *J. Bact.* **54**, 641.

SPLITTSTOESSER, D. F. & FOSTER, E. M. (1957). The influence of drying conditions on survival of *Serratia marcescens*. *Appl. Microbiol.* **5**, 333.

THOMAS, H. R. (1943). *Cercospora* blight of carrot. *Phytopathology*, **33**, 114.

THORNE, H. V. & BURROWS, T. M. (1960). Aerosol sampling methods for the virus of foot-and-mouth disease and the measurement of virus penetration through aerosol filters. *J. Hyg., Camb.* **58**, 409.

TORLONI, M. & BORZANI, W. (1958). A filtration method for the determination of concentration of micro-organisms in air. *Appl. Microbiol.* **6**, 252.

TYLER, M. E. & SHIPE, E. L. (1959). Bacterial aerosol samplers. I. Development and evaluation of the all-glass impinger. *Appl. Microbiol.* **7**, 337.

TYLER, M. E., SHIPE, E. L. & PAINTER, R. B. (1959). Bacterial aerosol samplers. III. Comparison of biological and physical effects in liquid impinger samplers. *Appl. Microbiol.* **7**, 355.

VANBREUSEGHEM, R. (1952). Technique biologique pour l'isolement des dermatophytes du sol. *Annls Soc. belge Méd. Trop.* **32**, 173.

VLODAVETS, V. V., GAIDOMOVICH, S. Y. & OBUKHOVA, V. R. (1960). Method of trapping influenza virus in the droplet phase of an aerosol. *Probl. Virol.* **5**, 728.

VRIES, DE, G. A. (1960). *Aspergillus fumigatus* and Actinomycetes in air. *Acta allerg.* **15**, 99.

WELCH, A. F. & TERRY, J. P. (1960). Developments in the measurement of atmospheric sulphur dioxide. *Am. ind. Hyg. Ass. J.* **21**, 316.

WELLS, W. F. (1955). *Airborne Contagion and Air Hygiene*, p. 122. Cambridge, Massachusetts: Harvard University Press.

WILLIAMS, R. E. O. (1952). Investigations into a method for counting the total number of bacteria in a suspension. *J. gen. Microbiol.* **7**, 89.

WILLIAMS, R. E. O. & HIRCH, A. (1950). The detection of streptococci in air. *J. Hyg., Camb.* **48**, 504.

WILSON, G. S. (1922). The proportion of viable bacteria in young cultures with especial reference to the technique employed in counting. *J. Bact.* **7**, 405.

WILSON, G. S. (1935). The bacteriological grading of milk. *Spec. Rep. Ser. med. Res. Counc.* no. 206. London: H.M.S.O.

LIBERATION MECHANISMS OF FUNGI

C. T. INGOLD

Department of Botany, Birkbeck College, Malet Street,
London, W.C. 1

INTRODUCTION

In considering how various types of fungal spore come to be present in the air spora it is interesting to look briefly at its composition. In the past fifteen years quantitative knowledge of the air spora has greatly increased due largely to the work of P. H. Gregory and his associates. It is not the intention here to review this work in general, but rather to consider an example in which a fairly detailed identification of the components of the spora has been attempted. Lacey (1962), using a Hirst spore-trap, analysed the air spora at a height of 0·5 m. at two sites 450 m. apart in a rural area west of London during a summer period (May to September). The catches from the two sites showed differences, but were, nevertheless, in substantial agreement (Table 1). The allocation of spores to different categories depends to some extent on ease of identification. Ballistospores shed from hymenomycete sporophores and discharged from the sterigmata of 'mirror yeasts' (Sporobolomycetaceae) are easily identified because of the characteristic projecting hilar appendix (Wells, 1965). Ascospores are much less easy to recognize and it is quite likely that in the category 'other spores' (Table 1) a fair number of these may be included. For this particular spora, 60–70% of the spores appear to be either ascospores or ballistospores, which are liberated by a process of violent discharge. Of the remainder, the single largest element is *Cladosporium*, the dry spores of which are not shot away.

In considering the release of spores into the air, it is easy to distinguish between violent and passive liberation. In violent discharge, potential energy engendered in the fungus itself is suddenly released for spore projection; in the so-called passive processes, the external kinetic energy of wind, falling raindrops or moving animals leads to the take-off of the spores.

VIOLENT DISCHARGE

In fungi there are two major kinds of violent discharge. In the first turgid living cells are involved, and, therefore, discharge can take place only under reasonably damp conditions. In the second discharge is associated with the process of drying.

Ascomycetes

Some spores are discharged by the controlled bursting of turgid living cells. This type of mechanism is found especially in Ascomycetes, the largest group of fungi. Although in some species ascospores are not discharged, they are shot away in the great majority of species. The mature ascus is essentially a turgid cell with a thin stretched cell wall. This is lined by an equally thin layer of cytoplasm which surrounds a large central vacuole of ascus sap in the upper part of which the spores are suspended. There is a considerable hydrostatic pressure within the ascus developed osmotically. Eventually the ascus ruptures apically by

Table 1. *Fungal spores in summer air, Silwood Park*

	Percentage total catch	
	Site S	Site M
Ascospores	14	7·5
Ballistospores	56	47·5
(Mirror yeasts)	(35)	(28·5)
Conidia	17	32
(*Cladosporium*)	(15·5)	(28·5)
Other spores	13	13

(Derived from the extensive data given by Lacey (1962).)

the development of a pore or by the hinging backwards of a lid. When this happens, the stretched ascus wall contracts and the contents are squirted out (Fig. 1 *a*).

In some asci the spores clearly escape in succession. For example, in *Trichoglossum hirsutum* when the apical pore develops, one of the eight long, needle-like, ascospores is driven into the pore temporarily stoppering the ascus. The spore then gathers speed and is shot away. Before there is significant loss of hydrostatic pressure, another spore occupies the apical pore and this process proceeds until all are discharged, a few seconds being involved in the discharge of each (Fig. 1 *b*). This kind of behaviour seems to be a feature of many Ascomycetes in which long narrow ascospores occur, for example in *Cordyceps militaris* and in *Leptosphaeria acuta*. However, in the majority of Ascomycetes, discharge of spores from an ascus appears to be simultaneous and the escape of the ascus contents occupies a few microseconds. Nevertheless, even in these, discharge is really successive in the sense that the spores pass one by one through the apical orifice, a process conditioned by the

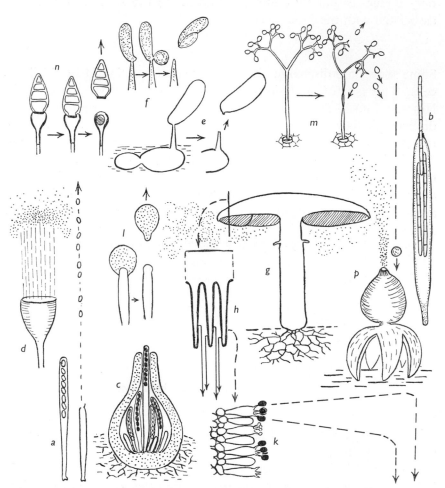

Fig. 1. *a*, Ascus of *Pyronema omphalodes* before and at the moment of discharge, × 250. *b*, Ascus of *Trichoglossum hirsutum*, the sixth spore is in the course of discharge, × 400. *c*, *Sordaria fimicola*, perithecium with an ascus about to discharge × 150. *d*, *Cookeina sulcipes*, apothecium puffing, × 1. *e*, *Sporobolomyces roseus*, yeast cell in slime bearing ballistospore on aerial sterigma, also discharged ballistospore showing minute projecting hilum, × 2,500. *f*, *Calocera cornea*, basidiospore discharge; drop (or bubble) exudation at the hilar appendage, and discharged spore apparently still with drop (after Buller, 1922). *g–k*, *Agaricus campestris*: *g*, longitudinal section of sporophore attached to mycelium in soil and with spore-cloud escaping × 1; *h*, tangential vertical section along indicated line in *g*; hymenium on gills shown by thick black line and trajectories of some discharged spores indicated, × 8; *k*, part of hymenium with basidia at various stages of development and trajectories of two discharged spores indicated, × 500. *l*, *Entomophthora coronata*; mechanism of spore discharge, × 500. *m*, *Peronospora tabacina*; spore discharge by conidiophore twirling on drying, highly magnified after Pinckard (1942). *n*, *Deightoniella torulosa*. Discharge of conidium following water-rupture in terminal cell of conidiophore. Gas-phase shaded. × 270 after Meredith.

fact that the width of the unstretched opening is less than the diameter of the escaping spores.

The ascus is a spore-gun of relatively long range. Ascospores may be shot to a distance of up to 50 cm. (e.g. in *Podospora fimicola*), although some are discharged to a much shorter distance. For most species the range is 0·5–2·0 cm. A major factor determining the range would seem to be spore size. It should, in passing, be noted that, for particles of the size of fungal spores, the difference between vertical and horizontal distance of throw appears to be negligible.

Long ago Buller (1909) suggested that the distance (D) of horizontal throw of a minute spherical projectile of radius 'r' discharged with a given velocity could be expressed by $D = Kr^2$, where K is a constant. If in asci the force of discharge (as indicated by the initial velocity given to the issuing projectile) is generally much the same, if the projectiles are spherical, and if the discharge situation is truly represented by $D = Kr^2$, a straight line should relate points on a graph of distance of discharge plotted against $V^{\frac{2}{3}}$, where V is the volume of the projectile. Available data from Ingold (1961) and from Walkey & Harvey (1966) are plotted in Fig. 2. No very clear straightline relationship is apparent, which suggests that differences in distance of throw are determined not merely by projectile size, but also by differences in vigour of discharge from species to species. It must also be borne in mind that the projectiles are not often spherical and that calculations of their sizes are based on the dimensions of the spores and take no account of associated ascus sap.

In spite of the absence of a regular association of projectile size and distance of discharge, Ascomycetes which shoot their spores to relatively great distances have large spores, or have the spores bound together into a single mass, or have both these features. For example, the 30 cm. discharge distance of *Dasyobolus immersus* is associated with a projectile of eight big spores (60×35 microns) glued together into a single mass (Buller, 1909). Spores of fungi such as this do not contribute to the air spora but are dispersed by animals. Most spores of the air spora are smaller and, indeed, tend to be around 10 microns or less in diameter. Ascospores of these dimensions are usually discharged to 0·5–2·0 cm., but even for ground-based ascocarps this distance is often sufficient to get the spores through the laminar boundary layer of air (which is still or in laminar flow) into the turbulent layers above, with consequent possibilities of significant dispersal. It is, however, to be noted that most of the Ascomycetes are not to be found on the ground, but as saprophytes on twigs, old herbaceous stems and leaves, or as parasites on the aerial parts of plants.

In flask fungi (Pyrenomycetes) a single ascus at a time normally elongates up the neck-canal of the perithecium to discharge its spores as soon as its tip projects through the ostiole (Fig. 1 c); whilst in cup-fungi (Discomycetes) the apothecium has an exposed hymenium of thousands of parallel asci intermixed with paraphyses. In the apothecium the simultaneous discharge of numerous ripe asci is possible. This phenomenon, 'puffing', tends to occur after a period of quiescence, triggered off by a gust of wind or by a shaft of sunlight suddenly falling on the

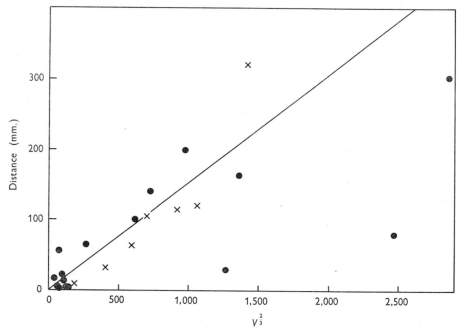

Fig. 2. Spore discharge in Ascomycetes. Average distance of discharge (mm.) plotted against $V^{\frac{2}{3}}$, where V is the mean volume in cubic microns of the projectile. The crosses derived from Ingold (1961, Table 3); the dots from Walkey & Harvey (1966, Table 3); the dot for *Podospora decipiens* (64-spore var.) falls far to the right of the figure with a distance of discharge of 365 mm. and a $V^{\frac{2}{3}}$ value of 4,793. The abitrary somewhat diagonal straight line serves only to indicate the general directional trend of dots and crosses.

hymenium. Thus 'puffing' is apt to occur under conditions which involve mechanical or thermal turbulence conducive to dispersal. From cup-shaped apothecia the issuing 'puff' tends to be a parallel beam of spores, because the positive phototropism of the individual asci directs the jet from each ascus towards the mouth of the apothecium (Fig. 1 d).

Generally speaking Ascomycetes are drought-enduring xerophytes. Although able to survive drying, apothecia and especially perithecia can function only after being wetted by rain. In dry air, spore discharge soon stops, to be renewed after the next shower. There are exceptions. Thus *Daldinia concentrica* and *Epichloe typhina* are not immediately dependent on rain for discharge; but the few exceptions only emphasize the rule. This relationship of spore expulsion to rainfall has been demonstrated repeatedly in relation to a number of plant pathogens (Ingold, 1965). It is also reflected in the nature of the damp-air spora noted by Gregory (1961) with its richness in elongated spores, probably mostly ascospores.

Provided that the water requirements of the fungus are fully satisfied, other factors may limit spore discharge in Ascomycetes. Some, perhaps the majority, are light-sensitive. In some (e.g. species of *Sordaria*, *Nectria* and *Ascobolus*) light strongly stimulates discharge; whilst in others (e.g. species of *Hypoxylon*, *Xylaria* and *Daldinia*) light has the opposite effect. Again, as would be expected, temperature is an important factor. Although there is not much critical information, in *Sordaria fimicola* it is known that little discharge occurs below 10° C, and this may well be fairly typical (Ingold, 1965).

Ballistospores

Ballistospores contribute a major element to the air spora particularly in rural areas. These spores are produced mainly by Hymenomycetes, the principal division of higher Basidiomycetes, and by the 'mirror-yeasts' (Sporobolomycetaceae) (Fig. 1 e). These yeasts are now recognized as extremely abundant, growing particularly as surface saprophytes on senescent leaves where they contribute largely to the flora of the 'phyllosphere'.

The ballistospore occurs asymmetrically at the end of a fine aerial sterigma. Near its junction with this the spore has a projection (hilar appendix). Immediately before discharge a drop (or bubble) appears there, grows in a few seconds to a definite size, and then suddenly the spore is shot away to a distance of usually 0·1–0·2 mm. (Fig. 1f). A spore gun of very short range is involved.

In Hymenomycetes each basidium usually produces four basidiospores and these are ballistospores. At maturity all four are almost always discharged in succession with up to half a minute intervening between the liberation of sister spores.

Basidia in Hymenomycetes occur in close palisade covering the surface of vertical geotropic gills (in agarics), lining exactly vertical tubes (in bolets and bracket polypores), covering geotropic teeth (in *Hydnum*) or on the surface of upright branches (as in coral fungi such as *Clavaria*). The basidia are for the most part horizontal and, except in clavarioid fungi, protected from rain, which can temporarily ruin the hymenium.

In contrast it may be noted that a hymenium of asci is largely unaffected by being wetted.

To take an agaric as an example (Fig. 1 g–k), the vertical gills, though closely packed, are farther apart than the distance of basidiospore discharge. The spores are shot more or less horizontally into the intergill spaces and then fall vertically. On emerging below the cap they stand a reasonable chance of dropping into turbulent air and thus being incorporated in the air spora. The thick stipe of the agaric has clearly two major functions. Its rigidity allows the spores to drop freely from the cap, and it raises the pileus above the ground so that effective dispersal of the liberated spores is more likely (Ingold, 1965).

In the Basidiomycetes, such as *Agaricus campestris*, the mushroom, three phases of the organism can be recognized: the long-lived feeding mycelium forming a three-dimensional network hidden away in the nutrient substratum, the soil; the short-lived but conspicuous sporophore, essentially an apparatus concerned with the production and liberation of spores; and the diffusing spore cloud, to which half a million spores a minute may be added from a fair-sized mushroom (Fig. 1 g).

The nature of the mechanism of ballistospore discharge is still uncertain. Discharge may occur by sudden rounding-off of spore and sterigma at the small, flat interface where they meet. This mechanism would be similar to that, described below, in *Entomophthora coronata* (Fig. 1 l). Again it has been suggested that sterigma may burst apically, squirting out a jet of fluid carrying the spore with it. This would be a *Pilobolus*-type of discharge on a microscopic scale. The difficulty here is that the successive discharge of spores from a basidium would involve the immediate sealing of each vacated sterigma to maintain the hydrostatic pressure in the basidium for the discharge of subsequent spores. Further, neither of these two suggestions explains the asymmetrical position of the ballistospore on its sterigma nor takes into account the production of the drop (or bubble) at the hilar appendix. Interest in the problem has been revived by the suggestion (Olive, 1964) that what is produced at the hilar appendix is a bubble, or gas-filled blister, which on reaching a certain size bursts thereby jerking the spore off the sterigma. No doubt this theory will be put to the test in the near future but there are still a few difficulties in the way of its acceptance.

Whatever may be the precise mechanism, it seems clear that only under damp conditions, when the cells involved are fully turgid, can ballistospore discharge occur. The sterigmata projecting from the gills of an agaric or into the tubes of a polypore are normally in a saturated atmosphere. Although drying soon leads to cessation of spore discharge in most hymenomycetes the response to rain is not so immediate, perhaps, as with Ascomycetes. However, in the phyllosphere of senescent leaves, response to changes in dampness of the air is much more rapid and the very early morning maximum of ballistospores of mirror-yeasts in the spora of country air is probably related to the necessity for high humidity for ballistospore development and discharge.

Conidial discharge

Many types of conidia are represented in the air spora, but few of these become airborne as a result of violent discharge. Nevertheless, in some conidial fungi (and conidial forms are to be found in all major groups of fungi) discharge does occur.

We may now consider types in which spore release is due to the activity of turgid cells and therefore damp conditions are necessary. Two subtypes can be recognized. In the first, discharge is due to the sudden rounding-off of distorted turgid cells; in the second actual bursting of turgid cells is involved.

The small phycomycete order Entomophthorales includes fungi, often parasites of insects, in which discharge is the rule. A well-known example is *Entomophthora coronata* (Martin, 1925) in which discharge of the single, large, terminal conidium to a distance of up to 4 cm. is effected by the eversion of part of the spore which, up to the instant of discharge, is pushed inwards as a columella at the end of the straight conidiophore (Fig. 1*l*). A similar rounding-off mechanism is responsible for the discharge of conidia in the downy mildew *Sclerospora philippinensis*, but in this the area of contact between spore and conidiophore is minute and flat (Weston, 1923). Nevertheless, the sudden rounding-off of spore hilum and conidiophore tip in this region is sufficient to discharge the spore, but only to a fraction of a millimetre. It might also be remarked that the violent discharge of aecidiospores in rust fungi (Uredinales) is due to the sudden rounding-off of these turgid spores in the exposed layers of the aecidial cups (Dodge, 1924).

Water-squirting mechanisms also occur. In *Entomophthora muscae*, fly cholera, the conidiophores, which erupt in band-like tufts from the abdomen of the parasitized fly after its death, burst and squirt their spores to a distance of 1–2 cm. A somewhat similar mechanism is responsible for violent discharge of the large black conidia of *Nigrospora sphaerica*, an imperfect fungus common on old grass stalks (Webster, 1952). Again it has been suggested that spore-release in *Pyricularia oryzae*, blast of rice, is due to bursting of the minute stalk-cell below the conidium (Ingold, 1964).

Passing to examples in which spore discharge occurs as a result of drying, two types may be recognized. First, those in which hygroscopic movements are involved; secondly, those in which the rupture of tensile water releases the mechanism of discharge.

Drying, twirling movements of the main axis of the conidiophore in *Peronospora tabacina* (Pinckard, 1942) throw off the finely poised spores (Fig. 1*m*), and a similar mechanism may possibly also operate at times in *Botrytis cinerea* (Jarvis, 1962). Again in some slime moulds, especially *Trichia* spp., hygroscopic movements of the spirally thickened elaters discharge the associated spores as an opened sporangium dries (Ingold, 1939).

A different type of mechanism has been described by Meredith (1961) in *Deightoniella torula*. In this the septate conidium is borne singly on an erect conidiophore. The uppermost cell of this is thick-walled, but the thickening is unequally distributed, a thinner zone occurring around the region where the conidium is attached. In dry air, as water evaporates from this cell, the consequent reduction in volume is accommodated by the apical part being drawn inwards. The cell, however, tends to return to its original shape and is retained in a distorted form only by the cohesion of the water molecules within and by their adhesion to the cell wall. The strain increases as evaporation proceeds. Ultimately the water within breaks. Instantaneously a gas phase, presumably water vapour, appears as the terminal cell of the conidiophore resumes its original shape, throwing off the conidium in so doing (Fig. 1*n*). Meredith has described a similar mechanism in a number of other genera of dematiaceous Hyphomycetes and it will probably be found to operate in many more. The same type of mechanism is involved in slinging spores out of the opened fern sporangium.

PASSIVE LIBERATION

We may now turn to processes of liberation in which the spores do not become part of the air spora as a result of violent discharge. Amongst the great range of conidial fungi two broad categories can be recognized: slime-spore and dry-spore types. In the former, spores cannot be blown from their parent sporophores by wind and either insects or water splash are involved in spore release. Splash dispersal has become increasingly recognized as a significant factor in the spread of many fungal diseases of plants. Here, however, we are concerned with this process only in so far as it adds to the population of spores in the air. In any comprehensive quantitative listing of the air spora slime-spore conidial fungi occur, but in total they rarely contribute greatly and are generally less than 1 % of the total. The two commonest genera are *Fusarium* and *Pullularia*.

Rain

The basic operation of splash in the liberation of slime-spores has been revealed by the work of Gregory, Guthrie & Bunce (1959). Particularly

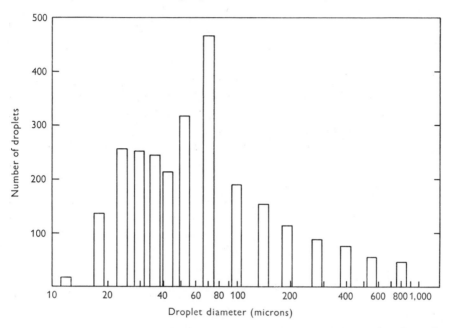

Fig. 3. Numbers of droplets classified in size-ranges from one splash from a drop 5 mm. in diameter falling 7·4 m. on to a wetted twig of *Acer pseudoplatanus* bearing conidial fructifications of *Nectria cinnabarina*. (After Gregory, Guthrie & Bunce, 1959.)

illuminating in the present connexion are their data relating to spore liberation from conidial stromata of *Nectria cinnabarina* growing on a twig. It was found that a large drop of water striking the already wet stromata broke into 2,000 or more reflected droplets (all of which carried spores) varying in size from 12 to 800 microns (Fig. 3). The great majority of reflected droplets in a situation of this kind are too large to stay airborne, although some may be thrown to a distance of 20–30 cm. However, the smaller ones, perhaps below 20 microns, add to the air spora.

Falling raindrops are also effective in causing the conidia of typically dry-spore fungi to become airborne. Jarvis (1962) studied the conidia of

Botrytis cinerea in the air of raspberry plantations when the fruit was ripe and affected by grey mould. Although the main spore liberation is most frequently associated with blow-off during windy midday periods of a dry day, a heavy shower on a relatively calm night may also result in massive spore liberation. Jarvis suggests that the percussion waves associated with the impact of large falling raindrops may blast spores from the mouldy fruit. This phenomenon has been the subject of experiments by Hirst & Stedman (1963) using a variety of dry-spore fungi. It is difficult to distinguish between two effects of a drop on impact: first the shaking given to the target and secondly the actual percussion waves generated. Hirst and Stedman suggest that a brief way of referring to these two processes would be 'rain tap' and 'puff'. So many conidial fungi grow on stems and leaves both living and dead that stem vibration and leaf flutter produced by heavy rain must be a significant factor in the 'passive' liberation of spores. The aerobiologists have repeatedly observed steep increases in the air spore on the onset of heavy rain. However, it must be remembered that continued heavy rain also is most effective in scrubbing spores out of the air (see: Ludlam, p. 12; Chamberlain, p. 155).

Large raindrops and drips from the leaf canopy of a wood are also involved in liberating spores by a bellows mechanism from puff-balls (*Lycoperdon* spp.) and earth-stars (*Geastrum* spp.) (Gregory, 1949). A large drop falling on the thin, dry, unwettable capsule momentarily depresses the capsule wall causing a visible puff of spores to escape through the ostiole to a height of several centimetres (Fig. 1 *p*).

Wind

For many dry-spore conidial fungi, wind is an important factor in spore release. In contact with the ground, or indeed with any surface, is a laminar boundary layer through which spores must pass to the turbulent regions beyond to have a chance of effective dispersal. This layer may be only a fraction of a millimetre thick, but at times, particularly at night in fine weather, it may become much thicker. Under conditions of strong turbulence, eddies can break through this skin and pick up dry spores from a surface. Nevertheless, even a slight elevation of the spores above the surface is probably a help in getting them airborne and the significance of relatively long conidiophores is no doubt associated with this. Most common mould fungi (e.g. species of *Cladosporium, Penicillium, Aspergillus, Trichothecium*) have conidiophores 100–200 microns high. Also it should be noted that relatively few conidiophores are situated at ground level. Most occur on living or dead vegetation some way above this general level. The air spora does not seem to be recruited to any extent from the abundant soil fungus flora. It might have been expected that many of the fungal propagules in the air would be associated with dust particles blown off soil. However, this does not seem to be so and an examination of slides from a Hirst spore trap suggests that most of the spores seen on them have been liberated directly from their sporophores into the air.

Few quantitative studies have been made of the 'passive' liberation of spores of microfungi by wind. Zoberi (1961) studied take-off from cultures grown in long horizontal tubes through which air at known speeds and of controlled humidity could be drawn. His results for *Trichothecium roseum* are fairly representative. Under the influence of a rapid air stream most spores were liberated at the outset and very reduced numbers later. The initial rate of blow-off was greater the stronger the air current, dry air being much more effective than damp air. Smith (1966) has studied blow-off of uredospores from sori of *Puccinia graminis in situ* using a set-up rather similar to that of Zoberi, but more satisfactory because the uredosori were placed in midstream of the horizontal tube which was essentially a small wind-tunnel. A direct relationship between wind speed and spore liberation was observed.

CIRCADIAN PERIODICITY

A striking feature of the air spora, revealed especially by studies involving the use of a Hirst trap, is the circadian periodicity shown by individual species when averaged over sufficiently long periods. For some the maximum is in the morning before dawn (e.g. 'mirror' yeasts), or shortly after sunrise (e.g. *Deightoniella*), or during late morning (e.g. *Phytophthora infestans*), or early in the afternoon (e.g. *Cladosporium, Alternaria, Ustilago*).

Periodicity as recorded in a trap operating at the usual 1 m. above ground does not necessarily reflect a corresponding rhythm in spore liberation. Thus if we consider a cup-fungus on the ground discharging its spores at a steady rate to a height of 1–2 cm., few spores liberated during fine nights, when the air tends to be still, would be caught by a nearby trap, but during the turbulent conditions so often associated with the middle part of the day many more would reach the trap.

Nevertheless, where the Hirst trap does reveal a circadian periodicity, this may often be related to periodic spore release.

Circadian periodicity of spore release is normally determined by one or more of the major environmental factors which also show rhythms of this kind, namely light, temperature, relative humidity and wind velocity. Of these the most emphatic periodicity is exhibited by light. Temperature also rarely departs from a daytime maximum and a minimum by night. Normally relative humidity is high at night and low during the day time, but this rhythm is often upset when high relative humidity persists during days on end. So far as wind is concerned in many regions it is only by averaging over relatively long periods that the greater windiness of the day as compared with night-time becomes apparent.

The periodicity of spore release in a certain fungus may be determined by a combination of these external factors, but probably more commonly a particular factor is involved. In a number of Ascomycetes, light seems to be the dominating factor provided that the water supply is not limiting. *Hypoxylon* spp. and *Xylaria* spp. are firmly nocturnal, whilst *Sordaria fimicola* and *Ascobolus* spp. are essentially diurnal. It is to be noted that light probably affects the last stages of maturation rather than the actual discharge mechanism. Probably in a number of fungi a day-time maximum in spore release is related to temperature. This seems to be so in *Fomes annosus* in which light does not affect discharge and the spores are set free in the still, saturated air of the hymenial tubes. High relative humidity is probably the determining factor in the peak occurrence of members of Sporobolomycetaceae in the air spora after midnight. However, light may also be involved. It has been shown (Bridger, 1967) that in Petri dish cultures exposed to 12 hr. light alternating with 12 hr. of darkness each day, discharge is mainly in the dark periods. So far as wind is concerned the midday periodicity of spores of *Ustilago nuda* (loose smut of barley) in the air seems to be related to wind, which on average is strongest at that time of day. The erect, stiff stalks with their terminal smutted ears stand above the heavy nodding healthy heads and scatter spores when they vibrate in the wind.

CONCLUSION

In fungi the spores are essentially airborne and on considering fungal structure this should be constantly borne in mind. It is becoming increasingly clear that the various types of structural organization relating to spore release are of profound significance in the success of fungi as terrestrial organisms.

REFERENCES

BRIDGER, D. H. (1967). Spore liberation in *Sporobolomyces* in relation to light. *Proc. Linn. Soc. Lond.* (in the Press).

BULLER, A. H. R. (1909). *Researches on Fungi. I.* London.

BULLER, A. H. R. (1922). *Researches on Fungi. II.* London.

DODGE, B. O. (1924). Aecidiospore discharge as related to the character of the spore wall. *J. agric. Res.* **27**, 749.

GREGORY, P. H. (1949). The operation of the puff-ball mechanism of *Lycoperdon perlatum* by raindrops shown by ultra-high-speed Schlieren cinematography. *Trans. Br. mycol. Soc.* **32**, 11.

GREGORY, P. H. (1961). *The Microbiology of the Atmosphere.* London: Leonard Hill Ltd.

GREGORY, P. H., GUTHRIE, E. J. & BUNCE, M. E. (1959). Experiments on splash dispersal of fungus spores. *J. gen. Microbiol.* **20**, 328.

HIRST, J. M. & STEDMAN, O. J. (1963). Dry liberation of fungus spores by raindrops. *J. gen. Microbiol.* **33**, 335.

INGOLD, C. T. (1939). *Spore Discharge in Land Plants.* Oxford.

INGOLD, C. T. (1961). Ballistics in certain Ascomycetes. *New Phytol.* **60**, 143.

INGOLD, C. T. (1964). Possible spore discharge mechanism in *Pyricularia*. *Trans. Br. mycol. Soc.* **47**, 573.

INGOLD, C. T. (1965). *Spore Liberation.* Oxford.

JARVIS, W. R. (1962). The dispersal of spores of *Botrytis cinerea* Fr. in a raspberry plantation. *Trans. Br. mycol. Soc.* **45**, 549.

LACEY, M. (1962). The summer air-spora of two contrasting adjacent rural sites. *J. gen. Microbiol.* **29**, 485.

MARTIN, G. W. (1925). Morphology of *Conidiobolus villosus*. *Bot. Gaz.* **80**, 311.

MEREDITH, D. S. (1961). Spore discharge in *Deightoniella torulosa* (Syd.) Ellis. *Ann. Bot.*, N.S. **25**, 271.

OLIVE, L. S. (1964). Spore discharge mechanism in Basidiomycetes. *Science*, **146**, 542.

PINCKARD, J. A. (1942). The mechanism of spore dispersal in *Peronospora tabacina* and certain other downy mildew fungi. *Phytopathology*, **32**, 505.

SMITH, R. S. (1966). The liberation of cereal stem rust uredospores under various environmental conditions in a wind tunnel. *Trans. Br. mycol. Soc.* **49**, 33.

WALKEY, D. G. A. & HARVEY, R. (1966). Studies of the ballistics of ascospores. *New Phytol.* **65**, 59.

WEBSTER, J. (1952). Spore projection in the hyphomycete *Nigrospora sphaerica*. *New Phytol.* **51**, 229.

WELLS, K. (1965). Ultrastructural features of developing and mature basidia and basidiospores of *Schizophyllum commune*. *Mycologia*, **57**, 236.

WESTON, W. H. (1923). Production and dispersal of conidia in the Philippine Sclerosporas of maize. *J. Agric. Res.* **23**, 239.

ZOBERI, M. H. (1961). Take-off of mould spores in relation to wind speed and humidity. *Ann. Bot.*, N.S. **25**, 53.

TAKE-OFF OF BACTERIA AND VIRUSES

O. M. LIDWELL

*Cross-Infection Reference Laboratory, Central Public Health
Laboratory, Colindale, London, N.W. 9*

INTRODUCTION

Bacteria and viruses are found in the air. How do they get there and how do the processes by which they become airborne affect this state? These micro-organisms have not developed any special structures to facilitate their dispersion into the atmosphere so that this can only occur as a consequence of adventitious physical disturbances (see Lidwell (1964) for a general discussion of the processes involved).

The increased nasal secretion during a cold, the coughing associated with a sore throat or pulmonary tuberculosis, and the diarrhoea accompanying most intestinal infections are examples of host responses which promote dispersal of the pathogen into the environment. The ability to provoke such responses is therefore a character advantageous to the pathogen which, having often only a limited residence time in the host, is more dependent than the saprophyte on transmission from host to host. Nearly all studies of the dissemination of micro-organisms into the air have been concerned with bacteria directly pathogenic to human beings or with species thought likely to serve as models for the spread of pathogens. The technical difficulty of isolating viruses from air have so far limited their study to a few preliminary observations. There is no reason to suppose that the general considerations governing their dispersal differ from those applying to the bacteria and, as methods improve, detailed studies of particular factors important for individual viruses will certainly be made.

TALKING, COUGHING AND SNEEZING

During talking, coughing and sneezing, fast air streams are forced through constricted apertures. The mucous surfaces are wetted with more or less viscous secretions. Some of the fluid is picked up by the air stream and broken down into droplets. The size distribution of these will depend on the velocity of the air stream, the viscosity of the fluid, and the extent to which the shape of the respiratory passages causes loss of sprayed particles by impingement. The physical parameters of these processes are discussed by Jennison (1942) who gives a useful list of references, and illustrates the act of droplet production by high-speed photographs.

Sneezing is the most vigorous action of the three, and commonly generates as many as a million droplets below 100 microns in diameter as well as many thousands of larger particles (Duguid, 1945). These are almost exclusively formed from the saliva at the front of the mouth (Bourdillon & Lidwell, 1941; Jennison, 1941), only occasionally is nasal secretion also expelled and this is not often effectively atomized, owing partly to its greater viscosity. In the early stages of an upper respiratory infection, however, the nasal secretion is greatly increased in quantity and reduced in viscosity so that the possibilities of its dispersal seem to be much greater than from healthy subjects, but there do not appear to be any satisfactory studies of this point.

Talking, apart from the contemptuous snort, is entirely a mouth activity. As a moment's casual observation shows, the numbers of droplets dispersed by different speakers differ very widely (Bourdillon, Lidwell & Lovelock, 1948). Most dispersal is obviously associated with the enunciation of the consonants, but the numbers are not large in normal speech. Duguid (1945) found an average of only 250 droplets on declaiming 100 words. (Hare & Thomas (1956) reported that dispersal of *Staphylococcus aureus* directly from the upper respiratory tract of nasal carriers of this organism was only achieved by vigorous snorting.)

Coughing is a semi-voluntary reflex designed to clear the pharyngeal region of obstruction, e.g. by viscous mucous secretion. This is brought forward into the mouth to be disposed of by spitting or swallowing. In addition to the direct dispersal of secretion formed in the pharynx, or reaching this area from the nose or bronchi, coughing may also contaminate the saliva with these secretions so that they may be subsequently dispersed by talking or sneezing. The preliminary deep inspiration which provides the air volume needed for a sneeze is usually omitted before coughing so that the expelled air stream is less in quantity and velocity. In addition, the surface of the palate acts as a baffle to trap a substantial proportion of any droplets produced. Consequently the numbers of droplets expelled in a cough are far fewer than in a sneeze and have a larger median diameter (Jennison, 1942; Duguid, 1945).

Not all the droplets expelled from the mouth become airborne. Wells (1934) reasoned that while aqueous droplets exceeding 100–200 microns diameter would fall to the ground before evaporation, those initially smaller than this would evaporate down to their non-volatile residuum in about 1 sec. or less and remain suspended as 'droplet-nuclei'.

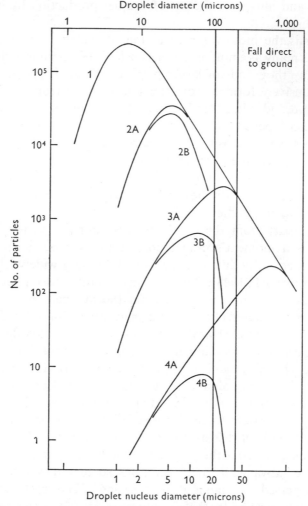

Fig. 1. The size distribution of the particles of secretion expelled by sneezing and of the resulting 'droplet nuclei'. The curves represent: 1, The numbers and size distribution of the expelled droplets produced by one average sneeze (10^6 droplets). 2 A, The numbers and size distribution of those droplets carrying one or more viable units for a level of infection in the secretion of 10^8 viable units per ml. 2 B, The relative exposure to the droplet nuclei of different sizes formed by evaporation of the droplets described by the curve 2 A. For exposure in a room 10 ft. high ventilated at four air changes per hour. 3 A, 3 B, 4 A, 4 B, The same distributions as illustrated in 2 A and 2 B but resulting from levels of infection in the secretion of 10^6 viable units per ml. for 3 A and 3 B, and 10^4 viable units per ml. for 4 A and 4 B. The figure is drawn on a double log scale so that a log-normal distribution of particle size would appear as a symmetrical curve with approximately linear tails. The scale at the top of the figure gives the sizes of the original droplets; the bottom scale gives the resulting droplet nuclei (curves B), assuming evaporation to a residuum of 1·25 %. The relative exposure is calculated from the droplet nucleus diameter, d microns, as $K/(0·036d^2+4)$, where K represents the proportion of droplets which evaporate before falling to the floor. K is taken as 1·0 for droplets less than 100 microns diameter, 0 for droplets over 200 microns diameter, 0·3, and 0·1 for droplets 125 and 150 microns diameter respectively. The settling rate of a particle in still air is taken as $0·36d^2$ ft./hr. The details of this kind of calculation are discussed by Lidwell (1948). The curves are based on the data given by Duguid (1946).

Duguid (1946) determined the size distributions of the droplets expelled during each of the three activities, and deduced the numbers and size distribution of those droplets which would contain one or more micro-organisms at a variety of assumed levels of infection of the

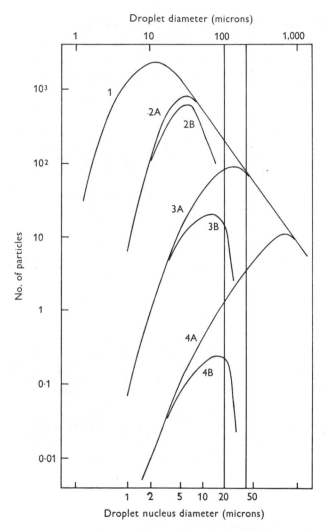

Fig. 2. The size distribution of the particles of secretion expelled by coughing or talking and of the resulting droplet nuclei. 1, The numbers and size distribution of the expelled droplets produced by two coughs or speaking loudly 4,000 words (10^4 droplets). 2 A, 3 A, 4 A, The numbers and size distribution of those droplets carrying one or more viable units for levels of infection in the secretion of 10^8, 10^6 and 10^4 viable units per ml. 2 B, 3 B, 4 B, The relative exposure to the droplet nuclei of different sizes formed by evaporation of the droplets described by the curves 2 A, 3 A, 4 A. The methods of representation and calculation are the same as for Fig. 1. The curves are based on the data given by Duguid (1946).

secretions. The combined effects of loss by sedimentation and density of viable organisms in the secretion are shown in Figs. 1 and 2, which are based on the data given by Duguid. The droplets produced by coughing and talking have a median diameter nearly twice those from a sneeze. Since, however, only the larger sized droplets are likely to contain viable cells, even at concentrations as high as 10^8 per ml. of secretion, the size distributions of the droplet nuclei resulting from these activities show only trivial differences. It is of interest also to note that if the secretion contains 10^6 viable units per ml. or less, then the size distribution of the

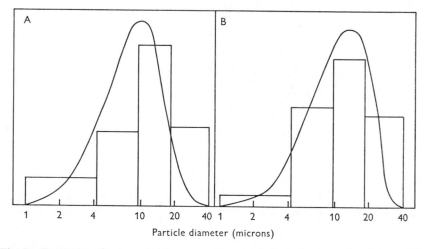

Particle diameter (microns)

Fig. 3. The size distribution of airborne particles, presumptively of mouth origin, carrying streptococci. A, The histogram shows the size distribution of all the mouth streptococci. The full line is the size distribution of the infected droplet nuclei produced by talking or coughing for a level of infection in the secretion of 10^7 viable units per ml. (comparable to curves 2 B, 3 B and 4 B in Fig. 2). B, The histogram shows the size distribution of those particles carrying *Streptococcus salivarius*. The full line is the size distribution of the infected droplet nuclei produced by talking or coughing for a level of infection in the secretion of 10^6 viable units per ml. (the same curve allowing for changes of scale, as 3 B in Fig. 2). The scale of particle size is logarithmic. All the curves have been normalized to enclose the same areas. The data for the airborne streptococcus-carrying particles are taken from observations made in a group of clerical offices (Kingston, Lidwell & Williams, 1962).

resulting airborne bacteria- (or virus-) carrying particles is almost invariant with a median equivalent particle diameter of about 13 microns. At these concentrations very few of the airborne particles will contain more than one independent viable unit, about 7% at 10^6 independent viable units per ml. As the concentration of micro-organisms in the secretion increases, however, so will the proportion of particles carrying more than a single viable unit, e.g. at a concentration of 10^8 per ml. the proportion will be over 40%, including most of those with an initial diameter exceeding 25 microns (corresponding to a dried particle size over 5 microns for a fluid such as saliva having a solid content somewhat less than 1 %).

Some field studies in occupied environments have shown reasonable agreement with this model. Viridans streptococci form the most numerous group of micro-organisms in normal saliva, usually between 10^7 and 10^8 per ml. *Streptococcus salivarius* comprises upwards of one-tenth of the mouth streptococci. The number of these organisms found in the air of school classrooms was found to be correlated with talking, rather than with the activity of the children, which suggested that they were indeed being dispersed into the air, at least principally, directly from the mouth. The sizes of the airborne particles involved were roughly estimated in these studies (Williams, Lidwell & Hirch, 1956), but a later series of observations in offices in Newcastle (Kingston *et al.* 1962) included estimates of the particle size distribution. These are shown in Fig. 3 compared with those deduced from Duguid's data. Both the absolute values of particle size and the slightly increased median particle size of the less numerous *Streptococcus salivarius* agree with expectation. The particle sizes deduced from the office observations are, however, rather greater than those predicted. This discrepancy may have been due to experimental error. The actual concentration of organisms in the mouth secretions was not known, and should perhaps be reduced by a factor to allow for the death of some of the organisms during the production of droplet nuclei.

THE DISSEMINATION OF *STAPHYLOCOCCUS AUREUS* INTO THE AIR

The great interest in the spread of staphylococcal infection in hospitals during the last decade has led to very extensive publication on all aspects of the subjects. Much of this is of limited value, but sufficient apparently reliable and independently confirmed experimental work has now been reported to form a picture of the dissemination process.

The references here given are, of necessity, very selective. In particular, similar ideas appear many times over a wide period of years with differing degrees of emphasis. No implication of priority attaches to the reference cited in a particular connexion. A classified list of 2,450 references (up to June 1960) on the control of staphylococcus and other hospital infections was published by the National Research Council of Canada (Bibliography, 1960, 1961).

Staphylococcus aureus is a common member of the normal nasal flora. The organisms can be recovered by swabbing from between 30 and 50 %

of healthy adults (Williams, 1963; Solberg, 1965), and is present in small numbers in the air of inhabited places. However, studies with nasal carriers showed that direct dispersal from the upper respiratory tract did not take place to any great extent under normal conditions, but that active movements might produce large numbers of infected airborne particles (Hare & Thomas, 1956; Shooter, Smith & Hunter, 1959). The bedclothes of carriers in hospital also rapidly became infected (Noble, 1962), and much effort was made to limit the dispersal of the organism from these secondary reservoirs by the use of residual disinfectants or particle-retaining oils, by more frequent changes to clean bed-coverings and by the use of different materials (Rubbo, Stratford and Dixson; 1960, Newcastle Reg. Hosp. Brd., 1962). Rubbo and his co-workers (Rubbo & Dixson, 1960; Rubbo, Pressley, Stratford & Dixson, 1960; Rubbo & Saunders, 1963) examined this form of dispersal very thoroughly and concluded that the numbers of airborne organisms dispersed were not correlated with the numbers of airborne wool-fibres from blankets but were associated with considerably smaller particles which they suggested might be cotton-fibre nuclei, the dominant component in the fine dust of the ward air, or 'Free' organisms. They also made the interesting observation that friction between two textiles appeared to be the most effective mechanism of aerial dispersion, so that placing a clean counter-pane over the blanket increased dispersal substantially. The effect disappeared if the counterpane was firmly attached to the blanket by pinning (Rubbo et al. 1962). Dispersion from textiles has usually been attributed to direct contamination of these from the upper respiratory tract followed by dispersion of the dried material, possibly attached to small fragments of textile fibre, by fricative processes. However, Hare & Thomas (1956) noted that organisms were dispersed from the naked skin of their volunteers, and large numbers of organisms presumed to have arisen from the skin were found in the air of coal mines coming from seams where the men were working completely stripped (Lidwell & Williams, 1956, unpublished observations). The microscopic examination of airborne particles from a hospital ward (Davies & Noble, 1962) showed that these included many skin scales, an observation which had been made more than 100 years earlier. They also showed that the rise in bacterial content of the air during bedmaking was closely paralleled by the rise in the numbers of airborne skin scales, and were able to obtain photomicrographs showing colonies of cocci growing on skin scales collected from the air and incubated on a nutrient agar surface.

It appears most probable therefore that the normal method of dispersal of *Staph. aureus* is by contamination of the skin from the upper respiratory tract, perhaps largely by hand contact in the first instance and that particles of desquamated skin are dispersed into the air either directly, as a result of skin movements, or after transfer to clothing or other textiles, by agitation of these.

The size distribution of the airborne particles carrying *Staph. aureus* is compatible with this hypothesis. The median equivalent particle diameter of the air-suspended skin scales was 8 microns (Davies & Noble, 1962). Although this is appreciably less than the 13 microns estimated for the particles carrying bacteria (Noble, Lidwell & Kingston, 1963) the larger skin fragments are more likely to be those carrying micro-organisms.

An interesting example of what appears to be direct dispersal from the upper respiratory tract has been reported by Eichenwald (Eichenwald, Kotsevalov & Fosso, 1960). A substantial proportion of the newborn infants in a nursery became colonized with *Staph. aureus*, phage type 80/81. Some of these infants were found to disperse large numbers of the organism into the air, as vigorously, for example, as infants infected with staphylococcal impetigo. But whereas dispersal from these latter was greatly reduced by enclosing the infant's body in a plastic bag, this procedure had no effect on the 'Cloud babies' as they were called. This enhanced dispersive capacity appeared to be closely associated with adenovirus or echovirus infection and was characterized by the small size of the particles dispersed. Most of the airborne staphylococci were associated with particles less than 5 microns in diameter, in contrast to the much larger particle sizes commonly found (Noble, Lidwell & Kingston, 1963). Direct spraying of upper respiratory tract secretion due to higher than normal air velocities through passages restricted by the action of the virus infection seems the most likely explanation of the phenomenon. However, in the absence of any confirmation of the effect it is uncertain how far this is a general phenomenon or whether it is peculiar to young infants.

Although the nose is commonly the principal or only site of multiplication of *Staph. aureus* in carriers, skin carriage can occur independently of nasal colonization. Infected lesions such as boils, small pustules or minor abrasions are obvious examples of this. Skin lesions of non-bacterial origin are especially liable to become infected, and the greatly increased rate of desquamation, as well as enhanced levels of skin carriage, often leads to such individuals acting as prolific dispersers. Selwyn (1965) conducted an investigation in some dermatological wards. The air counts of *Staph. aureus* were very high, and the dust contained a large proportion of keratin with many recognizable skin fragments. The high rate of dispersal was not significantly reduced by treating the nasal carriers with antibiotics (applied topically to the nose) but treatment of the skin with 'Rikospray antibiotic' (neomycin, bacitracin and colistin sulphate) greatly reduced both dispersal and the risks of acquisition of the organism by new patients.

The extent to which staphylococci, and *Staph. aureus* in particular, multiply on the normal skin is not known (Kligman, 1965; Blank, 1965). With *Staph. aureus*, however, multiplication on the skin appears to be of limited significance, since the treatment of nasal carriers by the application of antibiotics to the nose results in a decrease in the numbers of the organism recoverable from the skin, and of the number dispersed into the air, which corresponds closely to the decrease in the number present in the nose (Solberg, 1965). However, large numbers of *Staph. aureus* can regularly be recovered from the skin of the perineum of some individuals. Perineal carriers are often unusually active dispersers of the organism (Hare & Ridley, 1958; Ridley, 1959), and perineal carriage may exist or persist independently of nasal carriage. As the numbers of *Staph. aureus* found in the perineal samples may also be many times greater than in the faeces there seems little doubt that active multiplication can take place in this skin area. The conditions in and on the skin of the perineum differ in a number of ways from those pertaining over most of the rest of the body but the significant differences (Ridley, 1959) which lead to true carriage on this site in a minority of individuals are not known. The most extensive series of patients examined both for nasal and perineal carriage, that of Bøe, Solberg, Vogelsang & Wormnes (1964), showed 449 (12·8 %) out of 3,508 patients admitted to a medical ward to have *Staph. aureus* present on the perineum; 90 (2·8 %) of these were not carrying the organism in their upper respiratory tract. A much shorter series of 364 patients examined just before operation (Richards, Polakoff & Lidwell, unpublished observations) showed similar proportions. Forty-five (12·3 %) carried *Staph. aureus* on the perineum; of these 9 (2·5 %) were not nasal carriers and 7 (1·9 %) carried a strain on the perineum different from that found in the nose. It also appeared that independent perineal carriage was relatively much more frequent with hospital-type multiple-resistant strains than with those sensitive to all antibiotics or resistant to penicillin only. The possible importance of this in relation to the dissemination of hospital-type strains hardly needs emphasizing.

Recently, however, Solberg (1965) has attempted a fully quantitative study, and his results give the most detailed picture of carriage and dispersion yet produced. He used standardized sampling procedures to examine various areas of the body, and the numbers reported are counts per swab per person; faecal counts are organisms per gram, and hand counts were measured after a standard wash. His estimate of the total number of organisms dispersed into the air by the patient was based on a standard procedure which included occupation of a cubicle for a constant time during which the bed was made by a uniform technique and the staphylococci were enumerated by means of settle plates and air

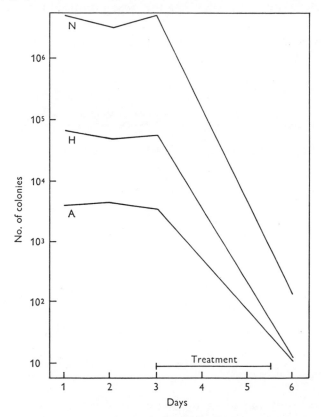

Fig. 4. Dispersion of staphylococci by nasal carriers treated with antibiotic nasal spray. The logarithmic vertical scale gives the numbers of *Staphylococcus aureus* recovered in samples taken in a standardized manner from, the nose (N), the hands (H), and the air of the room during and after bedmaking (A). During the treatment period the carriers were subjected to a nasal spray of a framycetin–gramicidin preparation 4 times a day. Data based on 40 carriers (Solberg, 1965).

samples. He examined 100 persistent nasal carriers, selected as yielding less than 1,000 *Staph. aureus* in samples from axillae, vagina, perineum and faeces, and found that the numbers of the organism recovered from the nose ranged between 10^3 and $3\cdot2 \times 10^7$ per subject. The numbers of staphylococci recovered in samples from the hands ranged up to 10^6,

and were highly correlated with the numbers found in the nose
($r > 0.8$). Only small numbers were recovered from skin areas, such as
the abdomen, which had no direct contact with the nose. The numbers
of staphylococci dispersed into the air during a standardized bedmaking
procedure varied from less than 25 up to 43,000, and were highly correlated with the nasal count ($r > 0.8$) and even more highly with the whole
hand counts ($r > 0.9$). Treatment of these carriers with an antibiotic
spray (framycetin-gramicidin) into the nose produced a parallel reduction in nasal carriage, in skin count and in air dispersal (Fig. 4). A
similar result was obtained by systemic treatment with fucidin (Bøe &
Solberg, 1965).

Table 1. *Skin contamination and aerial dissemination: perineal carriers*

No. of *Staph. aureus* (thousands)

No.	Sex	Perineum	Extra-perineal area	Hands	Air	Nose
1	F	2·5	<0·08	<0·5	<0·03	86
2	M	2·5	0·24	<0·5	0·1	12
3	M	4·0	<0·08	<0·5	0·1	38
4	M	5·5	<0·08	<0·5	<0·03	0·06
5	M	128	1·2	≮5·8	4·0	<0·04
6	F	135	≮0·08	≮0·3	2·3	<0·04
7	M	224	≮0·16	6	7	10
8	F	441	28	16	2·4	≮0·4
9	F	601	1·9	<0·5	1·2	95
10	F	621	1·0	62	19	10
11	M	640	16	26	25	0·04
12	M	1,800	9	43	11	15
13(*a*)	M	4,900	69	132	54	77
13(*b*)	M	16,800	418	930	143	10
14	M	17,600	28	455	233	112

13(*a*), 13(*b*) Two separate admissions of the same patient.
The numbers given are the mean of from two to five sets of specimens from each patient.
Adapted from Solberg (1965).

A further study was made by Solberg of fourteen persistent perineal
carriers, selected as yielding less than 1,000 *Staph. aureus* in samples
from the axillae, vagina or faeces, and less than 10^6 from the nose (in
only three did the nasal count reach or exceed the perineal count). The
numbers recovered in samples from the perineum varied between 10^3
and 2.3×10^7 (very similar to the range found in nose swabs from nasal
carriers), and these were highly correlated with the numbers recovered
from various skin area and dispersed into the air by bedmaking
(Table 1). Air contamination, however, reached much higher levels than
with the nasal carriers; the maximum estimated dispersal varied from
less than 25 up to 260,000, as much as five times greater. The effect of

antibiotic treatment was not explored with these patients, but twice daily washing of the perineum with a 3% hexachoraphane emulsion continued for 3 days almost eliminated the organism from the perineal area and greatly decreased numbers on the skin and dispersal in the air (Fig. 5). To avoid affecting the other skin areas with hexachlorophane

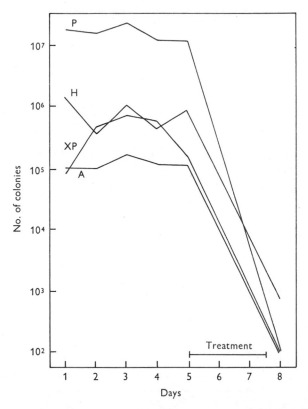

Fig. 5. Dispersion of staphylococci by a perineal carrier treated with hexachloraphane emulsion. The logarithmic vertical scale gives the numbers of *S. aureus* recovered in samples taken from: the skin of the perineum, P; the hands, H; the skin just outside the perineal area, XP; and the air of the room during and after bedmaking, A. During the treatment period the patient rubbed a 3% emulsion of hexachlorophane over the perineal area twice daily. Data from a male patient (Solberg, 1965).

directly, the emulsion was allowed to remain on the perineal area for 1 min. only before being washed off and all other areas were washed with ordinary soap.

When patients with staphylococcal-infected dermal lesions were examined, some with extensive pyodermias not only carried large numbers of the organisms in the infected lesion but (as in the patients studied by Selwyn, 1965), they dispersed these into the environment to

an even greater extent than the heaviest perineal carriers. More than
10^6 colonies of *Staph. aureus* were sometimes dispersed into the air
during bedmaking, five times greater than with the heaviest perineal
carrier. Treatment with antibiotics was ineffective, but washing the
lesions only twice daily with 3% hexachlorophane emulsion (the

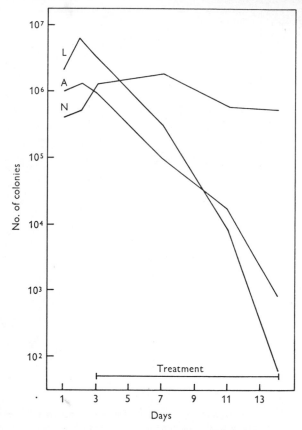

Fig. 6. Dispersion of staphylococci by a patient with dermal lesions. The logarithmic
vertical scale gives the numbers of *S. aureus* recovered in samples taken from: the lesion (L);
the air of the room during and after bedmaking (A); and from the nose (N). During the
treatment the lesions and perineal area were treated with a 3% hexachlorophane emulsion
twice daily. Data from a female patient with pyodermia involving thighs, buttocks and
lower part of the trunk (Solberg, 1965).

perineum also in the case of perineal carriers), while using ordinary soap
on the rest of the body, largely eliminated both skin carriage and dispersal, even although nasal carriage persisted (Fig. 6).

The observation of Duguid & Wallace (1948) that wearing normal
operating-room clothing only slightly reduced dispersal of micro-
organisms from the skin was repeated by Hare & Thomas (1956), but

little attention seems to have been paid to its significance in relation to the contamination of operating-room air until quite recently. Two studies (Bethune, Blowers, Parker & Pask, 1965; Blowers & McCluskey, 1965; Speers, Bernard, O'Grady & Shooter, 1965; Bernard, Speers, O'Grady & Shooter, 1965) showed that the wearing of sterile operating-room clothing did not significantly reduce dispersal of micro-organisms below the numbers liberated when wearing ordinary street clothes. Moreover, washing in a shower before donning the clean clothing often produced an increase in bacterial dissemination which was maximal about 15–30 min. after showering and did not return to normal levels until nearly 2 hr. later (Fig. 7). The mechanism of this

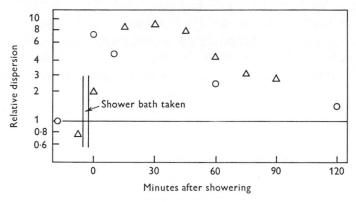

Fig. 7. Dispersion of micro-organisms before and after taking a shower bath. The circles represent samples taken from the air of the test chamber with the subjects clothed, the triangles similar samples taken when the subjects were naked. Median values have been estimated for each time from the data given by Speers, Bernard, O'Grady & Shooter (1965). (Small numbers of *S. aureus* were recovered in these experiments. Taken together, the samples collected immediately after showering and those taken 10, 60 and 120 min. after included $2\frac{1}{2}$ times as many colonies of *S. aureus* per sample as the pre-showering samples.)

increase (which was examined principally in terms of all species of micro-organisms found, not only for *Staph. aureus* specifically) has not been ascertained. It might result from the loosening of skin scales and the removal of grease and sweat which help to attach them to the skin, or it could be a consequence of rubbing bringing up bacteria from the pores and glands of the skin. Skin treatment with lanolin or with 70 % alcohol counteracted the effect, presumably by promoting mechanical adhesion of the skin scales in the first case and by disinfecting action in the second. The use of hexachlorophane soap in the shower did not reduce the total numbers of micro-organisms liberated subsequently (Bernard, Speers, O'Grady & Shooter, 1965 b; Speers, O'Grady, Shooter, Bernard & Cole, 1966). Confirmation that the dispersal was indeed derived from the skin was provided by showing that enclosing the body in an impermeable bag ('Polythene' or paper), or more usefully in a suit of tightly woven cloth ('Ventile' fabric with a nominal pore size below 10 microns), largely eliminated this source of contamination of the air. Dispersion was several times greater from below the waist than from upper parts of the body, so that the wearing only of particle-impermeable trousers effects a substantial reduction in dissemination (Bernard, 1966, personal communication). The problem of the 'heavy disperser' of staphylococcus seems to be largely explicable in terms of the numbers of organisms colonizing the carriage site, and the relative facility with which organisms from the site are able to contaminate the desquamating skin. The extensive dispersion sometimes associated with acutely ill or dying patients (Rountree & Bultean, 1965; Solberg, 1965; Lidwell, Polakoff, Robinson, Jevons & Parker, 1966) is probably explicable in terms of more widespread proliferation of the organism in these patients (Report, 1966). It is not clear whether there is any real difference between the sexes in respect of their liability to carry and disperse *Staph. aureus*. Bethune and his colleagues (Bethune *et al.* 1965) found it difficult to locate any female dispersers in a group of nurses and medical students. Solberg (1965), however, found no significant sex differences in his group of hospital patients. There are substantial changes in the conditions on the skin during sexual maturation (Behrendt, Green & Carol, 1964) and the relationship of these to skin carriage and shedding is quite unknown. Differences in clothing and ablution habits might also play a part. The rather widespread sale of soaps and other preparations containing hexachlorophane could easily lead to erroneous conclusions if not allowed for.

Hexachlorophane-containing powders and emulsions have been widely and successfully used to reduce dissemination and acquisition of *Staph. aureus* in infant nurseries but no experiments seem to have been reported on their general use in adult wards. On our present information about the dispersal of this organism, local skin treatment seems likely to be an effective control measure, although its long-term effects on the composition of the skin flora need watching (Shehadeh & Kligman, 1963).

DISPERSAL INTO THE AIR FROM SOLID SURFACES

Horizontal surfaces become bacteriologically contaminated by airborne material settling on to them. Vertical and downward-facing surfaces can attract airborne particles by electrostatic or thermal processes, demonstrated by the familiar pattern of staining above a radiator or on a heated ceiling (p. 48). Any surface may also become contaminated by direct contact with infected secretions.

The attractive forces between small particles and a smooth surface are considerable. It is therefore difficult to dislodge such particles directly into the air. No quantitative bacteriological data are available but a good deal of work has been done with various dusts especially with reference to radio-active materials (Corn & Stein, 1966; Masironi & Fisk, 1966). Only one-third of glass beads 30 microns in diameter were removed from a clean glass surface at wind speeds of over 10,000 ft./min. Corn and Stein conclude that 'the most likely mechanism for the contamination of air by particles redispersed from solid surfaces involves the transfer of momentum from the activity of human beings'. Where appreciable amounts of settled dust are allowed to accumulate, the uppermost particles will make no contact with the main surface and the large low density aggregates so formed will be much more easily lifted from the surface than individual particles. Once suspended in an air stream, the aggregates may then wholly or partially disintegrate and so give rise to airborne particles small enough to remain suspended for an appreciable time.

Many investigators have been impressed by the large numbers of micro-organisms which can be dispersed into the air by the dry sweeping of floors (p. 162). In view of the large amount of dust raised into the air only to settle again after a short time this is in any case an inefficient method of cleaning. By using water or, more effectively, oils or other mixtures which cause the individual dust particles to adhere to one another in more or less permanent large and heavy aggregates, the raising of dust can be greatly reduced (Thomas, 1941; Puck, Hamburger, Robertson & Hurst, 1945). Textiles, such as bedclothes, can also be treated with oils to reduce dispersal from them when shaken during bedmaking or other activities. Reference to many of these studies is made by Williams (1949). As an alternative to treating the surface the cleaning implement may itself be treated. This retains much of the effectiveness in reducing disposal during cleaning and avoids some of the difficulties associated with floor treatments (Burnham, 1962; Ødegaard, 1962; Kingston, 1963; Babb, Lilly & Lowbury, 1963). Vacuum cleaning with an efficient machine is probably the cleaning method producing least dust dispersal (Blowers & Bond, 1960; Bate, 1961). Dusting as a cleaning action is essentially similar to sweeping and the same considerations apply.

People walking about will certainly disperse dust from the floor

(p. 53) but, because the activity also leads to shedding of bacteria-carrying particles from the skin and clothes, it is not easy to assess the contribution to the air-suspended flora derived from the floor. One approach to this problem would be to contaminate the floor with dust containing a marker organism and examine the air under various amounts of activity in the room. In a preliminary experiment of this kind (Carson, 1966), walking into a room whose floor was contaminated to the extent of about 50 marker organisms per in.², produced a bacterial

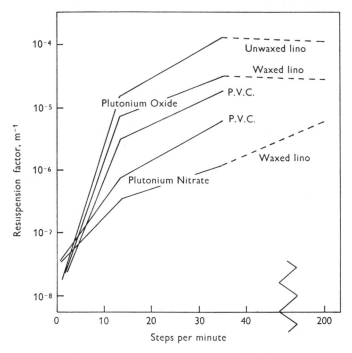

Fig. 8. Resuspension of dust from the floor by walking. The plutonium oxide dust had an activity median diameter of about 14 microns. Data given by Jones & Pond (1966).

count in the room (a single bed ward) of about 5 marker organisms per ft.³ of air sampled. A number of studies have been made on the resuspension of radioactive dusts, both from the open ground and from the floors of laboratories and changing rooms. The results have commonly been expressed in terms of a 'resuspension factor' (p. 162), K = (concentration in the air/density on the ground). This factor has the dimensions L^{-1} and the data given by the contributors to the Oak Ridge Symposium on Surface Contamination are expressed as metres⁻¹. Outdoor values ranged from 10^{-6} to 10^{-4} m.⁻¹ (Stewart, 1966; Fisk, Walker, Royster & Thompson, 1966). When staff were walking about indoors, values of about 10^{-4} m.$^{-1}$ were recorded (Brunskill, 1966) but with the floor contaminated with dust recently shed from 'dirty' clothing the resuspension factor reached 4×10^{-3}. (The corresponding figure for the bacterial experiment quoted above is about 2×10^{-3}.) In comparing different floor surfaces, powdered material (median diameter 14 microns) was more easily dispersed into the air by walking from unwaxed linoleum than from waxed and polished linoleum, PVC sheeting or bitumenized paper (Jones & Pond, 1966). If, however, the surfaces were contaminated by spilled liquid, which was allowed to dry before disturbance, the resulting surface contamination was most easily dispersed from the PVC sheeting (Fig. 8). The maximum levels, 10^{-4} m.$^{-1}$, reached with powdered material were about ten times greater than those derived from the spilled solutions. This last might be supposed to be in some way analogous to direct contamination with secretions, although their organic content will tend to anchor the organisms in them more firmly to the surface on drying.

EQUIPMENT AND LABORATORY PROCEDURES

Air-humidifying equipment is often difficult to sterilize: the many wet surfaces easily become contaminated and may serve as sites for the multiplication of bacteria, especially those of the Pseudomonas group. At the same time the passage of air through the apparatus can produce droplets and so disperse these micro-organisms as often reported. This possibility is particularly serious when the output of the apparatus is directly inhaled by a patient with some dysfunction of the respiratory tract or by an infant in an incubator (Anderson, 1959; Sever, 1959; Barrie, 1965; Phillips & Spencer, 1965; Edmondson, Reinarz, Pierce & Sanford, 1966). Contaminated secretions may themselves be dispersed into the air by the action of suction pumps used for aspiration (Ranger & O'Grady, 1958).

Almost any manipulation of liquid is capable of forming droplets. A comprehensive survey is given by Reitman & Weedum (1956). The fall of drops, or of a stream of liquid as in pipetting, is perhaps an obvious way of generating droplets small enough to evaporate and leave airborne residues. Another method of dispersal is sputtering when liquids are suddenly heated as in the flaming of loops or the insertion of a hot wire into an agar medium. Less obvious is the production of droplets when a liquid film is broken, for example when opening a bottle whose cap and seal have become wet (Tomlinson, 1957). This quite commonly occurs owing to distillation of the contents (bacteriological contamination of the distillate can occur by growth in the wet film from the body of the culture). These operations and others of similar character produce only small numbers of droplets. Homogenizing and grinding are more prolonged and energetic and therefore capable of dispersing much more extensively.

DISCUSSION

Micro-organisms are dispersed into the air by all those physical processes which can break up the original substrate in which they have multiplied into a sufficiently finely divided form. The account, as yet incomplete, of the dissemination of *Staph. aureus* into the air of occupied places illustrates the detailed investigation necessary to determine the sequence of events by which any particular species arrives in the atmosphere as an airborne particle. The recovery of pathogenic micro-organisms from the air is, of course, no proof that the related diseases are actually transmitted in this way to any significant extent. For the epidemiologist interested in the airborne route of infection a comparison of the different ways a particular species may appear in the air is necessary for an understanding of the natural history of the disease and for the initiation of rational control measures. The risks of infection by these modes of dispersion must also be compared with risks associated with contact transfer and ingestion. In our present state of knowledge, or ignorance, generalizations are wholly unwarranted and detailed studies of particular organisms are required.

REFERENCES

ANDERSON, K. (1959). *Pseudomonas pyocyanea* disseminated from an air-cooling apparatus. *Med. J. Aust.* i, 529.
BABB, J. R., LILLY, H. A. & LOWBURY, E. J. L. (1963). Cleaning hospital floors with oiled mops. *J. Hyg., Camb.* **61**, 393.
BARRIE, D. (1965). Incubator-borne *Pseudomonas pyocyanea* infection in a newborn nursery. *Arch. Dis. Childh.* **40**, 555.
BATE, J. G. (1961). Bacteriological investigation of exhaust air from hospital vacuum cleaners. *Lancet*, i, 159.
BEHRENDT, H., GREEN, M. & CAROL, B. (1964). Relation of skin pH pattern to sexual maturation in girls. *Am. J. Dis. Child.* **108**, 37.
BERNARD, H., SPEERS, R., O'GRADY, F. & SHOOTER, R. A. (1965 a). Reduction of dissemination of skin bacteria by modification of operating-room clothing and ultra-violet irradiation. *Lancet*, ii, 458.
BERNARD, H., SPEERS, R., O'GRADY, F. & SHOOTER, R. A. (1965 b). Airborne bacterial contamination. Investigation of human sources. *Arch. Surg. Chicago*, **91**, 530.
BETHUNE, D. W., BLOWERS, R., PARKER, M. & PASK, E. A. (1965). Dispersal of *Staphylococcus aureus* by patients and surgical staff. *Lancet*, i, 480.

BIBLIOGRAPHY (1960, 1961). *Bibliography on the Control of Staphylococcal and of other Hospital Infections*, vol. I, 1960; vol. II, 1961. National Research Council of Canada, Ottawa.

BLANK, I. H. (1965). The survival of bacteria on the skin. In *Skin Bacteria and their Role in Infection*. Ed. H. I. Maibach & G. Hildick-Smith, N.Y., U.S.A.: McGraw-Hill

BLOWERS, R. & BOUND, W. H. (1960). Air hygiene and vacuum cleaners. *Mon. Bull. Minist. Hlth*, **19**, 207.

BLOWERS, R. & McCLUSKEY, M. (1965). Design of operating-room dress for surgeons. *Lancet*, ii, 681.

BOURDILLON, R. B. & LIDWELL, O. M. (1941). Sneezing and the spread of infection. *Lancet*, ii, 365.

BOURDILLON, R. B., LIDWELL, O. M. & LOVELOCK, J. E. (1948). Efficiency of various types of masks in trapping bacteria emitted from the mouth. In 'Studies in air hygiene'. *Spec. Rep. Ser. med. Res. Counc.* no. 262. London: H.M.S.O.

BRUNSKILL, R. T. (1966). The relationship between surface and airborne contamination. In *Surface Contamination*. Ed. B. R. Fisk. Oxford: Pergamon Press.

BURNHAM, F. E. (1962). Floor maintenance in hospital wards. *Hospital, Lond.* **58**, 543.

BØE, J., SOLBERG, C. O., VOGELSANG, TH. M. & WORMNES, A. (1964). Perineal carriers of staphylococci. *Brit. med. J.* ii, 280.

BØE, J. & SOLBERG, C. O. (1965). Behandling av nasale Stafylokokbaerere med Fucidin. *Tidsskr. norske Laegeforen.* **85**, 527.

CARSON, W. (1966). Personal communication.

CORN, M. & STEIN, F. (1966). Mechanics of dust redispersion. In *Surface Contamination*. Ed. B. R. Fisk. Oxford: Pergamon Press.

DAVIES, R. R. & NOBLE, W. C. (1962). Dispersal of bacteria on desquamated skin. *Lancet*, ii, 1295.

DUGUID, J. P. (1945). The numbers and sites of origin of the droplets expelled during expiratory activities. *Edinb. med. J.* **52**, 385.

DUGUID, J. P. (1946). The size and duration of air-carriage of respiratory droplets and droplet-nuclei. *J. Hyg., Camb.* **44**, 471.

DUGUID, J. P. & WALLACE, K. R. (1948). Air infection with dust liberated from clothing. *Lancet*, ii, 845.

EDMONSON, E. B., REINARZ, J. A., PIERCE, A. K. & SANFORD, J. P. (1966). Nebulization equipment. A potential source of infection in Gram-negative pneumonias. *Am. J. Dis. Child.* **111**, 357.

EICHENWALD, H. F., KOTSEVALOV, O. & FOSSO, L. A. (1960). The 'cloud-baby'—an example of bacterial–viral interaction. *Am. J. Dis. Child.* **100**, 161.

FISK, B. R., WALKER, R. L., ROYSTER, G. W. & THOMPSON, J. L. (1966). Redispersion of settled particulates. In *Surface Contamination*. Ed. B. R. Fisk. Oxford: Pergamon Press.

HARE, R. & THOMAS, C. G. A. (1956). The transmission of *Staphylococcus aureus*. *Brit. med. J.* ii, 840.

HARE, R. & RIDLEY, M. (1958). Further studies in the transmission of *Staphylococcus aureus*. *Brit. med. J.* i, 69.

JENNISON, M. W. (1941). The dynamics of sneezing. Studies by high-speed photography. *Scient. Mon., N.Y.* **52**, 24.

JENNISON, M. W. (1942). Atomizing of mouth and nose secretions into the air as revealed by high-speed photography. In *Aerobiology*. Ed. F. R. Moulton. American Association for the Advancement of Science, publication no. 17, Washington, U.S.A.

JONES, I. S. & POND, S. F. (1966). Some experiments to determine the resuspension factor of plutonium from various surfaces. In *Surface Contamination*. Ed. B. R. Fisk. Oxford: Pergamon Press.

KINGSTON, D. (1963). Tests on dry, oiled and damp mops. *Mon. Bull. Minist. Hlth*, 22, 153.

KINGSTON, D., LIDWELL, O. M. & WILLIAMS, R. E. O. (1962). The epidemiology of the common cold. III. The effect of ventilation, air disinfection and room size. *J. Hyg., Camb.* 60, 341.

KLIGMAN, A. M. (1965). The bacteriology of normal skin. In *Skin Bacteria and their Role in Infection*. Ed. H. I. Maibach and G. Hildick-Smith. N.Y., U.S.A.: McGraw-Hill.

LIDWELL, O. M. (1948). Notes on the ventilation and sedimentation of small particles, with particular reference to airborne bacteria. In 'Studies in air hygiene'. *Spec. Rep. Ser. med. Res. Counc.* no. 262. London: H.M.S.O.

LIDWELL, O. M. (1964). Microbiology of the atmosphere and airborne infection. In *Medical Climatology*. Ed. S. Licht. Elizabeth Licht, New Haven, Connecticut, U.S.A.

LIDWELL, O. M., POLAKOFF, S., JEVONS, M. P. & PARKER, M. T. (1966). Staphylococcal infection in thoracic surgery: experience in a subdivided ward. *J. Hyg., Camb.* 64, 321.

MASIRONI, L. A. & FISK, B. R. (1966). Direct observations of particle re-entrainment from surfaces. In *Surface Contamination*. Ed. B. R. Fisk. Oxford: Pergamon Press.

NEWCASTLE REGIONAL HOSPITAL BOARD WORKING PARTY (1962). Blankets and air hygiene: a report of a trial of blanket disinfection. *J. Hyg., Camb.* 60, 85.

NOBLE, W. C. (1962). The dispersal of staphylococci in hospital wards. *J. clin. Path.* 15, 552.

NOBLE, W. C., LIDWELL, O. M. & KINGSTON, D. (1963). The size-distribution of airborne particles carrying micro-organisms. *J. Hyg., Camb.* 61, 385.

ØDEGAARD, A. (1962). Renhold av gulv på sykehus. Bakteriologiske undersøkelser ved prøving av nye metoder. *Nord. Med.* 67, 344.

PHILIPS, I. & SPENCER, G. (1965). *Pseudomonas aeroginosa* cross-infection due to contaminated respiratory apparatus. *Lancet*, ii, 1325.

PUCK, T. T., HAMBURGER, JR., M., ROBERTSON, O. H. & HURST, V. (1945). Effect of tri-ethylene glycol vapour on airborne beta hemolytic streptococci in hospital wards. II. The combined action of glycol vapour and dust control measures. *J. infect. Dis.* 76, 216.

RANGER, I. & O'GRADY, F. (1958). Dissemination of micro-organisms by a surgical pump. *Lancet*, ii, 299.

REITMAN, M. & WEEDUM, A. G. (1956). Microbiological safety. *Publ. Hlth Rep., Wash.* 71, 659.

REPORT (1966). Necropsy survey of staphylococcal infection in patients dying in hospital. A report of the Public Health Laboratory Service. *Brit. med. J.* i, 313.

RIDLEY, M. (1959). Perineal carriage of *Staphylococcus aureus*. *Brit. med. J.* i, 270.

ROUNTREE, P. M. & BULTEAN, V. G. (1965). Hospital infection with tetracycline resistant haemolytic streptococci. *Med. J. Aust.* p. 446.

RUBBO, S. D. & DIXSON, S. (1960). A contact-plate technique for determining bacterial contamination of fabrics. *Lancet*, ii, 394.

RUBBO, S. D., PRESSLEY, T. A., STRATFORD, B. C. & DIXSON, S. (1960). Transmission of airborne bacteria in hospital wards. *Lancet*, ii, 397.

RUBBO, S. D., STRATFORD, B. C. & DIXSON, S. (1960). Self sterilization of chemically treated blankets. *Med. J. Aust.* p. 331.

RUBBO, S. D., STRATFORD, B. C. & DIXSON, S. (1962). Spread of a marker organism in a hospital ward. *Brit. med. J.* ii, 282.

RUBBO, S. J. & SAUNDERS, J. (1963). Liberation of organisms from contaminated textiles. *J. Hyg., Camb.* **61**, 507.

SELWYN, S. (1965). Cross-infection in dermatological wards. *J. Hyg., Camb.* **63**, 59.

SEVER, J. L. (1959). Possible role of humidifying equipment in spread of infections from the newborn nursery. *Pediatrics*, **24**, 50.

SHEHADEH, N. H. & KLIGMAN, A. M. (1963). The effect of topical antibacterial agents on the bacterial flora of the axilla. *J. Invest. Derm.* **40**, 61.

SHOOTER, R. A., SMITH, M. A. & HUNTER, C. J. W. (1959). A study of surgical masks. *Brit. J. Surg.* **47**, 246.

SOLBERG, C. O. (1965). A study of carriers of *Staphylococcus aureus. Act. Med. Scand.* **178**, Suppl. No. 436.

SPEERS, R., BERNARD, H., O'GRADY, F. & SHOOTER, R. A. (1965). Increased dispersal of skin bacteria into air after showers. *Lancet*, i, 478.

SPEERS, R., O'GRADY, F., SHOOTER, R. A., BERNARD, H. & COLE, W. R. (1966). Increased dispersal of skin bacteria into the air after shower baths: The effect of hexachlorophane. *Lancet*, i, 1298.

STEWART, K. (1966). The resuspension of particulate material from surfaces. In *Surface Contamination*. Ed. B. R. Fisk. Oxford: Pergamon Press.

THOMAS, J. C. (1941). Reduction of dust-borne bacteria by oiling floors. *Lancet*, ii, 123.

TOMLINSON, A. J. H. (1957). Infected air-borne particles liberated on opening screw-capped bottles. *Brit. med. J.* ii, 15.

WELLS, W. F. (1934). On air-borne infection. Study II. Droplets and droplet nuclei. *Amer. J. Hyg.* **20**, 611.

WILLIAMS, R. E. O. (1949). Methods of maintaining bacterial purity of air. *J. Instn Heat. Vent. Engrs*, **16**, 404.

WILLIAMS, R. E. O. (1963). Healthy carriage of *Staphylococcus aureus*. Its prevalence and importance. *Bact. Rev.* **27**, 56.

WILLIAMS, R. E. O., LIDWELL, O. M. & HIRCH, A. (1956). The bacterial flora of the air of occupied rooms. *J. Hyg., Camb.* **54**, 512.

DEPOSITION OF PARTICLES TO NATURAL SURFACES

A. C. CHAMBERLAIN

Health Physics and Medical Division, Atomic Energy Research Establishment, Harwell, Berkshire

INTRODUCTION

The transport of microbes in the atmosphere, like the transport of man in space, can be considered in three stages: take-off, free flight and landing. Biological adaptations to assist take-off, illustrated by Ingold for the fungi (p. 102), will be of no advantage if the microbe is carried so far or so high in the atmosphere that it is killed by desiccation or ultra-violet light, or lands in a climatic region outside the range of the parent organism. In this chapter, the deposition to surfaces of particles in the size range 1–50 microns will be considered. The transport and deposition of larger particles, particularly sand grains, has been investigated by Bagnold (1941, 1960) and by Chepil (1941, 1945). Instances can be found of adaptions which influence the deposition process, but these are less numerous than those influencing take-off, and much of what follows applies to particles of a given size irrespective of their origin.

SEDIMENTATION VELOCITY AND RELATED CONCEPTS

It was sometimes assumed that sedimentation under gravity is the sole mechanism for the deposition of particles, and that any upward-facing surface will collect an aliquot of airborne particles of given size, shape and density. The work of Gregory (1961) showed that this is not so, but nevertheless sedimentation is a most important mechanism for pollens and the larger spores.

The force of gravity on a particle causes it to accelerate until it reaches a velocity at which the drag of the surrounding air becomes equal to the gravitational force. This equilibrium rate of fall is called the terminal velocity.

Stokes's Law gives the drag on a spherical particle of radius r cm. as

$$F = 6\pi\eta r v \text{ dynes,} \qquad (1)$$

where v (cm./sec.) is the velocity relative to the surrounding air and η the viscosity of air ($1 \cdot 81$ g. cm.$^{-1}$ sec.$^{-1}$ at $20°$C). Stokes's Law is accurate provided:

(i) the particle is large compared with the mean free path of the gas molecules (which is true for the range of particle sizes of interest here);

(ii) the Reynolds number $Re = 2rv/v$ is less than unity, where v is the kinematic viscosity, found by dividing the viscosity by the density of air.

For a particle of diameter 40 microns and unit density, falling at its terminal velocity of 5 cm./sec., Re is $0 \cdot 13$, so the second condition also is satisfied by spores and pollen (but not by most seeds).

The terminal velocity v_s of the particle is found by equating F to the negative buoyancy force giving

$$v_s = \frac{2}{9} r^2 g \left(\frac{\rho_s - \rho_a}{\eta} \right), \qquad (2)$$

where ρ_s and ρ_a are the densities of the particle and of air. Usually, ρ_a is small compared with ρ_s and (2) becomes

$$v_s = \frac{2r^2 g \rho_s}{9\eta} \qquad (3)$$

$$= \tau g, \qquad (4)$$

where $\tau = 2r^2\rho_s/9\eta$, which has the dimensions of time, is called the relaxation time of the particle. By considering the equations of motion of a particle suddenly released at rest in an air stream moving past it horizontally with velocity u, it can be shown that the drag of the air stream will give the particle a horizontal velocity $u(1-e^{-1})$ in time τ, where e is Euler's constant equal to $2 \cdot 7$. Conversely, if a particle is injected into still air with velocity v, its velocity will decrease to v/e in time τ. The relaxation time is thus a measure of the time taken for the particle to accommodate itself to the motion of surrounding air. In Table 1 the terminal velocity and relaxation times of spherical particles of unit density are shown. It may be found surprising that τ is so small —a few milliseconds for a large spore or a pollen grain.

A particle projected horizontally with velocity v into still air travels a distance S called the stopping distance before its horizontal motion is stopped by the drag of the air. S is given by

$$S = v\tau = \frac{vv_s}{g}. \qquad (5)$$

For given initial velocity, the stopping distance is proportional to v_s and hence to the square of the diameter of the particle, and large velocities must be given to very small particles to project them any distance. For example, a velocity of 30 m./sec. is required to project a 10-micron particle a distance of 1 cm.

Ingold (1939, 1965) has shown that the range of discharge of spores of cryptogams is correlated with the size of the projectile. In some species, the stopping distance is increased by the simultaneous ejection of a number of spores, or by the ejection of cell sap or a puff of air with the spores. The stopping distance regulates also the return journey back

Table 1. *Terminal velocity and relaxation time of spheres of unit density*

Diameter (microns)	Terminal velocity (cm./sec.)	Relaxation time (sec.)
1	$3 \cdot 5 \times 10^{-3}$	$3 \cdot 6 \times 10^{-6}$
2	$1 \cdot 3 \times 10^{-2}$	$1 \cdot 3 \times 10^{-5}$
3	$2 \cdot 9 \times 10^{-2}$	$3 \cdot 0 \times 10^{-5}$
5	$7 \cdot 8 \times 10^{-2}$	$8 \cdot 0 \times 10^{-5}$
10	$3 \cdot 0 \times 10^{-1}$	$3 \cdot 1 \times 10^{-4}$
20	$1 \cdot 2$	$1 \cdot 2 \times 10^{-3}$
30	$2 \cdot 7$	$2 \cdot 7 \times 10^{-3}$
50	$7 \cdot 1$	$7 \cdot 2 \times 10^{-3}$

through the viscous boundary layer of air to the surface at the end of the path travelled by the particle. Theories of the rate of deposition of particles to natural smooth surfaces have been based on the assumption that a 'sink' exists at a distance from the wall determined by the stopping distance of the particle (Friedlander & Johnston, 1957; Davies, 1965, 1966). The particle is carried by eddy diffusion to within a certain distance of the wall, and is then projected across the sublaminar layer. The difficulty with the theory is to determine the transverse eddy velocity of the particle just outside the sublaminar layer for insertion in equation (5) to give the stopping distance. Chamberlain (1966b) has shown that this theory may be applicable to rough surfaces also.

Factors modifying the rate of sedimentation of particles
Density

The terminal velocity v_s is proportional to the difference between the density of particle and air. Some pollen grains contain air sacs, and have a bulk density considerably less than unity. Particles which are filamentous, or are aggregates of smaller particles, also entrain air, and have bulk densities less than the parent material.

Shape

Provided that the shape of the particle is not too far removed from the spherical, the drag can be written:

$$F = 6\pi\eta\alpha rv \text{ dynes,} \tag{6}$$

where r is the radius of the sphere of equal volume to the particle and α is a constant called the dynamical shape factor (Fuchs, 1964). Equation (6) implies that the drag on a non-spherical particle is proportional to the relative velocity of particle and air, as for a spherical particle, and this is found experimentally to be true. It follows that the terminal velocity of the particle is $1/\alpha$ times that of the sphere of the same volume and density. A number of measurements of α have been made by observing

Table 2. *Dynamical shape factor*

(Ratio of terminal velocity of equivalent sphere to that of particle.)

Shape†	Ratio of axes	α	References
Ellipsoid	4	1·28	(1)
Cylinder	1	1·06	(1)
Cylinder	2	1·14	(1)
Cylinder	3	1·24	(1)
Cylinder	4	1·32	(1)
Two spheres touching	2	1·10	(2)
Two spheres touching	2	1·17	(3)
Three spheres touching, as triangle	—	1·20	(2)
Three spheres touching, in line	3	1·34	(2)
Three spheres touching, in line	3	1·40	(3)
Four spheres touching, in line	4	1·58	(2)
Four spheres touching, in line	4	1·56	(3)

† In all cases, preferential motion is perpendicular to long axes.
References: (1) see Fuchs (1964); (2) Megaw (1966, personal communication); (3) Kunkel (1948).

the rate of sedimentation of glass or metal particles of various shapes in viscous liquids, and the results are summarized in Table 2. For cylindrical particles or chain-like aggregates with lengths not more than four times their breadth, α does not exceed about 1·5, so for practical purposes no great error is made by taking the Stokes' Law velocity for the equivalent sphere to apply to those spores and pollens which are more or less regular in shape. For example, the conidium of *Helminthosporium* is approximately ellipsoidal in shape, with major and minor axes of 80 and 18 microns (Gregory, 1961, plate 5). The volume is about $1·8 \times 10^{-8}$ cm.³, and the radius of the equivalent sphere 75 microns. If of unit density, this sphere would have a terminal velocity of 1·7 cm./sec. and, applying a dynamical shape factor of 1·3, this would become 2·0 cm./sec., which is close to one experimental determination of the terminal velocity of the spore (Gregory, 1945, fig. 1).

Departures from Stokes's Law become very much greater where special adaptations occur, in particular among seeds of the higher plants. Thus the seed of Rosebay Willowherb (*Chamaenaerion angustifolium*) is about 0·8 by 0·2 mm. (Salisbury, 1961) and weighs 40 μg. The terminal velocity of the equivalent sphere would be about 1 m./sec., but attached to the seed is a parachute of 70 fine hairs each about 1 cm. long. These hairs present a large surface area, entraining and reducing the effective density so that the actual terminal velocity is 8 cm./sec. (Salisbury, 1961). In this way, the potential airborne dispersion of the seed is immensely increased, enabling the Willowherb quickly to colonize freshly exposed sites.

Interaction between particles and air in a cloud

The drag between a falling particle and the surrounding fluid acts in opposite directions on particle and fluid. If the concentration of particles is sufficiently great, the drag on the fluid will cause it to sediment as a local current. Currents of this sort, called turbidity currents, occur when mud is stirred up on the ocean floor, and may develop into powerful and fast-moving flows extending hundreds of miles across the ocean bottom (Holmes, 1965).

Turbidity currents can also occur in the atmosphere. Fuchs (1964) suggests that the *nuée ardente* which devastated the town of St Pierre after the eruption of Mont Pelée in 1902 was a turbidity current. The dust and ash present as an aerosol increased the density of the erupted gases, and despite their high temperature they descended the slopes of the mountain with hurricane force.

Fuchs (1964) gives a criterion to decide whether an aerosol will behave as a collection of individual sedimenting particles with the air blowing through the cloud or as a sedimenting cloud pushing aside the surrounding clean air. The former situation will occur if the terminal velocity v_s of the particles is greater than the rate of sedimentation v_c of the cloud as a whole. This rate is calculated by equating the negative buoyancy force on the cloud to the drag between the cloud and the surrounding air, assuming as an approximation that the cloud can be treated as though it were a balloon with a definite boundary. Applying Fuchs's method, the surprising result is reached that a spherical volume of air of diameter 1 m., containing 10 mg. of particles suspended in it, could acquire a bulk sedimentation velocity of 2 cm./sec., equal to the terminal velocity of a 30-micron particle.

The phenomenon of bulk sedimentation provides a possible reason for the observation of Gregory, Longhurst & Sreeramulu (1961) that the apparent velocity of deposition of *Lycopodium* spores released in the field decreased with distance downwind. Close to the source, before turbulent dispersion had taken effect on the cloud of released spores, bulk sedimentation may have operated to give an excessive apparent velocity of deposition.

IMPACTION

When air flows past an obstacle, the streamlines divide to pass either side. Particles in the air tend to carry straight on by virtue of their momentum and hit the obstacle. Figure 1 shows the trajectory of a

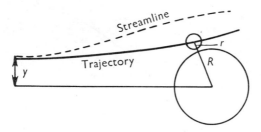

Fig. 1. Impaction of particle on cylinder.

particle which grazes a cylinder. The efficiency E of impaction is defined as the ratio of the number of particles striking the obstacle to the number which would have passed through the space occupied by it if it had not been there. In the example of Fig. 1, E is equal to y/R.

Theoretical investigations of impaction efficiency on cylinders and spheres are summarized by Green & Lane (1964) and by Fuchs (1964). The efficiency of impaction is a function of a parameter P defined by

$$P = \frac{S}{R} = \frac{uv_s}{gR},\tag{6}$$

where S is the stopping distance of the particle, u is the wind speed, R the radius of the cylinder or sphere, and v_s the terminal velocity of the particle (cf. p. 61).

The relation between E and P can be calculated only if the Reynolds number Re of the obstacle ($Re = 2Ruv^{-1}$) is either large (of order 10^3) or very small (of order 10^{-1}). At intermediate values of Re, interpolation formulae have to be used. In Fig. 2 the relation between E and P calculated by Davies & Peetz (1956) for large Re is shown, together with experimental values obtained by Chamberlain (1966b) using *Lyco-*

podium spores tagged with radioactivity and by Gregory (1951) using visual methods of counting. The range of Re was 10^2 to 10^3, so the theory for ideal flow should be applicable. The experimental values lie below the theoretical, but it is uncertain whether this represents a fault in the theory or a failure by the sticky cylinders to retain all the spores striking them.

The efficiency of impaction falls off very sharply as the diameter of the particle is reduced, since v_s and therefore S depends on the square of the diameter. For a 4-micron particle, $v_s = 5 \times 10^{-2}$ cm./sec., and if, for example, $u = 5$ m./sec. and $R = 0.325$ cm., equation (6) gives $P = 0.08$.

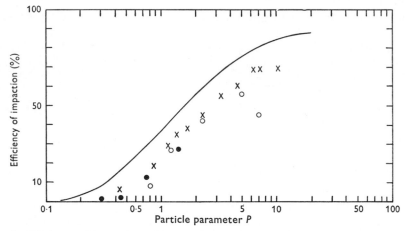

Fig. 2. Efficiency of impaction of *Lycopodium* spores on cylinders ●, Gregory 2·5 cm. diam. cyl.; ○, Gregory 0·5 cm. diam. cyl.; ×, Chamberlain 0·65 cm. diam. cyl.

Then from Fig. 2, E is vanishingly small. This was confirmed experimentally by Gregory (1961), who found that the spores of *Lycoperdon giganteum* (about 4 microns diameter) were not impacted on cylinders at any wind speed within the range tested. Conversely, however, E increases as the radius of the cylinder is reduced, and a thread or hair 100 microns thick would be efficient even for the smallest spores at normal wind speed.

The impaction of spores and pollen grains on leaves and twigs cannot be calculated theoretically, because natural obstacles are not rigid solids of revolution, nor do their surfaces necessarily retain all the particles which strike them. Gregory & Stedman (unpublished, quoted by Gregory, 1961) measured the collection efficiency of *Lycopodium* spores on leaflets of potato and broad bean in a wind tunnel. The petiole of the leaf was clamped and the leaf allowed to trail downwind. Very small efficiencies were obtained, especially at high wind speeds, and Gregory pointed out that turbulent deposition either failed to develop at the higher wind speeds or the spores were shaken off again in the wind.

Chamberlain (1966b) compared the impaction of *Lycopodium* spores and other particles on natural and artificial surfaces, using radioactive tagging to measure the catch. As far as possible the experiments were designed to distinguish between the effects of the size, posture, and rigidity of the surface and the effects of surface texture and stickiness. In one series of experiments, twigs of beech (*Fagus sylvatica*) were chosen which had a diameter of about 0·65 cm. (range 0·5–0·8 cm.). Sections of twig 5 cm. long were covered with stopcock grease, and other portions were wetted and kept wet during exposure to the cloud of tagged particles in the tunnel. The twigs were fixed horizontally at right angles to the direction of air flow, and sticky cylinders of 0·65 cm.

Table 3. *Efficiency of impaction of particles on beech twigs of diameter about* 0·65 *cm.* (*wind speed* 5 *m./sec.*)

	Efficiency E (%)		
Particle	Sticky surface	Wet surface	Dry surface
Lycopodium spores (30 microns)	36	29	4
Ragweed pollen (19 microns)	35	29	0·9

diameter were fixed above and below, to provide, by use of the results of Fig. 2, a measure of the dosage of particles in the tunnel. After exposure to the cloud of particles, the twigs were placed in the well of a scintillation counter for estimation of the activity of the spores caught on them. By comparison with the catch on the sticky cylinder, values of *E* were obtained, as shown in Table 3. The beech twigs treated with stopcock grease showed impaction efficiencies comparable with those of the sticky cylinders. The wet twigs showed efficiencies rather lower but still substantial, but the dry twigs gave efficiencies of only 4% for *Lycopodium* spores and 0·9 % for pollen of ragweed (*Ambrosia artemisiifolia*).

After the activity of the impacted spores had been measured, the twigs were replaced in the tunnel to see if further exposure to air flow caused any of the catch to be blown off. In fact, not more than a few per cent of the spores were blown off at a flow of 5 m./sec., whatever the initial treatment of the twig. Vigorous shaking of a dry twig also failed to dislodge spores. It seems, therefore, that the relatively poor catch of the spores and pollen grains on the dry twigs was due to 'bounce-off' and not 'blow-off', a conclusion in accord with the findings of Bagnold

(1941), who used somewhat larger particles. Bagnold found that rebound of sand grains from surfaces was a most important effect and that movement occurred in successive jumps, but that a smooth surface of fine sand or cement grains was not easily disturbed by wind alone. Similarly, Chepil (1941) found that quartz particles less than 50 microns in diameter were not moved by wind, even when the velocity was 16 m./sec. at 15 cm. above the ground.

In another series of experiments, Chamberlain (1966b) compared the deposition of particles on segments of real leaves with the deposition on sticky artificial leaves. A sward of artificial grass was made by fixing polystyrene strips 8 cm. long, 0·5 cm. broad and 0·025 cm. thick into a wax substrate. The strips were fixed at various orientations according to the method of Gregory *et al.* (1961), and formed a stand 4 m. long by

Table 4. *Deposition of particles on segments of plant leaves, and on filter paper, relative to deposition on sticky artificial leaves*

		Relative deposition				
Particle	Diameter (microns)	Grass	Plantain	Clover	Filter paper	Sticky PVC
Lycopodium spores	32	0·45	0·26	0·18	0·70	1·00
Ragweed pollen	19	0·15	0·11	0·23	0·68	1·00
Polystyrene	5	1·3	1·8	1·8	1·1	1·00
Tri-cresyl-phosphate	1	1·7	2·6	5·5	6·4	1·00
Aitken nuclei	0·08	1·1	1·7	0·9	1·5	1·00

30 cm. broad, filling the whole floor of the tunnel, and containing some 6,000 'leaves'. Segments 0·5 cm. wide were cut from leaves of a grass (*Lolium perenne*) a clover (*Trifolium pratense*) and a plantain (*Plantago lanceolata*) and these segments were stuck to blades of artificial grass which were then placed within the stand in the tunnel. Each composite leaf thus had the dimensions, posture and rigidity of the artificial leaves, but the surface was that of one of the three plant species. Care was taken to stick the segments of leaf to the spills so that the upper surface of the donor leaf was exposed on one side and the lower surface on the other. Composite leaves were also made by sticking filter paper to the PVC strips. The filter paper was not made sticky, but it was more hairy than any of the real leaf surfaces.

Table 4 gives the deposition to the segments of real leaves and filter paper relative to the deposition on equal areas of sticky artificial leaves. In the experiments with *Lycopodium* spores and ragweed pollen, the segments of leaves of grass, clover and plantain collected fewer particles than the sticky PVC 'leaves', and this is almost certainly due to bounce-off from the natural surfaces, because blow-off was imperceptible when the leaves were re-exposed after the deposition had been measured. By contrast when 5-micron spheres of polystyrene were used, the natural surfaces collected more than the artificial, and the same difference was even more marked when 1-micron droplets of tri-cresyl-phosphate tagged with P32 were used. For these very small particles, it seems that surfaces having hair-like roughness are much more efficient than smooth surfaces, whether sticky or not. Theoretical reasons why this is to be expected can be found when the mechanisms of transport across boundary layers are considered in detail (Davies, 1965, 1966), since hair-like elements, protruding into the sublaminar layer on a surface, trap micron-sized particles which otherwise follow the stream lines.

Some experiments were also done with Aitken nuclei, which are condensation nuclei naturally occurring in the atmosphere. The nuclei were tagged by attachment of ThB activity. With these particles the deposition on the test surfaces was less variable. This also is understandable, since the transport of Aitken nuclei to surface is mainly by Brownian motion, which carries particles of less than 0·1 micron diameter through the laminar boundary layer.

To sum up in general and perhaps over-simplified terms, impaction on to natural obstacles is a principal mechanism of deposition provided: (a) the main dimensions of the particle are of order tens of microns or more; (b) the dimensions of the obstacle are of order centimetres or less; (c) the approach velocity is of order metres per second or more; (d) the surface is wet, sticky or otherwise retentive of particles.

For particles of dimensions 1–5 microns, impaction is not efficient, and interception by fine hairs on vegetation is possibly the most effective method of catch. Below about one-tenth of a micron, Brownian motion becomes more important, and the nature of the surface is not so important as for larger particles.

DEPOSITION TO GRASSLAND AND OTHER EXTENDED SURFACES

The flow of air over the earth's surface is normally turbulent, and the components of the turbulent velocities in all directions at a distance from the ground are usually large compared with the sedimentation velocities of particles of 50 microns or less. For this reason, spores and pollen, like dust and smoke in the atmosphere, diffuse according to the eddy motion of the air, and are subject to the influence of convection which can carry them to great heights. Very near the surface, however, the scale of atmospheric turbulence is reduced, and the sedimentation of the particles causes them to depart significantly from the streamlines of air motion. Also vegetation and other roughness elements protruding into the lowest layer of the atmosphere provide impaction surfaces which filter out particles.

To a first approximation, the effects of sedimentation and impaction can be considered to be additive. If F is the flux of particles to the ground (number per cm.^{2} per second) and C is the volumetric concentration (number per cm.^{3}) at some height z above the surface, then the ratio F/C has the dimensions of a velocity and can be called the velocity of deposition v_g. To a first approximation

$$v_g = v_s + v_T,$$

where v_s and v_T are the transport velocities due to sedimentation and impaction respectively.

It is here assumed that lateral variations in concentration can be neglected. This is true provided that the distance of the sampling point from the source of the particle is much greater than the height of the sampling point above ground (say 100 times), but the condition is not always satisfied in experimental measurements of v_g.

Although defined above in terms of deposition to the ground, the velocity of deposition can be applied irrespective of the orientation of the surface. At a vertical surface, the term v_s vanishes, and deposition by turbulent transport is the only mechanism. Both v_s and v_T depend on the size, shape and density of the particle, but v_T also depends on the windspeed, roughness, and surface texture of the vegetation.

The separate determination of the two components of v_g in field experiments has not proved easy, because of the difficulties of measurement of F and C and the inherent variability of field conditions. In some long-range experiments, attempts have been made to determine v_g indirectly by calculation from the rate at which particles are lost from the cloud (Islitzer & Dumbauld, 1963). The trouble with this method is that very extensive measurements of volumetric concentration are needed over a grid of sampling positions widely spaced in both lateral and vertical directions to enable the concentration to be completely integrated. Most of the estimates of v_g made by this method seem to be inexplicably large compared with estimates from direct measurement of deposition to the ground. Eggleton & Thompson (1961) attempted to overcome the difficulty of the spatial integration of concentration by simultaneously emitting fluorescent particles and the radioactive noble gas xenon 133. From the relative concentration of particles and gas at various distances from the source, the loss of particles from the cloud was estimated, and v_g was found to be 15 cm./sec. This was a surprisingly large value for particles of a mass median diameter of about 2 microns and was two orders of magnitude greater than the velocity of deposition to grass measured by the direct method in a wind tunnel. Probably the loss of fluorescence by particles exposed for several hours to a normal polluted atmosphere accounts for the surprising result of Eggleton & Thompson's experiment. On the other hand, it is possible that some process in the natural environment as yet unidentified may remove particles more rapidly than can be accounted for by experiment.

Turning now to direct measurements of v_g in the field, the earlier work has been summarized by Gregory (1961). The difficulty of counting spores visually on natural surfaces such as leaves and soil, and the non-representative nature of the surface presented by traditional sampling devices such as Petri dishes and microscope slides, led Gregory and his associates to the use of 'artificial grass' previously described. Trays containing vertical strips of wood or plastic 8 cm. high were placed in the ground amongst short grass at various distances from a point where *Lycopodium* spores were dispersed. The volumetric concentration over the period of emission was measured by small slit samplers placed above the deposition trays, and the flux of spores to the artificial grass was determined by visual counting of the number of spores on the vertical strips and on the substrate.

Average values of v_g for six experiments were 8·8, 5·2 and 3·7 cm./sec. from measurements at distances of 2·5, 5 and 10 m. respectively, from the source. The reason for the apparent variation with distance is not known. Possible reasons for excess values near the source are bulk sedimentation of the cloud of spores (referred to above), insufficient diffusive spread of the cloud leading to unrepresentative volumetric samples, and the presence of clumps of particles. The terminal velocity of *Lycopodium* spore is about 2 cm./sec., and if the value of v_g at the 10 m. arc in the experiments of Gregory *et al.* (1961) is taken as representative, it suggests that v_g is not much larger than v_s. However, the experiments were conducted at moderate or low wind speeds (0·4–2·6 m./sec. at 1 m. above ground) and at such speeds the contribution of v_T would not be large.

Chamberlain (1966*b*) has extended Gregory's work to larger ranges using spores tagged with radioactive iodine. In the more recent experiments, iodine was adsorbed on the spores from the gaseous phase by distillation of a source of elemental iodine incorporating the radioactive isotope iodine-131. By weight, the total amount of iodine used was very small, about 50 mg./50 g. of spores. Consequently only about a monolayer of iodine was adsorbed on to the spores, and the sorption was found to be almost irreversible. The activity was sufficient for the presence of about 10 spores per g. of plant material to be detected. Radioactive tagging obviated the need for visual observation of the spores and the deposit on the natural herbage and underlying soil in the field could be measured. Furthermore, during the course of the work improvements in counting techniques enabled the range of the experiments to be increased from 20 to 50 and in some cases 100 m. When values of v_g from different ranges were compared, no significant differences were found.

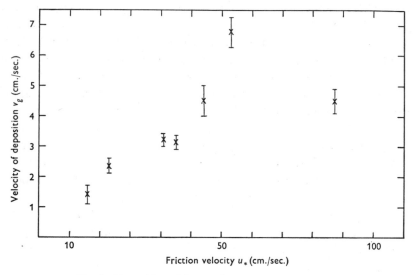

Fig. 3. Deposition of *Lycopodium* spores to grassland.

The results of the field experiments on the deposition of tagged *Lycopodium* spores are shown in Fig. 3, the velocity of deposition being plotted against the friction velocity u_*.[†]

In each trial, a value of v_g was obtained at each of about five sampling positions and in Fig. 3 the standard error as well as the mean of v_g is shown. The significant increase of v_g with friction velocity shows the reality of the contribution of turbulent transport to deposition.

[†] By definition, $\rho_a u_*^2$ is the shearing stress of the wind on the ground, and is a measure of the rate of turbulent transport of momentum by the atmosphere. Under certain conditions the variation of wind speed with height above the ground follows the law $u/u_* = (1/k)$ log (z/z_0), where z_0 is called the roughness length, a constant for a given surface, and k is Von Kármán's constant and equal to 0·4. For grass reaching a height of 10 cm., z_0 is about 2 cm. (for other conditions see Sutton, 1953, p. 232), and u_* is then approximately one-tenth of the wind speed at 1 m. above ground.

However, the highest value of v_g, 6·8 cm./sec., was obtained on a day when the wind speed was only moderate ($u_* = 64$ cm./sec.) and the grass was wet following rain.

The results of Fig. 3 suggest that the ratio of velocity of deposition to wind speed is about 0·01 for *Lycopodium* particles. This ratio is denoted p by Gregory (1961), and by reference to fig. 24 of his book the proportion of spores deposited within various ranges from the point of dispersal can be estimated. For example, if the height of release is taken as 10 cm. above ground, 50% of the spores would have a range of travel of 200 m. or more in average weather conditions.

The difficulty with field trials is that the experimenter cannot order conditions as he wishes, or repeat experiments which give interesting or surprising answers. The difficulty with laboratory experiments is to

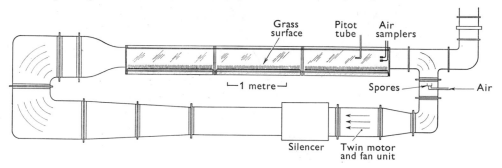

Fig. 4. Deposition of spores to grass in the wind tunnel.

apply results obtained on a very small scale to conditions in the field. In an attempt to obtain realistic arrangements in the laboratory, Chamberlain (1966 b) used a wind tunnel in which the floor of a working section 4 m. long can be covered with turves or with grass grown in shallow trays. Despite the limited cross-section of the tunnel (30 cm. wide by 40 cm. high) and the limited fetch over the deposition surfaces, experiments on the transport of gases to grass and grasslike surfaces in this tunnel showed that the boundary layer of air flow is sufficiently well developed to give results which agree well with field experiments (Chamberlain, 1966 a).

The tunnel, shown in Fig. 4, has been used to extend the field experiments on deposition of particles to a greater range of wind speed, surface characteristics and particle size than has been possible on the field. The particles, tagged with suitable radioactive tracers, were introduced into the tunnel just *downwind* of the working section, and allowed to circulate repeatedly until all were deposited. Volumetric samplers (suction

samples or sticky rods) were used to determine the volumetric concentration at two or more heights above the surface, and the flux to the
surface was measured by removing sections for counting after each
experiment.

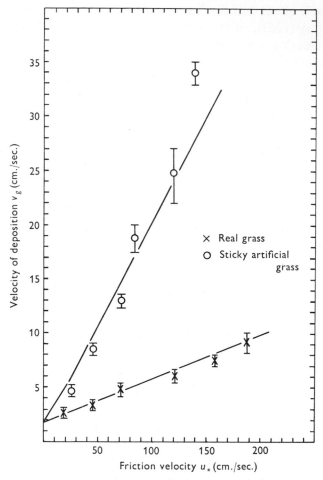

Fig. 5. Deposition of *Lycopodium* spores in wind tunnel.

The values of v_g found in the wind tunnel for the deposition of
Lycopodium spores to grass are shown in Fig. 5 (lower line). There is a
linear increase of v_g with u_* from a value 2·6 cm./sec. at $u_* = 19$ cm./sec.
to $v_g = 9·0$ cm./sec. at $u_* = 185$ cm./sec. The grass was about 6 cm.
high and was dry. When sections of the stand of grass were thoroughly
wetted just before an experiment, the deposition on the wetted grass was
found to exceed that on the dry grass by a factor varying from 1·1 at low
wind speed to 2·5 at high wind speed.

The increased deposition on wetted grass suggested that the retention of impacted spores on the leaves was a limiting factor especially at high wind speeds. As with the experiment with beech twigs previously described, it was possible to show that poor retention was the result of 'bounce-off' and not 'blow-off'. When the activity of the deposited spores was measured *in situ* in the tunnel by a portable beta counter, and the tunnel was then swept by a stream of fresh air, no decrease in activity was detectable whether the grass was wet or dry.

Further evidence of the importance of stickiness was provided by experiments in which the grass in the tunnel was replaced by a stand of sticky artificial grass (PVC strips treated with a glycerine jelly). Aerodynamically, the artificial and real grass were similar, although the artificial 'leaves' were somewhat more rigid than the real ones. The values of v_g for deposition of *Lycopodium* spores to the artificial grass, (also shown in Fig. 5), were much higher than for real grass, and at $u_* = 140$ cm./sec. the velocity of deposition was 34 cm./sec. so that v_T was very much larger than v_s. In this case the limiting factor on the deposition rate was not the impaction process but the rate at which the spore content of the air at the level of the artificial leaves was replenished by turbulent diffusion from above.†

Chamberlain (1966*b*) also measured deposition in the wind tunnel with a number of particles of varying sizes smaller than *Lycopodium* spores, as follows:

Particle	Method of preparation	Diameter (microns)	Radioactive tagging
Pollen of ragweed (*Ambrosia artemisiifolia*)	Dispersion of natural sample	19	Thorium B
Polystyrene spheres	Dispersion from spinning top of solution of polystyrene in xylene	5	Cobalt 51
Fluorescent particles of zinc-cadmium sulphide (density 4·5)	Dispersion of commercial sample	2	Zinc 65
Droplet of tri-cresyl-phosphate	La Mer generator	2	Phosphorus 32
Droplet of tri-cresyl-phosphate	La Mer generator	1	Phosphorus 32
Aitken nuclei	Naturally present in laboratory air	0·08	Thorium B

† The sticking probability is of greatest importance when large spores are impacted at high velocities. Many of the larger spore bodies ejected by cryptogams are rendered sticky by a film of mucilage on their surface and the spores are retained on the first surface hit, normally the leaves of vegetation. This is particularly advantageous to coprophilous fungi, which grow on the dung of herbivorous animals, since impaction on the tips of nearby herbage gives a good chance of ingestion by another animal (Ingold, 1965). The opposite effect is seen in some plants, which depend on wind-borne pollination. The receiving surface, the stigma, is sticky, and the chance of pollen reaching it is increased because the grains, which are not sticky, bounce off other surfaces such as leaves and twigs.

The ragweed pollen, kindly supplied by Mr G. Raynor of Brookhaven National Laboratory, was used for comparison with American work. The polystyrene spheres and tri-cresyl-phosphate droplets were mono-disperse, but the zinc–cadmium sulphide particles and Aitken nuclei had a range of particle sizes. The deposition surface for the particles was grass, grown to a height of about 6 cm., and filling the working section of the tunnel. Volumetric sampling was by isokinetic suction

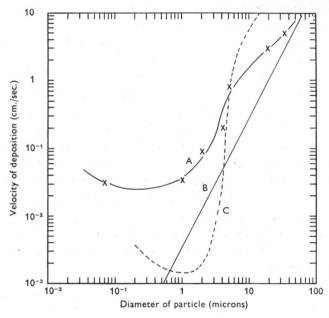

Fig. 6. Deposition of particles to grass in wind tunnel ($u_* = 70$ cm./sec.). Curve A: experimental results; curve B, terminal velocity; curve C, theoretical curve of Davies for smooth surface.

samplers (p. 66). The wind speed measured at a height of 15 cm. above the surface 5 m./sec. and the friction velocity was 0·7 m./sec. The results of the measurements of deposition velocity with these particles are shown in Fig. 6, both v_g and particle diameter being plotted on logarithmic scales.†

Figure 6 also shows a theoretical curve given by Davies (1965) for velocity of deposition of particles to a vertical smooth surface at a friction velocity of 1 m./sec. Although the mechanisms of deposition at rough and smooth surfaces are in some respects quite different, the similarity in general shape of the theoretical and experimental curves is

† The point for the zinc–cadmium particles (density 4·5) has been entered in Fig. 6 in a position corresponding to the mean diameter multiplied by 2·2 to allow for the effect of density on the terminal velocity.

striking, particularly the steep fall in v_g when the particle diameter falls to about 4 microns, and the minimum at about 1 micron. It seems that, quite apart from considerations of minimum viable cell size, spores much smaller than 4 microns would be ineffective transmitters of the parent organisms through inability to return to the ground within a reasonable distance. As it happens, 4 microns is also about the particle size at which impaction by raindrop becomes ineffective (see Gregory, 1961, figure 16), an aspect discussed in the next section.

WASHOUT OF PARTICLES BY RAIN

Impaction on raindrops

The efficiency E of the impaction of particles radius r on raindrops radius R is a function of the parameter P given by

$$P = \frac{v_s V_s}{gR},\qquad(8)$$

where v_s and V_s are the terminal velocities of particle and raindrop respectively. It is assumed that V_s is much greater than v_s, so that V_s can be taken as the relative velocity of drop and particle, and equation (8)

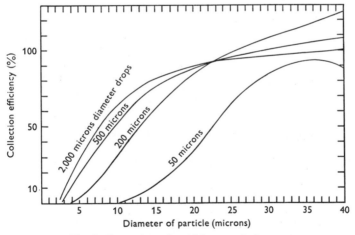

Fig. 7. Impaction of particles on raindrops.

is thus of the same form as the corresponding equation for impaction on cylinders (equation 6), with the fall velocity of the raindrop in place of the wind speed.

Langmuir (1948) calculated E as a function of P for the two cases where the flow of air round the falling drop is of the potential and viscous type, corresponding to large and small values of the Reynolds number of the raindrop. Langmuir gave an interpolation formula of doubtful theoretical validity for intermediate values of *Re*. The calculation was extended by Fonda and Herne (see Herne, 1960) and Mason (1957) to take account of the finite size of the particle, by virtue of which its centre need pass only within distance *r* of the drop for grazing contact to occur. Hocking (1959) examined theoretically the case where *R* and *r* are of comparable magnitude, and Picknett (1960) obtained experi-

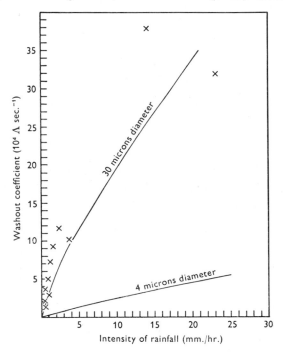

Fig. 8. Washout of particles by rain (× = May's experiments).

mental results which agree well with Hocking's theory. The efficiency of capture as a function of diameter of raindrop and particle is given in Fig. 7, in which *E* for the larger drops has been taken from Mason's calculation and *E* for the 50-micron mist or cloud droplets from Hocking's paper. For particles of about 20 or 30 microns, which would include most pollens and the larger spores, the efficiency of capture by raindrops is high, but it falls off very sharply for particles of 5 microns diameter or less. This latter conclusion was reached also experimentally by Walton & Woodcock (1960), who used particles of methylene blue with sizes between 2 and 10 microns. It was found that water-drops falling at their terminal velocities had very poor collection efficiencies for particles in the respirable range up to 3 microns. The only feasible method for removal of the smaller particles was to use pressurized sprays emitting droplets at speeds much greater than their terminal velocities.

By applying Langmuir's values of E to the spectrum of raindrop sizes given by Best (1950), Chamberlain (1953) calculated the wash-out coefficient Λ as a function of the terminal velocity of the particles and the intensity of rainfall. Λ has dimensions sec.$^{-1}$, and is the proportion of the cloud of particles washed out per second. Value of Λ for 30-micron particles ($v_s = 2$ cm./sec.) and 4-micron particles ($v_s = 0.05$ cm./sec.) are given in Fig. 8. Also shown are experimental values of Λ obtained by May (1958) who measured the washout of *Lycopodium* spores tagged with radio-iodine in the open air during rain. Reasonably

Table 5. *Effect of rainfall of intensity 2 mm./hr. on concentration in atmosphere of particles with diameter 4 or 30 microns*

	C/C_0	
Time (min.)	4 microns	30 microns
15	0·96	0·60
30	0·92	0·36
60	0·85	0·12
120	0·72	0·01

good agreement with the theory was obtained in May's experiments, which covered a range of rainfall intensity from 0·06–23 mm./hr. It is an over-simplification to suppose that the spectrum of raindrop size depends only on intensity, since frontal rain tends to consist of smaller drops than thundery rain, but the general agreement with theory shows that the basic assumptions are correct. If loss by deposition directly to the ground, and replenishment by fresh emission are both neglected, washout reduces the concentration of particles in air exponentially according to the equation

$$C = C_0\, e^{-\Lambda t}. \tag{9}$$

As an example, the variation of C/C_0 with time is given in Table 5 for a rainfall intensity of 2 mm./hr. The concentration of 30-micron particles is reduced to 0·36 of its initial value after 30 min. of rainfall or a total fall of 1 mm. of rain. By comparison, the experimental results of Hirst (1953), indicate an even more rapid removal of spores from the air. During a thunderstorm in July 1951 which terminated a previously dry spell, 0·95 mm. of rain fell in the first 30 min., during which the airborne concentrations of various categories of spores were measured. The count of pollens, and spores of *Ustilago* and *Erysiphe* were reduced to 1/6, 1/3 and 1/2 of their previous values respectively during the 30 min. of heavy rain.

Impaction by falling raindrops is not the only mechanism of wash-out. Particles carried up into the rain-forming layer may be captured by cloud droplets, or indeed droplets may actually form round them. Radioactive debris from nuclear explosions, which is mainly of sub-micron particle size, is precipitated in rain. Also, heavy rainfall, whether of convective or frontal type, usually occurs in conjunction with vertical and horizontal movements of air masses with different origins and therefore different particle concentrations.

Rates of wash-out

The relative effectiveness of direct deposition to the ground and wash-out by rain depends on the vertical extent of the cloud of particles. Data of Rempe (quoted by Gregory, 1961) indicate that the effective height $\bar{h}$ of the cloud of pollen† above a German forest was about 1,000 m. during day time and 300 m. at night. The velocity of deposition v_w due to wash-out is equal to $\Lambda\bar{h}$, and if $\bar{h}$ is taken as 500 m., then v_w is $5 \times 10^4 \Lambda$ cm./sec. For the wash-out of 30-micron particles in rainfall of 1 mm./hr., Λ is 3×10^{-4} sec.$^{-1}$ from Fig. 8, and the velocity of deposition is 15 cm./sec. This exceeds any likely value of v_g for direct deposition by sedimentation and impaction even when the vegetation is wet. However, the average daily rainfall in lowland Britain is between 1·5 and 3 mm., corresponding to an intensity of 1 mm./hr. for between 1·5 and 3 hr. daily, so the above value of v_w must be reduced by an order of magnitude to give a comparison of the yearly average contributions of wash-out and dry deposition. The two mechanisms are therefore likely to be of comparable long-term importance in the deposition of the larger spores and pollen. As Gregory (1961) points out, rainfall seems to be effective also with small spores which are deposited only slowly and ineffectively by other means. The exact mechanism of wash-out of small spores is, however, still in doubt.

DEPOSITION INDOORS

Even in a closed room, the air is never quite still, and convection currents are almost always present in sufficient strength to give air velocities at least comparable with the sedimentation velocities of the larger spores

---

† $\bar{h}$ is defined by the equation $\bar{h}C_1 = \int_0^\infty C(z)dz$, where $C(z)$ is the concentration at height z and C_1 the concentration near the ground.

and pollen (p. 140). Microbes entering through ventilation openings, or liberated indoors, are carried quite rapidly to all parts of a building. However, the rate of replacement of air in a building, even with good ventilation, is very small, a matter of changes per hour inside compared with changes per second in an equivalent volume outside.

Bourdillon, Lidwell & Lovelock (1946) showed that the effects of ventilation and deposition on the concentration of airborne microbes indoors can be evaluated as removal coefficients analogous to the wash-out coefficient previously discussed. When an initial population of microbes is created by human activity, and then left to die away, the volumetric concentration of viable organisms at time t is given by

$$C = C_0 e^{-\lambda t}, \tag{10}$$

and Bourdillon et al. (1946) show cases where the exponential decay of C continues for many minutes.

The removal coefficient λ (units time^{-1}) can be written

$$\lambda = \lambda_D + \lambda_R + \lambda_S, \tag{11}$$

where the suffixes D, R and S refer to death of the organisms, removal by ventilation, and removal by deposition respectively. If the air is reasonably well stirred λ_S can be equated approximately to v_s/H, where v_s is the sedimentation velocity and H the height of the room.

Table 6. *Rate coefficients for disappearance of particles of diameter* 4 *or* 30 *microns in a ventilated room* 3 *m. high*

		λ (sec. $^{-1}$)
Sedimentation (λ_S)	4 microns	$1 \cdot 6 \times 10^{-4}$
	30 microns	$1 \cdot 1 \times 10^{-2}$
Ventilation (λ_R)	2 changes/hr.	$5 \cdot 6 \times 10^{-4}$
	10 changes/hr.	$2 \cdot 8 \times 10^{-3}$

Table 6 gives values of λ_s for 30-micron particles and 4-micron particles assuming $H = 3$ m., with two typical values of λ_R for comparison. Evidently, sedimentation is likely to be more effective than ventilation in removing the 30-micron particles, but less effective for 4-micron particles. The dust 'rafts' which carry most of the bacteria and viruses in the atmosphere are mostly smaller than 4 microns, so that ventilation is the most effective way of removing them. Considering next the case of particles entering the air of a room from outside, suppose that C_0 is the concentration out-of-doors and that a proportion f of particles is removed by impaction and sedimentation in air passages on their way in. Neglecting any loss of viability, the equilibrium concentration C_i indoors is given by equating the net rate of entry to the rate of deposition of particles, as follows:

$$\lambda_R(fC_0 - C_i) = \lambda_S C_i. \qquad (12)$$

The ratio of concentrations indoors and out is

$$\frac{C_i}{C_0} = \frac{\lambda_R f}{\lambda_S + \lambda_R}. \qquad (13)$$

For 30-micron particles entering a room with two air changes per hour, the ratio C_i/C_0 is $0.05f$, and this explains why sufferers from hay fever do well to stay indoors.

In this discussion, the role of turbulent deposition on to walls and ceiling has been neglected. Deposition of dust particles on wallpaper is sometimes only too obvious, but little is known about the rate of deposition. The lower air velocities, and in general smoother surfaces

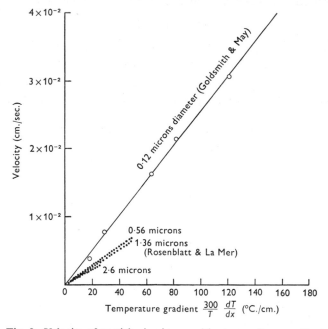

Fig. 9. Velocity of particles in air caused by temperature gradient.

indoors compared with outdoors would tend to minimize the turbulent transfer component of deposition in comparison with sedimentation, particularly for the larger particles. Another fact of practical importance is the thermal deposition of particles (p. 131). Particles tend to move down temperature gradients in the air, and this is the principle of the thermal precipitator (see, for example, Green & Lane, 1964, p. 265). The velocity due to thermal gradients, shown in Fig. 9, is not strongly dependent on particle diameter in the range 0·1–3 microns.

The temperature gradient between air and wall in a room is greatest where warm air rises turbulently from hot water pipes and radiators and comes into contact with cool walls. A very approximate upper estimate of the temperature gradient in the boundary layer might be 50 per cm. (boundary layer 2 mm. thick, 10° C difference between air and wall), and from Fig. 9 the induced velocity of deposition would be of order 10^{-2} cm./sec., which is comparable with the rate of turbulent deposition of micron-sized particles to grass-covered soil (Fig. 6).

In the outdoor environment, conditions most nearly approaching those indoors are found in forests, where the canopy restricts the exchange of air. Some particles carried in the air will be lost by impaction in the canopy, but the effect of sedimentation in the comparatively stagnant air below is more important. This is Raynor's explanation (in a personal communication) of the beneficial effects of a forest environment on sufferers from the allergy caused by ragweed pollen.

Re-suspension of dust

As previously shown from the experimental data on impaction, particles of 30 microns diameter or less, once deposited on surfaces, are not easily removed by air movement alone. The reason for this has been clearly stated by Bagnold (1960). First, small particles are submerged within a continuous viscous boundary layer which protects them from the buffeting of turbulent eddies. Secondly, should any particle nevertheless be disturbed and enter the air stream, it is slowed down as it re-enters the viscous boundary layer, and has insufficient velocity and momentum on impact to disturb other grains. Bagnold describes a desert in Anatolia, where the soil is very fine and powdery, and devoid of vegetation. When the wind is strong and the ground is disturbed by a flock of sheep, a dust cloud is created but this dies away rapidly as soon as the hoof marks are eroded, and the air becomes dust free. If, however, a desert surface contains large as well as small sand grains, a chain reaction is set up by the impact of one grain disturbing others, and dust clouds are continuously generated.

Re-suspension caused by mechanical disturbance of dust is important in hospital wards and theatres (Bourdillon et al. 1946), and also in nuclear energy establishments, where radioactive dust particles may be present on laboratory surfaces. By the use of suitable instruments, the radioactivity A of dust per m.² of floor surface, and the activity C per m.^{3} of the air can be measured. The ratio C/A, with units m.$^{-1}$, is called the re-suspension factor and denoted by K. K depends on the particle size of the dust, the amount of disturbance, and the roughness and texture of the surface. Measurements of K have been made both in laboratories and in the open air, following deposition of radioactive dusts in nuclear weapon tests (Stewart, 1966). In extreme conditions indoors, with air thick with dust, K was found to be 2×10^{-4} m.$^{-1}$ (Chamberlain & Stanbury, 1951), but in a more representative series of experiments in laboratories, where plutonium oxide dust of median diameter about 10 microns was dispersed, K ranged from 10^{-6} to 5×10^{-5} m.$^{-1}$. There was a marked reduction in K, by about a factor of five, when the linoleum on the floor was treated with a wax polish, but K increased with the amount of human activity in the room (measured in steps/min.). One interesting finding in later unpublished work was that K was greatly increased if the occupants of the room wore canvas overshoes of a type used to protect footwear from radioactive contamination. The overshoes are loose fitting, and when the wearer walks about there is some flapping and bellows action of the overshoes. There was no increase in K when the occupants walked about in PVC overshoes.

It is also known that the shaking of blankets causes a steep increase in the airborne bacteria of a hospital ward (p. 122) (Bourdillon *et al.* 1946). It is possible that the critical factor is the forcing of air through the surface of a textile material, which subjects particles to air movement not conditioned by the viscous boundary layer associated with air flow along the surface. The possible effect of such mechanisms can be seen by considering the experimental values of K in relation to the surface area of a room. If the surface is say 100 m.^{2}, and K is 10^{-5} m.$^{-1}$, then the suspension of particles is equivalent to the distribution into the air space of the contamination on 10 cm.^{2} of surface. Thus any process which effectively re-disperses particles even from a small surface area will lead to a sharp increase in K.

REFERENCES

BAGNOLD, R. A. (1941). *The Physics of Blown Sand and Desert Dunes*. London: Methuen. (Reprinted 1960.)

BAGNOLD, R. A. (1960). The re-entrainment of settled dusts. *Int. J. Air Pollut.* **2**, 357.

BEST, A. C. (1950). The size distribution of raindrops. *Q. Jl R. met. Soc.* **76**, 16.

BOURDILLON, R. B., LIDWELL, O. M. & LOVELOCK, J. E. (1946). Studies in air hygiene. *Spec. Rep. Ser. med. Res. Counc.* no. 262. London: H.M.S.O.

CHAMBERLAIN, A. C. (1953). Aspects of the travel and deposition of aerosol clouds and vapours. *A.E.R.E. Rep. HP/R* 1261. London: H.M.S.O.

CHAMBERLAIN, A. C. (1966 *a*). Transport of gases to and from grass and grass-like surfaces. *Proc. R. Soc.* A, **290**, 236.

CHAMBERLAIN, A. C. (1966 *b*). Transport of *Lycopodium* spores and other small particles to rough surfaces. *Proc. R. Soc.* A (in the Press)

CHAMBERLAIN, A. C. & STANBURY, G. R. (1951). The hazard from inhaled fission products in rescue operations. *A.E.R.E. Rep. HP/R* 737. Atomic Energy Research Establishment, Harwell, Berks.

CHEPIL, W. S. (1941). Relation of wind erosion to the dry aggregate structure of a soil. *Scient. Agric.* **21**, 488.

CHEPIL, W. S. (1945 & 1946). Dynamics of wind erosion. I to IV. *Soil Sci.* **60**, 305, 397, 475; **61**, 167.

DAVIES, C. N. (1965). The rate of deposition of aerosol particles from turbulent flow through ducts. *Ann. occup. Hyg.* **8**, 239.

DAVIES, C. N. (1966). Deposition of aerosols from turbulent flow through pipes. *Proc. R. Soc.* A, **289**, 235.

DAVIES, C. B. & PEETZ, C. V. (1956). Impingement of particles on a transverse cylinder. *Proc. R. Soc.* A, **234**, 269.

EGGLETON, A. E. J. & THOMPSON, N. (1961). Loss of fluorescent particles in atmospheric diffusion experiments by comparison with radioxenon tracer. *Nature, Lond.* **192**, 935.

FRIEDLANDER, S. K. & JOHNSTONE, H. F. (1957). Deposition of suspended particles from turbulent gas streams. *Ind. Engng Chem.* **49**, 1151.

FUCHS, N. A. (1964). *The Mechanics of Aerosols.* (Translation edited C. N. Davies.) Oxford: Pergamon Press.

GOLDSMITH, P. & MAY, F. G. (1966). Diffusiophoresis and thermophoresis. In *Aerosol Science* ed. by C. N. Davies. London and New York: Academic Press.

GREEN, H. L. & LANE, W. R. (1964). *Particulate Clouds: Dusts, Smokes and Mists*, 2nd edn. London: Spon.

GREGORY, P. H. (1945). The dispersion of airborne spores. *Trans. Br. mycol. Soc.* **28**, 26.

GREGORY, P. H. (1951). Deposition of airborne *Lycopodium* spores on cylinders. *Ann. appl. Biol.* **38**, 357.

GREGORY, P. H. (1961). *The Microbiology of the Atmosphere.* London: Leonard Hill.

GREGORY, P. H., LONGHURST, T. J. & SREERAMULU, T. (1961). Dispersion and deposition of airborne *Lycopodium* and *Ganoderma* spores. *Ann. appl. Biol.* **49**, 645.

HERNE, H. (1960). The classical computations of the aerodynamic capture of particles by spheres. *Int. J. Air Pollut.* **3**, 26.

HIRST, J. M. (1953). Changes in atmospheric spore content: diurnal periodicity and the effects of weather. *Trans. Br. mycol. Soc.* **36**, 375.

HOCKING, L. M. (1959). The collision efficiency of small drops. *Q. Jl R. Met. Soc.* **85**, 44.

HOLMES, A. (1965). *Principles of Physical Geology.* Revised edn. London: Nelson.

INGOLD, C. T. (1939). *Spore Discharge in Land Plants.* Oxford: Clarendon Press.

INGOLD, C. T. (1965). *Spore Liberation.* Oxford: Clarendon Press.

ISLITZER, N. F. & DUMBAULD, R. K. (1963). Atmospheric diffusion—deposition studies over flat terrain. *Int. J. Air Pollut.* **7**, 999.

KUNKELL, W. B. (1948). Magnitude and character of errors produced by shape factors in Stokes's law estimates of particle radius. *J. appl. Phys.* **19**, 1056.

LANGMUIR, I. (1948). The production of rain by a chain reaction in cumulus clouds at temperatures above freezing. *J. Met.* **5**, 175.

MASON, B. J. (1957). *The Physics of Clouds*. Oxford: Clarendon Press.

MAY, F. G. (1958). The washout of *Lycopodium* spores by rain. *Q. Jl R. met. Soc.* **84**, 451.

PICKNETT, R. G. (1960). Collection efficiencies for water drops in air. *Int. J. Air Pollut*. **3**, 160.

ROSENBLATT, P. & LA MER, V. K. (1946). Motion of a particle in a temperature gradient. *Phys. Rev.* **70**, 385.

SALISBURY, E. J. (1961). *Weeds and Aliens*. London: Collins.

STEWART, K. (1966). The re-suspension of particulate material from surfaces. In *Surface Contamination*. Ed. B. R. Fisk. London: Pergamon Press (in the Press).

SUTTON, O. G. (1953). *Micrometeorology*. London: McGraw-Hill.

WALTON, W. H. & WOODCOCK, A. (1960). The suppression of airborne dust by water spray. *Int. J. Air Pollut.* **3**, 129.

THE INHALATION AND RETENTION OF PARTICLES IN THE HUMAN RESPIRATORY SYSTEM

H. A. DRUETT

Microbiological Research Establishment, Porton, Salisbury, Wiltshire

INTRODUCTION

The retention of particles in lungs, and in particular in human lungs, has been studied over many years and intensively during the past two decades. The field has been reviewed by Casarett (1960), Davies (1949, 1952), Hatch & Gross (1964), Morrow (1960), and Task Group (1966), I have attempted to present the information broadly and in its historical perspective for the benefit of non-specialists.

The unhealthy atmosphere of mines has been recognized since the earliest times, and criminals and prisoners of war were often condemned to labour in them until relieved by death. Agricola (1556) gave a description of the general pathology associated with metal dusts, while Bubbe in 1775 described the pathological effects caused by stone breaking. The connection between dust and tuberculosis was soon recognized. Benoiston de Chateauneuf (1831) wrote 'De l'influence de certaines professions sur le developpement de la Phtisie pulmonaire' which was echoed by Lombard (1834).

During the nineteenth century awareness grew of the hazards associated with the inhalation of dust. The biological and microgeological contents of the air were studied by Ehrenburg in the 1830's. Work on the occupational hazards continued. In 1843 Holland surveyed the vital statistics of Sheffield. In 1857 Hall's 'Discussion of diseases of Sheffield Grinders' was published. The discovery of bacteria opened a new field to investigators. In 1868 Lister reported that exhaled air had lost its power to cause putrefaction of blood and Tyndall (1881) demonstrated that light-scattering particles were removed by passage through the lungs.

The experiments of Koch in 1884, later repeated by many others, suggested that infection in animals could be initiated by the inhalation of fine particles of dust containing tubercle bacilli. In 1888 Büchner (Büchner, 1888; Büchner & Merkel, 1888; Büchner & Enderlen, 1888) demonstrated the ability of an airborne powder of *B. anthracis* to cause infection. Thus experimental support was afforded to the ideas of Girolano Fracastoro (1483–1553) expounded in his work *De Contagione*.

Throughout the nineteenth century various commissions in Great Britain alternated between putting the most blame on dust or on fumes as the cause of industrial respiratory disease. The Miners' Phthisis Commission of 1903, which studied conditions in the Witwatersrand Mines, reported: 'It is urgently necessary to prevent the discharge of minute hard angular particles of dust into the mine atmosphere', and recommended the use of water spray to suppress these small dust particles. At this period the average life of a white miner at the rock face was 8 years. In 1905 an attempt to stimulate research into the prevention of dust diseases was the offer of a prize of £20 for an acceptable dust-arresting respirator.

The examination of silicotic lungs for dust particles emphasized the role played by the smaller particles in initiating respiratory disease. McCrae (1913) found that 70% by number of the particles were below 1 micron in diameter and that the largest did not exceed 10·5 microns. Watkins-Pitchford & Moir (1916) reported that only 1 particle in 10^5 was as large as 14 microns and 80% of particles were less than 2 microns. In 1923 Mavrogordato defined phthisis-producing dust as particles of free silica from 0·5–5 microns diameter. These early findings agree well with the recommendations of panels of the M.R.C. Industrial Pulmonary Disease Committee (1952) and the Johannesburg International Pneumoconiosis Conference (1959) which specify a cut-off for instruments simulating dust retention by the lung of 7·1 microns diameter for unit density spheres. Recognition of the importance of small particles was reflected by improved instrumentation for particle size analysis such as the Konimeter introduced by Kotze in 1916 and later modified into its circular form by Boyd (1928), the Greenburg & Smith (1922) impinger and the thermal precipitator of Green & Watson (1935).

During these years the importance of the airborne route of infection by micro-organisms as compared with other methods of contagion was hotly contested. Indeed in many respects the problem is still unresolved (Downie *et al.* 1965). After some severe reverses a new impetus was given to the study of airborne infection during the third decade of this century by the work of W. F. Wells (later published in book form in 1955) who showed that droplets expelled during coughing and sneezing would not necessarily fall to the ground, as their initial large size would suggest, but could evaporate to infective droplet nuclei small enough to be inhaled (e.g. p. 117). In retrospect, the droplet nuclei theory seems to overemphasize a particular method of aerosol generation, and it seems likely that the indirect generation of fine aerosols from dust or blankets may be more important with certain hardy organisms (Hare, 1964).

Meanwhile, considerable progress was made in the experimental study of dust retention in the human lung. After early work by Lehmann, Saito & Girörer (1912) and Baumberger (1923), a systematic attack was made on the problem by Drinker and his associates (Drinker, 1925; Drinker, Thomson & Finn, 1928; Drinker & Field, 1933). Their method, which set the basic pattern for this type of experiment, was to inhale dust-laden air from a cabinet and exhale it through a dust-collecting device, in this case an electrical precipitator. A spirometer was used to measure the volume breathed.

Drinker's work was expanded by C. E. Brown (1931 *a,b*) who studied the parameters controlling deposition using calcium carbonate dust and magnesium oxide fumes as the test aerosols. He found that deposition increased with the particle size of the inhaled aggregate and was inversely proportional to the minute-volume breathed. Below 20 respirations per minute, deposition was inversely proportional to respiration rate. Higher respiration rate did not increase deposition. Percentage deposition was independent of the relative humidity of the inspired air, vital capacity and volume per respiration, the last mentioned being the only disagreement with the subsequent theoretical findings.†

THE RESPIRATORY SYSTEM

The respiratory system may conveniently be divided into:

(*a*) The respiratory or gaseous exchange portion formed by the respiratory bronchioli, alveolar sacs, and alveoli.

(*b*) The conducting portion consisting of the trachea and a bifurcating system of air passages by which air taken in through the nose or mouth is distributed as uniformly as possible to the respiratory region during inhalation and conversely during exhalation.

(*c*) The upper respiratory portion consisting of the naso-pharynx and/or mouth.

† *Note.* Technical terms describing respiration may be defined as follows. *Tidal air*: the volume of air inhaled or exhaled per breath in normal breathing. *Complemental air*: the volume of air which can be inhaled by a forcible inspiratory effort after normal inspiration has ceased. *Supplemental air*: the volume of air which can be expelled from the lung by a forcible contraction of the muscles after normal expiration has ceased. *Residual air*: the volume of air which cannot normally be expelled from the lungs. *Vital capacity* = complemental + supplemental + tidal air. *Functional residual air* = supplemental + residual air. *Lung volume* = complemental + supplemental + tidal + residual air. *Minute volume* = the volume of air inhaled or exhaled per minute in normal breathing. *Ventilation rate* = tidal volume × number of breaths per minute.

During breathing the volume of the lung is increased and decreased by the action of the muscles of the chest and diaphragm. This causes a tidal flow of air to sweep through the system about 18 times per minute in each direction. The volume change takes place essentially in the respiratory portion of the lung. Inspiration lasts about three-quarters of the time taken in expiration and in normal breathing a short pause occurs after expiration. This pattern may be varied according to the demand of the tissues for oxygen, and can be altered by voluntary control to meet special needs, for example, while swimming. The respiratory rate is variable and depends on the age, size, and physical condition of the subject, the state of muscular activity and nervous condition, and on pathological conditions such as emphysema, asthma, pneumonia and silicosis.

In normal breathing (Starling, 1952) about 500 cm.³ of air (measured at N.T.P.) or 600 cm.³ of air (measured saturated at 37° C) is inhaled at each breath. Of this some 140 cm.³ (or 28%) does not penetrate to the respiratory tissues and this volume is known as the 'dead space'. If aerosol retention in the respiratory tissues is expressed in terms of aerosol inhaled, it is therefore impossible to achieve a retention greater than about 70% even if there is a complete removal of particles which have penetrated to these tissues. The remaining 30% may (or may not) be removed in the conducting portion of the lung.

After normal expiration is complete a forcible contraction will expel a further 1,300 cm.³ of reserve or supplemental air. In addition, there is a further 1,000 cm.³ of residual air which cannot be expelled. The supplemental and residual air collectively occupy 2·9 l. which is nearly 6 times the volume of the tidal flow. Owing to the rapid diffusion of gases the exchange of oxygen and carbon dioxide between the tidal and non-tidal volumes is efficient but the exchange of massive particles is limited by their much slower diffusion. For this reason measurements of gaseous exchange based on carbon dioxide content cannot be taken as indicative of the efficiency of aerosol exchange. Similarly, small particles are not readily transported by the airflow into the deepest parts of the alveolar structure although some will penetrate due to mixing and diffusion.

It is convenient to discuss separately the respiratory structures lying above and below the trachea. A full description of these can be found in standard reference books: only information relevant to deposition and removal of particulate matter is given.

The trachea (Fig. 1)

The trachea is a thin-walled tube, U-shaped in cross-section, about 11 cm. long and 2·2 cm. in diameter. It is prevented from collapsing by C- or Y-shaped hyaline cartilages which encircle the tube except for its flattened posterior portion. The inside of the trachea is covered with a ciliated epithelium and is well supplied with mucus-secreting cells.

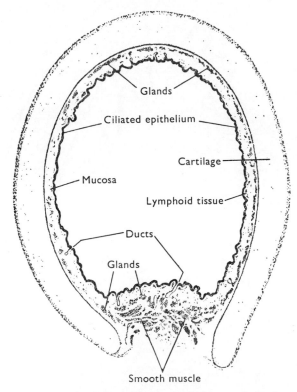

Fig. 1. Cross-section through trachea of a 9-year-old boy. ×6. (Redrawn and modified from Kölliker-von Ebner.)

Figs. 1–4. By permission from *A Text Book of Histology* (8th ed. by Bloom, W. & Fawcett, W. (1962). Philadelphia: W. B. Saunders Co.).

The bronchi (Figs. 2, 3)

At its lower end the trachea bifurcates into two main bronchi which enter the left and right lungs respectively. The right bronchus divides into three and the left into two branches which serve the lobes of the lung. The branches then subdivide for the most part by dichotomy into bronchi of several orders (the exact nomenclature and number of which depends on the authority consulted), and the diameter of the tubes becomes progressively smaller. Before the bronchi enter the lungs their structure is similar to that of the trachea but, once inside, the cartilage rings are replaced by cartilage plates. These plates surround the bronchus, which then takes a more circular section although in the larger bronchi the walls show marked longitudinal folding. As the tube

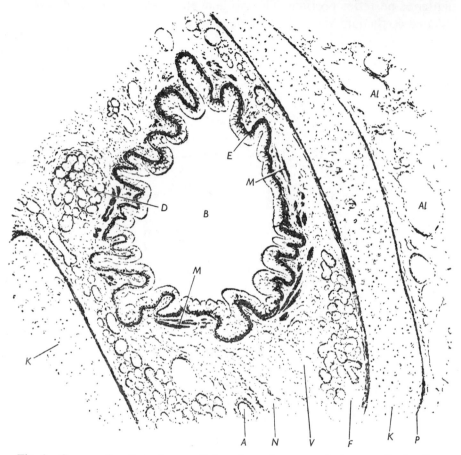

Fig. 2. Cross-section through a small bronchus of a man. *A*, Artery; *Al*, alveoli; *B*, bronchus; *D*, mixed glands; *E*, ciliated epithelium with goblet cells; *F*, fat tissue; *K*, cartilage; *M*, circular muscle; *N*, nerve; *P*, perichondrium; *V*, vein. Mallory's connective tissue stain. × 30. (After Schaffer.)

diameter decreases, the cartilage becomes less evident and finally disappears when the bronchioles, which have a diameter less than 1 mm., are reached. Miller (1947) defines the bronchioles as being free from cartilage, while Hayward & Reed (1952) state that the first bronchioles carry occasional plates. At the same time the mucus and mucerous glands, which are plentiful in the trachea and bronchi, cease and the epithelium which has been ciliated in the trachea and bronchi gradually becomes non-ciliated. Finally the bronchioles subdivide into respiratory bronchioles.

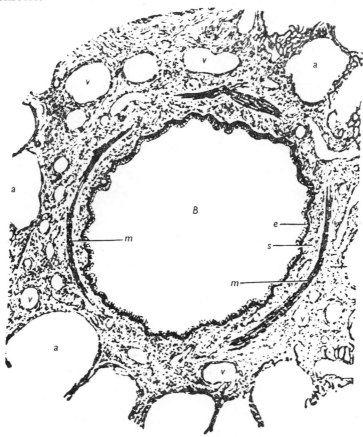

Fig. 3. Cross-section through a bronchiole (*B*) 0·7 mm. in diameter. *a*, Alveoli; *e*, epithelium; *m*, circular muscle; *s*, lamina propria with cross-sections of elastic fibres; *v*, veins. Lung fixed by filling it with alcohol. × 55. (After von Ebner.)

The respiratory portion (Fig. 4)

The respiratory bronchioles in man are about 0·5 mm. in diameter with a similar wall structure to the terminal bronchioles but the structure is interrupted where single or small groups of alveoli are opposed to the lumen (Weibel, 1963) and hence the term 'respiratory'. The alveolar ducts are respiratory bronchioles in which almost the entire wall has been completely alveolated and only a fine mesh work of elastic and thin collagenous and smooth muscle fibres remain. They follow a tortuous course through the respiratory tissue with frequent branching, throughout which they are closely beset with thin-walled openings which may lead to single alveoli or alveolar sacs from which the mouths of numerous alveoli open. The alveolar wall consists of a background of

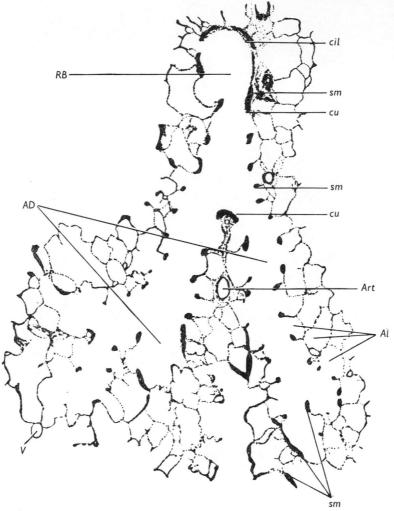

Fig. 4. Section through respiratory bronchiole (*RB*) and two alveolar ducts (*AD*) of human lung, showing the smooth muscle, *sm* (in black), in the walls of the alveolar ducts; *cil*, ciliated epithelium; *cu*, cuboidal epithelium; *Al*, alveolar sacs; *Art*, arteriole; *V*, vein. (Slightly modified from Baltisberger.)

reticular and elastic fibres supporting an anastomosing network of capillaries. The electron micrographs of Low (1952) and also of Karrer (1958) show that there is a thin continuous cellular covering of the alveolar wall arising from epithelial cells below which lies a thin continuous basement membrane.

Table 1. *Schematic representation of the respiratory system according to Findeisen (1935)*

Lung parts	Branching factor	No.	Inside dia. (cm.)	Length (cm.)	Cross-sectional area (cm.²)	Flow speed† (cm./sec.)	Flow-through time (sec.)
A. Trachea	1	1	1·3	11·0	1·3	150	0·07
B. Main bronchi	2	2	0·75	6·5	1·1	180	0·04
C. Bronchi, first order	6	12	0·4	3·0	1·5	130	0·02
D. Bronchi, second order	8	100	0·2	1·5	3·1	65	0·02
E. Bronchi, third order	8	770	0·15	0·5	14	14	0·04
F. Bronchiole terminales	70	$5·4 \times 10^4$	0·06	0·3	150	1·3	0·22
G. Bronchiole respiratorii	2	$1·1 \times 10^5$	0·05	0·15	220	0·9	0·17
H. Ductuli alveolarii	240	$2·6 \times 10^7$	0·02	0·02	8,200	0·025	0·82
I. Saculi alveolarii	2	$5·2 \times 10^7$	0·03	0·03	$1·47 \times 10^5$‡	approx. 0	1·2

† For ventilation rate of 200 cm.³ per sec.
‡ Total surface area of sphere-shaped saculi alveolarii.

FINDEISEN'S MODEL OF THE LUNG

Findeisen's (1935) approximation to the lung consisted of a system of branching tubes (Table 1) whose length and diameter and number conformed to the best available anatomical data. The only exception to this rule were the alveolar sacs which were assumed to be spherical in form. The subdivisions studied consisted of the trachea, four orders of bronchi, two orders of bronchioles and the alveolar ducts and sacs. The airflow during inspiration and expiration was treated as constant at 200 ml./sec. and the respiration rate was 15 cyc./min. It was assumed that branching to tubes of lower orders was at 30° to the axis of the higher order tube and for sedimentation calculations the tubes were assumed to be randomly orientated. Owing to the moist nature of the

Table 2. *Deposition of airborne particles as a percentage of those entering the trachea*

(4 sec. respiratory cycle 200 cm.³/sec. flow rate.)

Particle radius (microns)	0·03	0·1	0·3	1·0	3·0	10	30
Conducting portion	8·4	4·2	2·7	7·9	44·9	98	100
Respiratory portion	57·6	30·9	30·5	88·5	55·1	0	0
Total retention	66	35·1	33·2	96·4	100	98	100

walls, any particle touching them was assumed to be retained. Three physical processes were considered by which particles would be removed from the air flowing in these tubes: sedimentation, inertial effect (impaction) and diffusion. A correction was also made for the effect of finite particle size in air flowing near the tube boundaries. Formulae were derived for the probability of deposition due to each of these processes in each division of the lung. Table 2 summarizes the results obtained for the deposition of particles entering the trachea in the conducting portion (terminal bronchiole and above) and in the respiratory portion of the lung.

Findeisen's method of calculation shows more clearly to the reader of his paper than later methods the regions in which the various physical factors are important. Removal by diffusion (inversely related to particle size) plays a dominant role in removing submicron particles in the respiratory portion of the lung. Removal by sedimentation (which depends on particle density and the square of the diameter) operates most powerfully in the bronchioles in limiting the penetration of larger particles to the respiratory portion, but is responsible for the deposition of those particles which do reach this vulnerable area. Impaction causes particles to be removed higher in the respiratory system than removal by sedimentation alone, without greatly influencing the overall retention or removing those particles with a potentiality of penetrating to the respiratory region.

DEVELOPMENT OF THEORETICAL AND EXPERIMENTAL APPROACHES

If allowance is made for particle density and shape the predictions of Findeisen showed general agreement with the measurements of Van Wijk & Patterson (1940) who used mineral dust (Table 3) inhaled through the nose at a respiration rate of 19 per min. and a ventilation rate of 17 l./min. In these experiments, particle size measurements were made with a thermal precipitator and results showed an orderly decrease in retention from over 90 % at 5 microns to 28 % at 0·2 microns. Findeisen's calculation underestimated the volumes of the alveolar

Table 3. *Results of Van Wijk & Patterson* (1940) *for the retention of mine dust* (*chiefly quartzite*)

Apparent diameter of particles (microns)	0·2	0·2	0·4	0·8	1·2	1·6	2·0	2·5	3·0	4·0	5·0
Removed by breathing	21·0	27·8	37·8	52·8	63·0	76·3	79·5	84·7	89·4	96·1	92·6

ducts and sacs and consequently underestimated the retention of the submicron particles. Landahl (1950a) attempted to overcome this defect by increasing the number of alveolar sacs so that the model conformed to the actual resting volume of the lung. At the same time, he added the 'mouth' and pharynx as separate regions. His mathematical procedure differed from that of Findeisen in that probabilities for all the deposition processes were combined in each region. In a formalized breathing pattern each inspiration and expiration occupied three-eighths of the cycle, separated by one-eighth cycle at the termination of each process. During inspiration and expiration the volume flow was assumed constant. Retentions were computed for each subdivision of the respiratory tract for a range of particle sizes, and four different conditions of respiration frequency and tidal volume. These theoretical predictions were compared with the experimental findings of Landahl & Herrman (1948) and good agreement was found. These experimenters inhaled an aerosol of heterogeneous particle size from a reservoir via a tube held in the mouth. After two or three breaths to equilibrate the lungs, the aerosol was exhaled into a 6-stage size-discriminating sampler. Similar 6-stage samples were taken directly from the aerosol, consisting of corn oil, sodium bicarbonate, or glycerol. Corresponding stages were compared. This technique was considerably improved in accuracy (but severely limited in the type of aerosol) by the introduction of the homogeneous aerosol technique of Sinclair & La Mer (1949) to generate the inhaled cloud (Landahl, Tracewell & Lassen, 1951, 1952). This greatly simplified the sampling because a single critical jet impinger could be used instead of a 6-stage size-discriminator, enabling cloud concentration to be examined in four successive fractions of the exhaled air. The operation of valves was automatically controlled and the experimental subject synchronized his mouth position on the inhaling or exhaling tube. The standardized

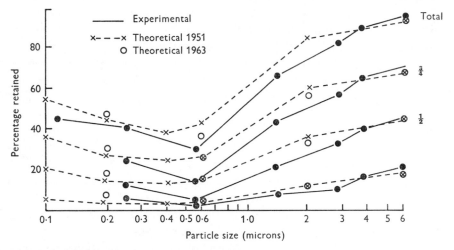

Fig. 5. Comparison of theoretical and experimental results for 12 sec. cycle 1,350 cm.³ tidal air, per cent retention in lungs of human subjects as a function of particle diameter in microns (impaction equivalent). The upper curves represent total retention. The lower curves represent retention in successive fractions of the expired air cumulatively modified from Landahl, Tracewell & Lassen (1951) and Landahl (1963).

breathing cycle described above was used. Because the successive fraction of the exhaled volume represents air which has penetrated progressively deeper into the lung structure, the deposition of particles increases. Figure 5 shows that for large particle sizes theoretical and practical values for retention agree well in all fractions of the exhaled cloud. For small sizes the theoretical estimates exceeded the experimental values appreciably.

The study of the retention of aerosol in successive fractions of exhaled air was further extended by Altshuler, Yarmus, Palmes & Nelson (1957). In their studies, an aerosol of triphenyl phosphate (density 1·31) of homogeneous size was inhaled and the concentration of particles in the exhaled air was continuously monitored by means of light scattering measurements. Respiratory flow was recorded by a pneumotachograph and carbon dioxide concentration measured by an infra-red gas analyser. The carbon dioxide concentration was used to estimate the respiratory dead space.

Results obtained for total deposition showed appreciable differences between the three experimental subjects. Minimum retention always occurred at 0·4 micron and slower, deeper breathing produced a greater retention than the converse. It was also observed that differences due to respiratory rate were greater with 1·6 micron particles than with 0·14 micron particles. This was attributed to the dependence of sedimentation removal (of 1·6 micron particles) on time, whereas Brownian removal (of 0·14 micron particles) is proportional to the square root of time. Subsequently, Altshuler *et al.* (1959) examined the information contained in their measurements in more detail and in particular analysed the mixing of the tidal air with the functional residual air. In these investigations the particle sizes studied were 0·2, 0·4 and 0·8 microns which are close to the value for minimum lung retention. In the first instance the aerosol was assumed capable of following the bulk movement of the gas and participating in its bulk mixing with the residual air without partaking in the rapid diffusive mixing of the gas molecules. Later, the deposition of particles was considered. The aerosol particle thus becomes a tracer for the investigation of bulk mixing. The subject started with a few breaths of clean air, then took nine breaths of aerosol followed by several breaths of clean air. Aerosol concentrations were monitored in all exhalations. The first four breaths of the aerosol (the 'wash in' phase) showed a build-up in the expired aerosol to a constant value ('steady state'). After the ninth aerosol breath, the concentration of exhaled aerosol fell rapidly ('wash-out' phase). After four breaths of clean air the concentration in the exhaled air was virtually zero. By assigning probabilities to the various mixing and deposition processes it was clearly demonstrated that aerosol exchange between the tidal and the functional residual air differed greatly from gaseous exchange. Whereas the gaseous exchange might amount to 70% of the tidal flow, the aerosol exchange might be less than 15%. The difference between aerosol and gas mixing volumes is much greater when comparing residual volumes. Whereas almost all the functional residual capacity participates in the gas exchange, less than one-tenth participates in exchange of aerosol. The studies again revealed appreciable differences between the three experimental subjects. Subsequently, Altshuler (1959) developed a model of the lung based on

Table 4. *Schematic representation of respiratory tract according to Landahl, revised, 1962*

Region (r)	Number	Volume (cm.³)	Relative volume (V)	Diameter (2R) (cm.)	Length (cm.)	Cross-sectional area (cm.²)	Velocity (cm./sec.)	Passage time (r') (sec.)	Fraction passing
Mouth (1)	1	20	0·04	2	7	3	100	0·07	1·00
Pharynx (2)	1	20	0·04	3	3	7	45†	0·07	0·96
Trachea (3)	1	24	0·06	1·6	11	2	150	0·07	0·92
Prim. bronchi (4)	2	10	0·02	1·0	6·5	1·6	190	0·03	0·86
Sec. bronchi (5)	12	4	0·01	0·4	3	1·5	200	0·015	0·84
Ter. bronchi (6)	100	5	0·01	0·2	1·5	3·1	100	0·015	0·83
Quart. bronchi (7)	770	7	0·015	0·15	0·5	14	22	0·02	0·82
Terminal bronchioles (8)	5·4×10⁴	45	0·10	0·06	0·3	170	2	0·15	0·81
Resp. bronchi (9)	1·1×10⁵	33	0·07	0·05	0·15	300	1·4	0·10	0·72
Alveolar ducts (10)	2·6×10⁷	(160)‡	(0·63)	(0·02)‡	(0·02)‡	8,000	—	—	0·65
Alveolar sacs (11)	5·2×10⁷	(730)‡	—	(0·03)‡	(0·03)‡	—	—	—	—

Retention in various regions of the respiratory tract

Region (r)	300 cm.³/sec. 4 sec. cycle 450 cm.³ tidal air					300 cm.³/sec., 8 sec. cycle 900 cm.³ tidal air					300 cm.³/sec., 12 sec. cycle 1,350 cm.³ tidal air					1,000 cm.³/sec., 4 sec. cycle 1,500 cm.³ tidal air				
	20	6	2	0·6	0·2	20	6	2	0·6	0·2	20	6	2	0·6	0·2	20	6	2	0·6	0·2
M 1	15	0	0	0	0	14	1	0	0	0	14	1	0	0	0	18	1	0	0	0
P 2	8	0	0	0	0	8	1	0	0	0	8	1	0	0	0	10	1	0	0	0
T 3	10	1	0	0	0	11	1	0	0	0	11	1	0	0	0	19	3	0	0	0
PB 4	12	2	1	0	0	13	2	1	0	0	13	1	1	0	0	20	5	1	0	0
SB 5	19	4	1	0	0	17	4	2	0	0	18	5	5	1	0	21	12	2	0	1
TB 6	17	9	2	1	0	20	9	2	0	0	21	10	2	2	0	9	20	5	1	2
QB 7	6	7	2	1	1	8	7	1	1	1	8	7	1	1	1	1	10	2	2	5
TB 8	6	19	6	4	6	6	24	7	4	6	6	24	8	8	6	1	9	8	3	3
RB 9	0	11	5	3	4	0	10	7	6	6	0	12	11	11	5	0	3	3	2	2
AD 10	0	25	25	8	11	0	27	44	17	23	0	27	48	22	25	0	13	26	10	13
AS 11	0	5	0	0	0	0	5	4	2	3	0	5	11	11	10	0	18	17	6	7
Totals	93	83	41	16	22	97	91	66	30	40	99	94	82	38	47	99	95	59	21	29

† Glottis velocity = 150.
‡ Values as estimated. These values are corrected to 2·5 l. at end of expiration.

the analogy of a continuous tubular filter bed and derived equations relating regional deposition, distribution of aerosol in the expired air and efficiency of removal at different depths in the respiratory tract.

In 1963 Landahl recalculated his previous work. In this he reverted (Table 4) to Findeisen's original estimate of the number of alveoli but adjusted their volume to correspond with the mean lung volume (i.e. the deflated lung volume plus half the tidal air volume). Other improvements were made to the mathematical theory. Agreement between these calculations and the experimental results of Landahl *et al.* (1951) was

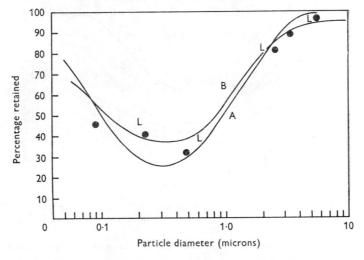

Fig. 6. Total retention in the human lung 1,350 cm.³. Tidal volume 12 sec. breathing cycle. A, Beeckman's calculation on Landahl's data (1950). B, Beeckman's calculation on Weibel's lung model A. L, Landahl's calculation 1963. ●, Experimental results of Landahl, Tracewell & Lassen (1951).

very close (Fig. 5). This work has been extended by Beeckmans (1965a, b) who made use of an electronic computer to introduce refinements that would have been impossibly tedious by classical methods. Both intrapulmonary gas mixing and recycling of undeposited aerosol were taken into account. In his first paper (Beeckmans, 1965a) he used the same model of the respiratory system as Landahl but in a subsequent paper (Beeckmans, 1965b) he used Weibel's model 'A' of the lung which has twenty-seven subdivisions. This more complicated model did not materially improve the agreement with experimental data (Fig. 6). Agreement between theory and experiment is now so close that considerable weight can be given to theoretical predictions where no direct experimental evidence is available. Where practical aerosols are concerned the main causes of uncertainty in the interpretation of data lies in

assessing the influence of hygroscopicity, shape and heterogeneity of
density amongst the various particles.

Beeckman's calculations demonstrating the effect of tidal volume on
aerosol deposition in the lung for a constant minute volume is shown
in Fig. 7. Figure 8 demonstrates the pronounced effect of the particle
density on the position of the maximum of alveolar retention. The value

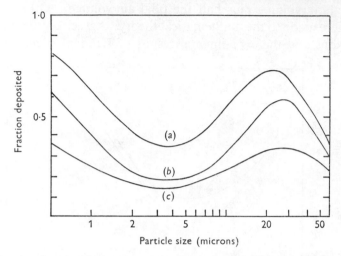

Fig. 7. Fraction deposited in lungs *vs.* particle size at constant minute rate: *a*, 1,600 cm.³
tidal volume 16 sec. breathing cycle; *b*, 800 cm.³ tidal volume 8 sec. breathing cycle;
c, 400 cm.³ tidal volume 4 sec. breathing cycle.

Figs. 7, 8. Reproduced by permission of the National Research Council of Canada from
Can. J. Physiol. Pharmac. **43**, 157–172, 1965.

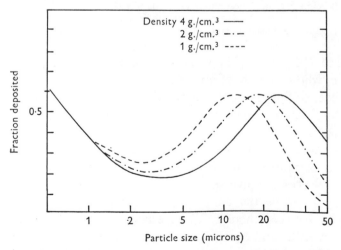

Fig. 8. Fraction deposited in lungs *vs.* particle size as a function
of density.

of the maximum is virtually unaltered. Both the position and the value of the minimum alter with density.

Wilson & La Mer (1948) measured retention in a localized alveolar region. They produced monodisperse aerosols of glycerol and water which had been nucleated with Na²⁴Cl. Breathing rates varied from 5½ to 20 cyc./min. Relative alveolar retentions were measured with a suitably screened Geiger–Mueller counter placed in the axillary region.

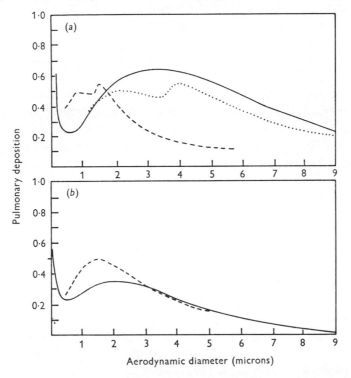

Fig. 9. From Task Group (1966). Reproduced from *Hlth Phys.* **12**, 180 (1966), by permission of the Health Physics Society. (*a*) Pulmonary deposition of particles entering trachea: —, theoretical 15 resp./min. 700 cm.³ tidal volume (data of Wilson & La Mer); - - -, diameters as inhaled; . . . . ., diameters at 99·5% R.H. (*b*) Pulmonary deposition for nasal breathing 15 resp./min. 750 cm.³ tidal volume. —, Calculated; - - -, Hatch's estimate. Based on work of Brown, J. H., Cook, Ney & Hatch (1950).

In this position the counter was relatively remote from the larger air passages and primarily picked up radiation from the peripheral portion of the lung near the chest wall. Measurements of the exhaled aerosol were made by breathing into a filter, and retention at various particle sizes could be computed from a subsequent assay. These measurements showed a general agreement with those of Van Wijk & Patterson (1940). The relative alveolar retention produced a double peaked curve with a maximum retention at 0·4 and 0·8 microns droplet radius. If allowance is made for the increase in size of the droplets due to the high humidity (99·5%) in the lung these results agree well with theoretical values.

Results for total retention with nasal breathing were obtained by J. H. Brown, Cook, Ney & Hatch (1950) using a constant minute-volume and 6, 15 and 20 respiratory cyc./min. and these agreed with the results of Van Wijk & Patterson (1940). Retention increased at all sizes with decreasing respiration rate. No minimum was observed down to 0·25 micron. The influence of breathing frequency on retention was investigated by Dennis (1961) using stearic acid particles. In these experiments the subject controlled his respiration frequency and allowed the minute volume and tidal air to accommodate this change. The values of all three quantities were recorded. As the respiration rate decreased below 15 per min., deposition of the inhaled aerosol increased (as found by C. E. Brown) but above this frequency an increase in deposition occurred. This result was observed at all particle sizes investigated (1–5 microns) but became less marked with increasing size. Dennis ascribes the increased retention above 15 respirations per min. to increased inertial deposition.

The deposition of particles in the submicron range has been intensively studied by Dautrebande (1962) who has applied aerosols of pharmacologically active substances to the treatment of various respiratory diseases. Owing to the high diffusion rate of very small particles the retention of those reaching the alveolar spaces is almost complete, although in terms of the inhaled aerosol retention seldom exceeds 60% due to the physical dead space. It is the tragedy of this form of treatment that the condition which renders it necessary usually makes the penetration of aerosol to the infected part of the lung less likely. Dautreband & Walkenhorst (1961) studied the retention of coal dust and sodium chloride crystals in this range (Fig. 10). If the sodium chloride crystals were measured dry after exhalation there was no agreement between the two curves, but if somewhat arbitrary assumption were made regarding the degree of hydration undergone by the sodium chloride due to the high relative humidity in the lung the two curves could be brought into close agreement and showed a well-defined minimum retention of approximately 30% at a particle size of 0·5 microns. The aerosol was sampled with a thermal precipitator and particle sizing was carried out under the electron microscope. A further example of the influence of the hygroscopicity of particles is afforded by comparing the results of Wilson & La Mer with calculated pulmonary retention under the same conditions (Fig. 9). The considerable difference observed can be almost eliminated by correcting the measured size of the glycerol droplets to their equilibrium size at 99·5% relative humidity. The problems associated with hygroscopic particles have been discussed by Milburn, Crider & Morton (1957), and the Task Group (1966); and the theory of droplet growth by Fuchs (1959). In contradistinction the lower curve of Fig. 9 shows a comparison between

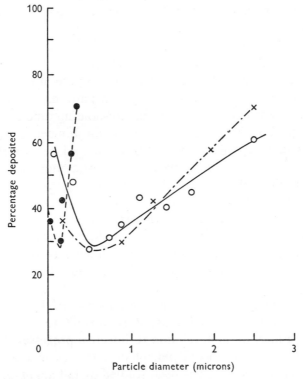

Fig. 10. Lung retention of water droplets, sodium chloride and coal dust particles. Modified from Dautrebande & Walkenhorst in *Inhaled Particles and Vapours* (C. N. Davies, ed., pp. 116–117. Pergamon Press, New York, 1961). —·—·—, Water–NaCl droplets; – – – –, NaCl measured dry; ———, coal dust.

theoretical prediction and Hatch's (1960) estimate of alveolar retention based on the work of J. H. Brown *et al.* (1950) with non-hygroscopic particles which in view of the inherent uncertainties involved shows a considerable measure of agreement.

Bacterial suspensions have been used for many years to produce aerosols of almost homogeneous particle size. Micro-organisms have many advantages for use in aerosol studies (Kethley, Orr, Fincher & Dallavale, 1957). Their main disadvantage for human studies lies in the difficulty of ensuring that the culture used is completely non-pathogenic. Thus *Serratia marcescens* used by Rooks (1939) for aerosol studies was believed at that time to be completely non-pathogenic, but some strains of this organism have subsequently been shown to be pathogenic in a variety of circumstances (e.g. Hawe & Hughes, 1954). Since the only certain way of demonstrating the non-pathogenicity of a given culture to man is by human challenge the method must always involve a risk of infection, but in many cases (e.g. *B. subtilis* var. niger alias 'BG') this is known to be vanishingly small. C. E. Brown (1961) used washed BG spores atomized from a 'Vaponefrin' nebulizer into a 4½ l. bottle as the test cloud. The experimenter inhaled the bacterial aerosol and exhaled into a tube leading to a slit sampler controlling the flow by turncocks. Estimates were made of the respiratory flow pattern.

From measurements after various breath-holding times, C. E. Brown was able to demonstrate an exponential relationship between percentage exhalation and time, with a time constant of -17% per sec. Extrapolation to zero holding time gave an initial exhalation of 81%. Values were similar for oral and nasal breathing and percentage exhalation tended to decrease with increased tidal volume. Over 95% of the total exhaled spores were contained in the first exhalation. In the discussion of this paper, Spendlove quoted work by Crider showing that 1 micron particles will grow to over 2 microns in diameter before reaching the alveoli, and Hatch stated that his experiments indicated an even greater increase in particle size of BG spores based on their retention compared with hygroscopically inert materials. Because bacterial particles become larger in highly humid conditions, it is difficult to interpret results obtained with inert dusts in relation to infective processes.

The deposition of triphenyl phosphate particles in the respiratory tract during breath holding has been studied by Palmes *et al.* (1965). A full text of this work is not available at present but their results again show an exponential relationship between the percentage exhaled and breath-holding time for particle sizes between 0·15 and 0·7 microns with re-exhalation at zero time of about 80% of the inhaled cloud. Their curves show variations between experimental subjects, but the data given for aerosol recovery of 1–1·2 micron particles after 15 sec. are higher than those indicated in Brown's experiments, a further indication of the increase in size of the bacterial particle in humid conditions.

EXAMINATION OF HUMAN LUNG TISSUES
FOR RETAINED DUST

There exists no method by which the immediate alveolar retention, or retention in the respiratory portion of the human lung can be directly measured. Information on the size and nature of dust retained in the lungs can be obtained from the lung tissues of cadavers who have succumbed after a life time spent in dusty environments. Typically the lungs are excised, dried, extracted with formamide or with acid and alcohol and the residual dust examined. This approach has been exploited over many years (McCrae, 1913; Mavrogordato, 1923) but it is only since electron microscopy has become generally available that adequate particle size distributions have been made. More recently the method has been used by Policard, Collet & Giltaire-Ralyte (1952, 1953), Zebel (1956), King, Maguire & Nagelschmidt (1956), Schlipköter & Colli (1956), Rivers, Wise, King & Nagelschmidt (1960), Arnold, Sasse & Einbrodt (1961), and Cartwright & Nagelschmidt (1961). The interpretation of this data to yield information on respiratory retention is beset with many difficulties since exposure may have extended over many years, and, as working conditions may have changed greatly, an accurate estimate of the particle size in the inhaled aerosol is obviously impossible. Concentrations of aerosol may have varied and the breathing pattern and lung structure of the exposed person may not have remained constant. As long ago as 1921, Fenn observed variations in the rate of uptake of various materials by phagocytes, and Drinker (1925) cast doubts on whether the rate of phagocytosis was independent of particle size. Since an electron microscope gives an essentially two-dimensional estimate of particle size, and as dust particles vary greatly in shape, various mathematical conventions have to be used which purport to change the measurements into equivalent spheres of unit density. Moreover, several workers attempting to study airborne respiratory infection by introducing small volumes of bacteria-containing liquid into the nasal region of animals have demonstrated that the bacteria can become widely distributed in the lung almost at once. Perhaps a similar engulfing of material impacted in the upper respiratory system may partly account for the occasional large particle. It is also uncertain whether all the particles observed entered the lung as separate entities or whether they are the residue of a larger mass which dispersed or partly dissolved after arrival.

In spite of these shortcomings information can be gleaned. Davies (1964) reviewed the literature and attempted after some arbitrary

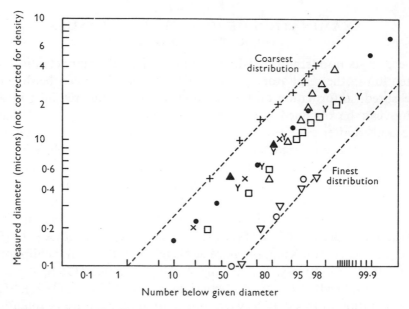

Fig. 11. Cumulative size distribution of lung dusts plotted from the observations of various workers from C. N. Davies (*Ann. Occ. Hyg.* **7**, 177, 1964), by permission of *Ann. Occ. Hyg.* Rock and quartz dust; ○, △, □, ▽; coal dust: ▲, ●, +, X, Y.

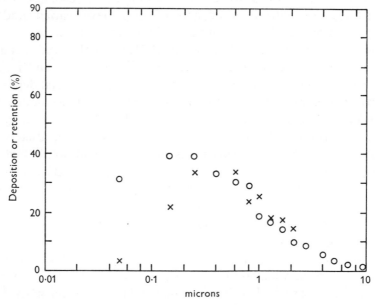

Fig. 12. Lung retention of dust particles calculated from 'coarsest' and 'finest' distributions observed in lung dusts and the coarsest and finest aerosol distribution in the working environments modified from C. N. Davies (*Ann. Occ. Hyg.* **7**, 180, 1964), by permission of *Ann. Occ. Hyg.* Symbols as above.

assumptions to set upper and lower bounds to the size distributions of
the inhaled clouds and to the particulate distribution recovered from
lungs. He then deduced the limits within which lung deposition and
alveolar deposition must lie. The experimental data used were 'not
corrected for the density of the particles because this correction is
balanced to some extent by the reduction from projected area to Stokes'
diameter'. Graphs showing the size distribution of retained dusts for
lung dust retention and Davies's deduced curve for alveolar retention
are shown in Figs. 11 and 12. Figure 11 shows a general agreement with
the results from experimental aerosols in cut-off size but shows striking
differences in retention values particularly in the 1–2 micron range. This
discrepancy is currently being investigated by a number of workers and
is providing the stimulus for much re-thinking about what goes on in
the terminal region of the lung passages.

CLEARANCE OF DEPOSITED PARTICLES FROM THE LUNG

A comprehensive review of clearance models has recently been published (Task Group, 1966). The clearance of particulate matter from the
lung tissue depends both on the chemical nature of the material and the
site of deposition. Material deposited on those parts of the lung tissue
possessing ciliated epithelial cells (i.e. above the terminal bronchioles)
will in large measure be swept upwards with the mucus layer into the
trachea and thence to the gastro-intestinal system. This process is rapid,
being variously estimated at 0·15–0·30 cm./min. in the bronchioles,
0·25–1·0 cm./min. in the bronchi, and 3–4 cm./min. in the trachea
(Lucas & Douglas, 1934; Hilding, 1948, 1957, 1959; Barclay &
Franklin, 1937; Florey, Carlton & Wells, 1932).

This process is liable to inhibition, for instance by viral infections,
and by fumes or particulates of a toxic nature (SO_2 and tobacco smoke).
Areas may be rendered vulnerable for the deposition of infective agents
by presence of parasites which locally destroy cilliary action. Particulate
matter which is soluble may be removed in solution either with the
mucus or via the circulatory system. The criterion for solubility must be
based on solution in the lung environment and not that observed in
water.

The upward progress of the mucous layer is not uniform since the
flow must be diverted around the junctions with other bronchioles and
this often results in the accumulation of particles at bronchiolar branch
points (Casarett, 1958). There are also small whirlpool areas (Hilding,
1957) where material may reside for longer than normal, while even the

normal human lung contains small islands of squamous cells (Casarett, 1960). These areas are of particular interest to the aerobiologist since organisms deposited fortuitously in them would stand a much better chance of initiating infection than in the more rapidly flowing stream. For instance, a primary pustule at the bifurcation of the bronchi has often been observed in naturally occurring infections of *B. anthracis* ('Woolsorters Disease').

Clearance of particles from the lung parenchyma (respiratory bronchioles, alveolar ducts and alveoli) is effected by a number of processes the mechanisms of which are ill-defined and depend greatly on the physical and chemical nature of the particles involved. One of the earliest mechanisms to be observed was the phagocytosis of particles by 'dust cells' which subsequently migrated out of the respiratory portion of the lung and in large measure to the ciliated removal system of the bronchioles. The origin of these 'dust cells' or alveolar macrophages has been, and still is, a matter of dispute. Policard *et al.* (1956) showed that the alveolar membrane contained cells of three types. The first of these was the 'small epithelial cell'. The nucleus of these cells was usually found in the central depression of the capillary meshes, while its cytoplasm extended laterally over considerable areas as a thin layer 0·2–0·5 micron thick. Some evidence of pinocytic activity was shown by the presence of numerous small rounded invaginations. In this continuous epithelium are interspersed 'large alveolar cells'. These cells have numerous short cilia on their free surface and they do not form lateral extensions. They are in close contact with the surrounding small alveolar cells. The alveolar macrophages are free cells which may be superimposed on the uninterrupted alveolar epithelium in which they can remain in loose contact. They extend cytoplasmic processes of varying length which show signs of phagocytosis (Karrer, 1958; Policard, Collet & Pregermain, 1956) and the perinuclear cytoplasm may contain inclusion bodies derived from this process. The free alveolar cells are believed to have originated from the large alveolar cells (Policard, 1956) which, under the stimulus of endocytosed matter, have become detached and act as migrating phagocytes. On the other hand, the view that alveolar cells are not phagocytic has been widely held and some support for this view has been afforded by the work of Low & Sampaio (1957), who showed no uptake of thorium oxide in the epithelial cells of rats after intratracheal instillation. These authors expressed the view that in spite of obvious morphological similarities the alveolar epithelium is of entodermal and the macrophages of mesodermal origin. The possibility that their origin lies, at least in part, in monocytes that have migrated

from the blood-stream cannot be disregarded (Florey, 1954). Labelle &
Brieger (1959, 1961) found that the number of free phagocytes in the
lungs of rats could be increased tenfold by the intratracheal injection of
carbon particles and several fold by the inhalation of carbon particles.
This type of experiment can produce misleading results unless the dose
and material is carefully chosen, since infections or the presence of
inflammatory or irritative material may cause a migration of phagocytic
cells from the blood-stream into the alveolar lumen and these cells may
greatly exceed the dust cells in number (Elliot, 1926; Forkner, 1930;
Robertson & Loosli, 1938).

As the stimulus causing the migration of the phagocytes towards the
ciliated region is unknown it has been suggested that mechanical processes exist which propel a proteinaceous layer containing cells and
debris upwards from the respiratory area (Gross, 1953; Antweiler,
1958). There is evidence that foreign matter is more readily cleared from
the alveoli when greater demands are made on the respiratory system
owing to exercise (Klosterkotter, 1957), but the work of Friedberg (1960)
does not confirm this. In addition to the commendable activity of
phagocytes in removing foreign matter from the respiratory region to
the ciliated epithelium it has been suggested that some removal to other
parts of the lung structure may occur with less happy results. Some
particulate matter may prove indigestible while other substances such as
silica are cytotoxic and the ultimate site of release is of importance.
Bacteria may prove extremely resistant to phagocytosis. Rogers &
Tompsett (1952) found that virulent staphylococci ingested by granu-
locytes were not killed but multiplied vigorously in the cytoplasm
eventually killing the cell and escaping into the surrounding fluids.
Further investigations by Rogers & Melly (1960), and Melly, Thomison
& Rogers (1960) showed that virulent staphylococci could live for some
time inside the leucocyte and undergo division within the cell. Sometimes an organism may actually be protected by its intracellular position
from bactericidal substances present in blood and tissues (Florey, 1964).
This process was put forward by Ross (1957) as responsible for the
removal of anthrax spores to the lymphatics, following deposition in the
lung of an inhaled cloud, and for the consequent initiation of infection.
The importance of this mechanism, and indeed its very existence has
been heavily attacked by many investigators who favour direct penetration of particles into the lung tissues (Antweiler, 1958; Schiller,
1956). However, the importance of a given mechanism in bacterial
invasion may depend on a relatively few or even one organism reaching
a favourable site for multiplication and this may represent a minute

fraction of the total number of organisms inhaled. In contrast, dust diseases demand the accumulation of appreciable amounts of the inhaled material over a period of time. The criteria are therefore different and a mechanism which is of importance to bacterial infection may be of negligible import in dust disease.

The use of fluorescent antibody and autoradiographic technique has allowed particles to be located in quantities which would be undetectable by other means. In this way radioactive materials have been located in the alveolar epithelium, interstitially in cells classed as histiocytes and in association with structural elements, for many months and even years after exposure (Morrow & Casarett, 1961), probably undergoing slow solution and phagocytosis. The method by which particles may penetrate to the interstitium is unknown. Hatch & Gross (1964) draw an analogy with the 'movement of gross objects such as needles' through the body without leaving demonstrable evidence of their transit or suggests alternatively that there may be micro-erosion of the surface of the alveolar membrane. Another suggestion (Von Hayek, 1942) is that the alveolar surface cells can retract their cytoplasmic extension as a reaction to the irritation produced by dust particles. Hatch & Gross (1964) adduce evidence that penetration is more likely in the regions adjacent to bronchi, bronchioles, and blood vessels. One of the grounds for favouring direct penetration of particles is the rapidity with which they appear in the lymphatic system following inhalation. Hamburger & Robertson (1941) found pneumococci in the hilar lymph nodes of dogs 10 min. after inhalation, and Drinker & Field (1933) recovered nickel silicate particles in the fluid of the cannulized lymphatic of a dog within minutes of an intratracheal injection. Whatever the mechanism it would be surprising to find that particulate matter was able to penetrate rapidly to the lymphatics but that phagocytes were unable to follow a similar path.

While the mechanism may be obscure, it is certain that dust particles penetrate into the lung tissues, that a considerable proportion eventually find their way into the lymphatic system and that this is an important method of long-term clearance. Over a period of 6 months some 10–20 % of the lung clearance may be by this route (Nagelschmidt *et al.* 1957; Klosterkotter & Bünemann, 1959) although experiments with transuranic oxides have suggested a rather lower figure.

The processes of particle clearance from the lung have been summarized by the 'Task Group':

(1) Dust deposited (soluble or insoluble) on the ciliated epithelium will have a clearance half time of minutes.

(2) Initially the recruitable phagocytes plus the ciliary mucus transport will effect a rapid clearance of the alveolar region with an (exponential) half-time of about 24 hr. (Phase 1).

(3) After the initial phase there is a slower and dominant alveolar phase whose rate appears to be largely governed by the physico-chemical properties of the dust particles. This clearance depends on a variety of mechanisms (Phase 2). The change-over between these two regions is not clear-cut.

(4) The apportionment of processes and pathways for the elimination of dust via the lymph tract and blood-stream relies largely on intuition.

As a clearance model for deposited soluble dusts it is assumed that two-thirds pass rapidly into the gastro-intestinal tract while one-third enters the circulation. For deposited insoluble dusts, two-thirds pass rapidly to the gastro-intestinal tract, one-sixth more reaches it during the first day and the remaining sixth undergoes prolonged retention with a half life of the order of 120 days. The Task Group's report tabulates data for the half-time appropriate to a wide variety of substances. Similar data are given by Hatch & Gross (1964). If the initial dust burden is large, the initial rapid clearance may disappear, possibly due to the saturation of the available lung phagocytes.

In addition to the generalized removal of dust particles from the lung in certain conditions, dust plaques consisting of cohesive proliferated alveolar cells may arise. These formations on the alveolar wall cause it to lose its capillary and basement membranes and so the inner layers of dust cells are in contact with the interstitium. As the constituent cells disintegrate dust particles are released into the lymphatics. The rate at which this occurs will depend on the cytotoxicity of the dust.

RETENTION OF PARTICLES IN THE NASAL REGION

The nasal region is divided into left and right cavities (fossae) by a partition called the septum whose anterior portion is formed by the cartilage dividing the left and right nostrils and whose posterior portion is formed by a vertical plate of bone. The base of the nasal cavity is formed by the palate. On the lateral walls of the fossae there are three shell-like projections called the superior, middle and inferior conchae (or turbinate bones) which almost divide the air channel into three air ways. Each air way (meatus) is named superior, middle or inferior after the concha lying immediately superior to it. Above the superior concha lies the olfactory region into which the main airflow does not extend during normal breathing. In sniffing, the air is deflected upwards from its normal course so that some of it reaches the olfactory region.

Air enters the nose through the anterior nares and passes through a slight dilation (the vestibule) into one of the three airways, and thence through a posterior nare (choana) into the pharynx. The lower part of the vestibule possesses coarse hairs (vibressae) which curve downwards towards the nares and through these the air stream passes. The whole of the nasal cavity is lined with ciliated epithelium with the exception of the olfactory area and the region between the nares and the vestibule. The ciliated region is richly supplied with goblet cells and the underlying tissue contains many mucous glands which keep the walls of the cavity moist.

MODEL OF THE NASAL REGION

The retention of particles in the nasal region was investigated theoretically by Landahl (1950*b*). Four subregions were considered:

(*a*) The external nares and vestibule. To allow for the variability of the nasal hairs, Landahl assumed two sizes—of 70 and 130 microns diameter respectively and each set were assumed to occupy one-quarter of the projected area perpendicular to the air flow.

(*b*) A rectangular tube 1·2 cm. high, 0·25 cm. wide and 1 cm. long with a 30° bend lying 2 cm. behind the external nares.

(*c*) A rectangular tube 0·2 cm. wide and 3 cm. high with a 20° bend.

(*d*) Two subregions in parallel, one somewhat narrower (0·1 cm.) and more tortuous and representing the upper passages, the other wider (0·2 cm.) and representing the more direct lower passages. The passages were taken to be 4 cm. high and 5 cm. long. The upper passage was assumed to take a 45° turn and the lower a 20° turn; the floor of the passage was assumed to be sloping.

This 'rather crude model' clearly indicated the dominance of inertial deposition in the nasal region. Sedimentation was only appreciable in the turbinate region and at the lowest flow rate. Diffusion was negligible although it would take on a dominant role for particles in the milli-micron range. Landahl's results showing the deposition in the four regions for a flow rate of 18 l./min. and unit density spheres is shown in Fig. 13. These calculations indicate that the nasal hairs play a major role in nasal filtration and that the bulk of the particulate deposition takes place in regions (*a*) and (*b*). Results for flow rates of 4·5 and 72 l./min. follow a similar pattern when allowance is made for the change in the impaction parameter. Since the retention of particles by the nasal hairs depends on the adhesion of the particle on contact, the efficacy of this mechanism will be dependent on the nature of the aerosol. Greater penetration of particles with poor adhesive properties such as some pollens and fungal spores beyond region (*a*) would therefore be expected. Landahl compared his calculated curve for nasal penetration with the experimental results obtained by Landahl & Black (1947) and Landahl & Tracewell (1949). In these experiments a heterogeneous aerosol was generated from a spray or a dust dispenser

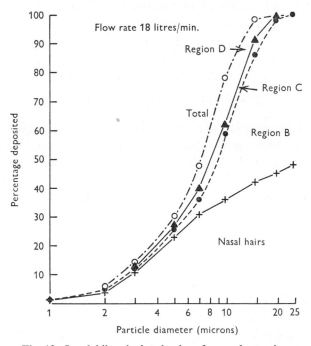

Fig. 13. Landahl's calculated values for nasal retention.

and collected in a reservoir. The sampling system consisted of a cascade impactor backed by an impinger and filter making a six-stage particle size discriminator. Samples were taken from the initial cloud and compared with those led in through the nose and out from the mouth of the subject who held his breath during the experiment. The flow rate was usually 17 l./min., although flow rates of 10, 29 and 60 l./min. were also used. The substances used included corn oil, dusts of sodium bicarbonate and calcium triphosphate, atomized solutions of sodium bicarbonate, methylene-blue, bismuth sub-carbonate, glycerol, sodium sulphate and tyrosine. Results from these experiments and Landahl's theoretical curve showed a 'fairly satisfactory' agreement for a flow rate of 18 l./min. in the case of non-hygroscopic particles. The plots of the various aerosols were reduced to a common curve by the use of the 'equivalent particle diameter' d'. This is defined by $d' = \sqrt{(\rho d^2)}$ where ρ and d are the actual density and particle diameter of the material and d' is the equivalent diameter of a unit density sphere having the same impaction characteristics. Above a flow rate of 18 l./min., sedimentation in the upper respiratory system is negligible but the authors state in contrast to the later papers that retention does not follow a simple relationship based on impaction parameters since reflex changes occur in the configuration of the nasal passage. Pattle (1961) investigated the nasal penetration of methylene-blue particles of homogeneous size produced by the spinning top method. He found a close agreement with the empirical formula, based on the impaction parameter

$$P = 95(1 - 0 \cdot 5 \log_{10} [D^2 W/20 \cdot 2]),$$

where P is the penetration per cent, D is the diameter in microns and W the flow rate in litres per minute. Pattle drew attention to the appreciable retention of small particles and showed this could not be due to the supersaturation of the inhaled air or to vestibular hairs. The 'Task Group' (1966) have transformed Pattle's equation into

$$N = -0 \cdot 62 + 0 \cdot 475 \log D_a^2 \, W \text{ (for inhalation)},$$

where D_a is the aerodynamic size, and N the fraction deposited during inhalation. They have shown that this equation adequately describes both Pattle's and Landahl's results for $1 \cdot 5 < \log D_a^2 W < 3$. The differences between hygroscopic and non-hygroscopic particles do not appear significantly different on this plot although the log scale would tend to mask the effect of small changes in diameter. Dennis (1961) has demonstrated that changes in particle size do occur during passage through the nose. All investigators have so far used a constant flow rate in their experiments and no experimental evidence is available on the pulsating flows that occur in normal breathing. The 'Task Group' (1966) have suggested the use of an equation similar to Pattle's for mouth breathing.

CLEARANCE FROM THE NASAL REGION

With the exception of the anterior unciliated area of the nose, particles deposited in the nasal region are swept backwards towards the naso-pharynx. The rate of clearance varies with experimental subject (Proctor & Wagner, 1966) and with site of deposition. The fate of inhaled particles has been studied by Meneely et al. (1953), Albert &

Arnett (1955), and Freiberg & Holma (1961) using radioactive tracer methods. Measurement of the average clearance flow rates of radioactive particles by the mucus stream with double collimated detectors gives values of 3–6 mm./min. Particles are effectively cleared from most areas of the nose within 10–30 min. (Proctor & Wagner, 1966). There is at present no satisfactory way of following the clearance of individual inhaled particles from their site of deposition. In airborne infection, the interest lies primarily in those organisms which reach sites from which they can invade the tissues, and the movement of the majority towards the pharynx may be of little importance compared to the occasional organism which has reached the olfactory region or some area in which ciliary removal is inefficient.

CONCLUSION

The immediate retention of particles in various parts of the human respiratory system can be calculated by the application of the physical laws governing sedimentation, impaction and diffusion. Such predictions agree well with results from inhalation experiments. The test aerosols in such experiments usually consist of spherical particles or droplets which are physically closely similar to droplet nuclei. How does this impinge upon the field of airborne infection? Figure 14 shows that the infective dose for some bacterial diseases (in animals) is greatly influenced by particle size which controls site of deposition. In other diseases the infective dose may alter little, but the course of the disease and the pathological observations may alter with particle size (Druett *et al.* 1956 *a, b*). Retention of the invading organism within the respiratory system is a necessary, but by no means sufficient condition for the infection of the host. Many bacteria and their spores are well adapted by their size to reach respiratory portion of the lung, but invasion is fortunately uncommon. This is due in part to the inefficiency of natural processes in generating finely dispersed bacterial aerosols and to the limited life of many airborne pathogens. It is also due to the many obstacles and hazards which the invader has still to overcome, e.g. immunity of the host, phagocytosis, and removal on the ciliary escalator. Clear-cut particle-size infection effects can only be expected when one part of the respiratory system is much more susceptible to the invading organism than the rest. If the respiratory portion of the lung is the susceptible region, spectacular increases in the number of inhaled organisms required to initiate infection may occur with increasing particle size (Fig. 14). If the susceptible region lies in the upper respiratory system particles of all inhalable sizes may be deposited in it with varying efficiency and particle size effects will be less marked. The influence of the hygroscopicity of the particle on retention has been stressed: this will depend on the materials from which the aerosol has

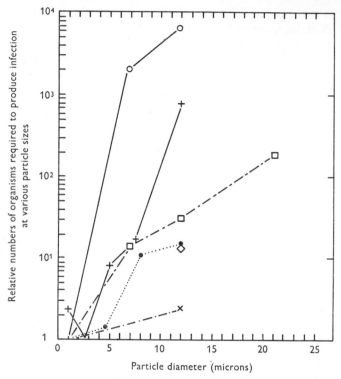

Fig. 14. Relative numbers of organisms required to produce infection at various particle sizes:

○ *P. tularensis* in guinea-pigs
□ *P. tularensis* in rhesus monkeys   } Goodlow & Leonard (1961)
+ *Br. suis* in guinea-pigs
● *B. anthracis* in guinea-pigs
◇ *B. anthracis* in rhesus monkeys   } Druett *et al.* (1953, 1956*a*, *b*)
× *P. pestis* in guinea-pigs

been generated such as buffer or spent culture in artificially produced aerosols or mucoid materials in the case of droplet nuclei. In assessing the chances of invasion full account must be taken of the inhibition of the ciliary defence mechanism by other organisms, air pollutants or previous damage. In a population including bronchitics, the smokers, the dwellers in industrial conurbations, how many have 'normal' respiratory systems?

In conclusion attention is drawn to a number of interesting and important articles which will shortly appear (autumn 1966) as the *Proceedings of the Second International Symposium* organized by the British Occupational Hygiene Society and to which I have not been able to make adequate reference.

REFERENCES

AGRICOLA, G. (1556). *De Re Metallica.* Translated by H. C. & L. H. Hoover. Salisbury House, London (1912).

ALBERT, R. E. & ARNETT, L. C. (1955). Clearance of radioactive dust from the human lung. *Arch. Ind. Hlth*, **12**, 99.

ALTSHULER, B. (1959). Calculation of regional deposition in the respiratory tract. *Bull. math. Biophys.* **21**, 257.

ALTSHULER, B., PALMES, E. D., YARMUS, L. & NELSON, N. (1959). Intrapulmonary mixing of gases studied with aerosols. *J. appl. Physiol.* **14**, 321.

ALTSHULER, B., YARMUS, L., PALMES, E. D. & NELSON, N. (1957). Aerosol deposition in the human respiratory tract. *Arch. Ind. Hlth*, **15**, 293.

ANTWEILER, H. (1958). Über die Funktion des Flimmerepithels der Luftwege insbesondere unter Staubbelastung. *Beitr. Silikoseforsch. Sonderband*, 3, 509.

ARNOLD, M., SASSE, D. & EINBRODT, H. J. (1961). Statistische Untersuchungen über die Korngrossenverteilung von Staub aus anthrakotischen Lungen. *Beitr. Silikoseforsch.* **74**, 1.

BARCLAY, A. E. & FRANKLIN, K. J. (1937). Rate of excretion of India ink injected into lung. *J. Physiol., Lond.* **90**, 484.

BAUMBERGER, J. P. (1923). The amount of smoke produced from tobacco and its absorption in smoking as determined by electrical precipitation. *J. Pharmac. exp. Ther.* **21**, 47.

BEECKMANS, J. M. (1965 a). The deposition of aerosols in the respiratory tract. (1) Mathematical analysis and comparison with experimental data. *Can. J. Physiol. Pharmac.* **43**, 157.

BEECKMANS, J. M. (1965 b). Correction factor for size-selective sampling results, based on a new computed alveolar deposition curve. *Ann. occ. Hyg.* **8**, 221.

BENOISTON DE CHATEAUNEUF (1831). De l'influence de certaines professions sur le développement de la phtisie pulmonaire. *Ann. d'Hyg., Paris*, **4**, 5 to 49.

BLOOM, W. & FAWCETT, D. W. (eds.) (1962). *A Textbook of Histology*, 8th ed. Philadelphia: W. B. Saunders.

BOYD, J. (1928). The estimation of dust in mine air in the Witwatersrand. *Jl S. Afr. Instn Engrs*, **26**, no. 7.

BROWN, C. E. (1931 a). Quantitative measurements of the inhalation, retention and exhalation of dusts and fumes by man. II. Concentrations below 50 mg. per cubic meter. *J. ind. Hyg. Toxicol.* **13**, 285.

BROWN, C. E. (1931 b). Studies in dust retention. III. Factors involved in the retention of inhaled dusts and fumes by man. *J. ind. Hyg. Toxicol.* **13**, 293.

BROWN, C. E. (1961). Human retention from single inhalations of *Bacillus subtilis* spore aerosols. In *Inhaled Particles and Vapours*, p. 122. Ed. by C. N. Davies. London: Pergamon Press.

BROWN, J. H., COOK, K. M., NEY, F. G. & HATCH, T. (1950). Influence of particle size upon the retention of particulate matter in the human lung. *Am. J. Publ. Hlth*, **40**, 450.

BUBBE, J. (1775). *Precis d'oper chirung.* Paris. Vol. 1, p. 561: on pathological effects of stonebreaking.

BÜCHNER, H. (1888). Untersuchungen über den Durchtritt von Infectionserregern durch die intacte Lungenoberfläche. I. Historisches v. Kritisches. *Arch. Hyg.*, *Berl.* **8**, 145.

BÜCHNER, H. & MERKEL, F. (1888). Untersuchungen über den Durchtritt von Infectionserregern durch die intacte Lungenoberfläche. II. Versuche über Inhalation trockenzerstaubter Milzbrandsporen. *Arch. Hyg.*, *Berl.* **8**, 165.

BÜCHNER, H. & ENDERLEN, E. (1888). Untersuchungen über den Durchtritt von Infectionserregern durch die intacte Lungenoberfläche. III. Inhalation von mass-zerstaubten Milzbrandsporen und Stäbchen und von Hühnercholera-bacillen. *Arch. Hyg.*, *Berl.* **8**, 190.

BÜCHNER, H. (1888). Untersuchungen über den Durchtritt von Infectionserregern durch die intacte Lungenoberfläche. IV. Specielle Bedingungen des Durch-trittes von Infectionserregern durch die intacte Lungenoberfläche. *Arch. Hyg.*, *Berl.* **8**, 217.

CARTWRIGHT, J. & NAGELSCHMIDT, G. (1961). The size and shape of dust from human lungs and its relation to relative sampling. In *Inhaled Particles and Vapours*, p. 445. Ed. by C. N. Davies. London: Pergamon Press.

CASARETT, L. J. (1958). Ph.D. Thesis, Rochester, N.Y.

CASARETT, L. J. (1960). Some physical and physiological factors controlling the fate of inhaled substances. II. Retention. *Hlth Phys.* **2**, 379.

DAUTREBANDE, L. (1962). *Microaerosols.* New York: Academic Press.

DAUTREBANDE, L. & WALKENHORST, W. (1961). Über die Retention von Koch-salzteilchen in der Atemwegen. In *Inhaled Particles and Vapours*, p. 110. Ed. by C. N. Davies. London: Pergamon Press.

DAVIES, C. N. (1949). Inhalation risk and particle size in dust and mist. *Br. J. ind. Med.* **6**, 245.

DAVIES, C. N. (1952). Dust sampling and lung disease. *Br. J. ind. Med.* **9**, 120.

DAVIES, C. N. (1964). Deposition and retention of dust in the human respiratory tract. *Ann. occup. Hyg.* **7**, 169.

DENNIS, W. L. (1961). Discussion of paper by C. N. Davies: A formalised anatomy of the human respiratory tract. In *Inhaled Particles and Vapours*, p. 88. Ed. by C. N. Davies. London: Pergamon Press.

DOWNIE, A. W., MEIKLEJOHN, M., ST VINCENT, L., RAO, A. R., SUNDARA BABU, B. V. & KEMPE, C. H. (1965). The recovery of smallpox virus from patients and their environment in a smallpox hospital. *Bull. Wld Hlth Org.* **33**, 615.

DRINKER, P. (1925). The size-frequency and identification of certain phagocytosed dusts. *J. ind. Hyg. Toxicol.* **7**, 305.

DRINKER, C. K. & FIELD, M. E. (1935). *Lymphatics, Lymph and Tissue Fluid.* Baltimore: Williams and Wilkins Co.

DRINKER, P., THOMSON, R. M. & FINN, J. L. (1928). Quantitative measurements of the inhalation, retention and exhalation of dusts and fumes by man. I. Con-centration of 50–450 mg. per cubic metre. *J. ind. Hyg. Toxicol.* **10**, 13.

DRUETT, H. A., HENDERSON, D. W., PACKMAN, L. & PEACOCK, S. (1953). Studies on respiratory infection. I. The influence of particle size on respiratory infection with anthrax spores. *J. Hyg., Camb.* **51**, 359.

DRUETT, H. A., HENDERSON, D. W. & PEACOCK, S. (1956 a). Studies on respiratory infection. III. Experiments with *Brucella suis. J. Hyg., Camb.* **54**, 49.

DRUETT, H. A., ROBINSON, J. M., HENDERSON, D. W., PACKMAN, L. & PEACOCK, S. (1956 b). Studies on respiratory infection. II. The influence of aerosol particle size on infection of the guinea-pig with *Pasteurella pestis. J. Hyg., Camb.* **54**, 37.

EHRENBURG, C. G. (1830). See *Three Centuries of Microbiology*, by Lechevalier, H. A. & Solotorovsky, M. (1965), pp. 536. New York: McGraw Hill.

ELLIOT, C. (1926). The origin of the phagocytic cells in the rabbit. *Johns Hopkins Hosp. Bull.* **39**, 149.

FENN, W. O. (1921). The phagocytosis of solid particles. I–III. *J. gen. Physiol.* **3**, 439, 465, 575.

FINDEISEN, W. (1935). Über das Absetzen kleiner, in der Luft suspendierten Teilchen in der menschlichen Lunge bei der Atmung. *Pflügers Arch ges Physiol.* **236**, 367.

FLOREY, H. W. (1954). *Lectures on General Pathology.* Ed. by H. W. Florey. London: Lloyd-Luke.

FLOREY, H. W., CARLETON, H. M. & WELLS, A. Q. (1932). Mucus secretion in the trachea. *Br. J. exp. Path.* **13**, 269.

FORKNER, C. E. (1930). The origin of monocytes in certain lymph nodes and their genetic relation to other connective tissue cells. *J. exp. Med.* **52**, 385.

FRIBERG, L. & HOLMA, B. (1961). External measurement of lung clearance. *Archs. envir. Hlth*, **3**, 420.

FRIEDBERG, K. D. (1960). Quantitative Untersuchungen über die Staubelimination in der Lung und ihre Beeinflussbarkeit im Tierexperiment. *Beitr. Silikoseforsch.* **69**, 1.

FUCHS, N. A. (1959). *Evaporation and Droplet Growth in Gaseous Media.* London: Pergamon Press.

GOODLOW, R. J. & LEONARD, F. A. (1961). Viability and infectivity of micro-organisms in experimental airborne infection. *Bact. Rev.* **25**, 182.

GREEN, H. L. & WATSON, H. H. (1935). Physical methods for the estimation of the dust hazard in industry. *Spec. Rep. Ser. med. Res. Counc.* no. 199, 56 pp. London: H.M.S.O.

GREENBURG, L. & SMITH, G. W. (1922). A new instrument for sampling aerial dusts. *U.S. Bur. Mines Rep. Invest.* no. 2392.

GROSS, P. (1953). The mechanism of dust clearance from the lung. A theory. *Am. J. clin. Path.* **23**, 116.

HALL, J. C. (1857). Diseases of special occupations. No. 1. Sheffield Grinders. *Br. med. J.* ('Vol. for 1857'), pp. 218, 234, 249, 293, 313.

HAMBURGER, M. & ROBERTSON, O. H. (1941). Unpublished experiments quoted by O. H. Robertson in: Phagocytosis of foreign material in the lung. *Physiol. Rev.* **21**, 112.

HARE, R. (1964). The transmission of respiratory infections. *Proc. R. Soc. Med.* **57**, 221.

HATCH, T. (1960). *Proceedings of the Pneumoconiosis Conference, Johannesburg, 1959*, p. 120. Ed. by A. J. Orenstein. London: J. A. Churchill.

HATCH, T. & GROSS, P. (1964). *Pulmonary Deposition and Retention of Inhaled Aerosols.* New York: Academic Press.

HAWE, A. J. & HUGHES, M. H. (1954). Bacterial endocarditis due to *Chromobacterium prodigiosum. Br. med. J.* i, 968.

HAYWARD, J. & REID, L. M. (1952). Observations on the anatomy of the intra-segmental bronchial tree. *Thorax*, **7**, 89.

HILDING, A. C. (1948). Experimental sinus surgery: some experiments on ventilation and sinusitis. *Laryngoscope, St Louis*, **58**, 1098.

HILDING, A. C. (1957). Ciliary streaming in the bronchial tree and the time element in carcinogenesis. *New Engl. J. Med.* **256**, 634.

HILDING, A. C. (1959). Ciliary streaming through the larynx and trachea; relation to direction of ciliary beat and significance in sites of respiratory disease. *J. thorac. Surg.* **37**, 108.

HOLLAND, G. C. (1843). *The Vital Statistics of Sheffield.* London: Tyas.

KARRER, H. E. (1958). The ultrastructure of the mouse lung. The alveolar macrophage. *J. biophys. biochem. Cytol.* **4**, 693.

KETHLEY, T. W., ORR, C., FINCHER, E. L. & DALLAVALE, J. M. (1957). Airborne microorganisms as analytical tools in aerosol studies. *J. Air Pollut. Control Ass.* **7**, 16.

KING, E. S., MAGUIRE, B. A. & NAGELSCHMIDT, G. (1956). Further studies of the dust in lungs of coal miners. *Br. J. ind. Med.* **13**, 9.

KLOSTERKÖTTER, W. (1957). Tier experimentelle Untersuchungen über das Reinigungsvermögen der Lung. *Arch. Hyg. Bakt.* **141**, 258.

KLOSTERKÖTTER, W. & BÜNEMANN, G. (1959). Untersuchungen über die Ausscheidung inhalierte Staub im Tierexperiment. *Beitr. Silikoseforsch. Sonderband*, **3**, 145.

KOCH, R. (1884). The aetiology of tuberculosis. *Berl. KlinWoch.* **19**, 221.

LABELLE, C. W. & BRIEGER, H. (1959). Synergistic effects of aerosols. II. Effects on rate of clearance from the lung. *Arch ind. Hlth*, **20**, 100.

LABELLE, C. W. & BRIEGER, H. (1961). Patterns and mechanisms in the elimination of dust from the lung. In *Inhaled Particles and Vapours*, p. 356. Ed. by C. N. Davies. London: Pergamon Press.

LANDAHL, H. D. (1950 *a*). On the removal of airborne droplets by the human respiratory tract. I. The lung. *Bull. math. Biophys.* **12**, 43.

LANDAHL, H. D. (1950 *b*). On the removal of airborne droplets by the human respiratory tract. II. The nasal passages. *Bull. math. Biophys.* **12**, 161.

LANDAHL, H. D. (1963). Particle removal by the respiratory system: note on the removal of airborne particulates by the human respiratory tract with particular reference to the role of diffusion. *Bull. math. Biophys.* **25**, 29.

LANDAHL, H. D. & BLACK, S. (1947). Penetration of airborne particulates through the human nose. *J. ind. Hyg. Toxicol.* **29**, 269.

LANDAHL, H. D. & HERRMAN, R. G. (1948). On the retention of airborne particulates in the human lung. *J. ind. Hyg. Toxicol.* **30**, 181.

LANDAHL, H. D. & TRACEWELL, T. (1949). Penetration of airborne particulates through the human nose. *J. ind. Hyg. Toxicol.* **31**, 55.

LANDAHL, H. D., TRACEWELL, T. N. & LASSEN, W. H. (1951). On the retention of airborne particulates in the human lung. II. *Arch. ind. Hyg.* **3**, 359.

LANDAHL, H. D., TRACEWELL, T. N. & LASSEN, W. H. (1952). Retention of airborne particulates in the human lung. III. *Arch. ind. Hyg.* **6**, 508.

LEHMANN, K. B., SAITO, Y. & GIRÖRER, W. (1912). Über die Quantitative Absorption von Staub aus der Luft durch den Menschen. *Arch. Hyg. Bakt.* **75**, 152.

LISTER, J. (1868). Antiseptic system treatment in surgery. *Br. med. J.* ii, 53.

LOMBARD, H. C. (1834). De l'influence de la profession sur la phtisie pulmonaire. *Ann. Hyg. Publique*, **11**, 1.

LOW, F. N. (1952). Electron microscopy of the rat lung. *Anat. Rec.* **113**, 437.

LOW, F. N. & SAMPAIO, M. M. (1957). The pulmonary alveolar epithelium as an entodermal derivative. *Anat. Rec.* **127**, 51.

LUCAS, A. M. & DOUGLAS, L. C. (1934). Principles underlying ciliary activity in the respiratory tract. II. A comparison of nasal clearance in man, monkey and other mammals. *Archs Otolar.* **20**, 518.

MCCRAE, J. (1913). The ash of silicotic lungs. *Publs. S. Afr. Inst. med. Res.* (unnumbered).

MAVROGORDATO, A. (1923). Value of the koniometer, being an investigation into the method and results of dust sampling as at present practised in the mines of the Witwatersrand. *Publs S. Afr. Inst. med. Res.* **17**, 14.

MEDICAL RESEARCH COUNCIL (1952). Dust Committee on Industrial Pulmonary Disease. Recommendations of the M.R.C. Panels Relative to selective sampling. London, 4 March 1952.

MELLY, M. A., THOMISON, J. B. & ROGERS, D. E. (1960). Fate of Staphylococci within human leukocytes. *J. exp. Med.* **112**, 1121.

MENEELY, G. R., AUERBACH, S. H., WOODCOCK, C. C., KORY, R. C. & HAHN, P. F. (1953). Transbronchial instillation of radioactive gold colloid in the lung of the dog: distribution studies, survival and pathology. *Am. J. med. Sci.* **225**, 172.

MILBURN, R. H., CRIDER, W. L. & MORTON, S. D. (1957). The retention of hygroscopic dusts in the human lungs. *Arch. ind. Hlth*, **15**, 59.

MILLER, W. S. (1947). *The Lung*, 2nd edition. Springfield, Illinois: Thomas.

MORROW, P. E. (1960). Some physical and physiological factors controlling the fate of inhaled substances. I. Deposition. *Hlth Phys.* **2**, 366.

MORROW, P. E. & CASARETT, L. J. (1961). An experimental study of the deposition and retention of a plutonium 239 dioxide aerosol. In *Inhaled Particles and Vapours*, p. 167. Ed. by C. N. Davies. London: Pergamon Press.

NAGELSCHMIDT, G., NELSON, E. S., KING, E. J., ATTYGALLE, D. & YOGANATHAN, M. (1951). The recovery of quartz and other minerals from the lungs of rats. *Arch. Ind. Hlth*, **16**, 188.

PALMES, D., ALTSHULER, B. & NELSON, N. (1965). Persistence of airborne aerosol particles in the human respiratory tract during breath holding. *Proc. 2nd Int. Symp. Br. occup. Hyg. Soc.* 1965 (in the Press).

PATTLE, R. E. (1961). Retention of gases and particles in the human nose. In *Inhaled Particles and Vapours*, p. 302. Ed. by C. N. Davies. London: Pergamon Press.

POLICARD, A., COLLET, A. & PREGERMAIN, S. (1956). Electron microscope studies on alveolar cells from mammals. *Proc. Stockholm Conf. Electron Microscopy*, p. 244. Ed. by F. Sjostrand and J. Rhodin. Stockholm: Almqvist and Wiksell.

POLICARD, A., COLLET, A. & GILTAIRE-RALYTE, L. (1953). Étude au microscope électronique des poussières de houille renfermées dans les poumons des mineurs au charbon. *C. r. hebd. Séanc. Acad. Sci., Paris*, **236**, 1458.

POLICARD, A., COLLET, A. & RAYLTE, L. (1952). Electron microscope studies of lung fibrosis in silicosis. *Presse méd.* **60**, 1419.

PROCTOR, D. F. & WAGNER, H. N. (1966). Mucociliary particle clearance in the human nose. 2nd Int. Symposium. *Br. occup. Hyg. Soc.* (in the Press).

RIVERS, D., MORRIS, T. G., WISE, M. E., COOKE, T. H. & ROBERTS, W. H. (1963). The fibrogenicity of some respirable dusts measured in mice. *Br. J. ind. Med.* **20**, 13.

RIVERS, D., WISE, M. E., KING, E. J. & NAGELSCHMIDT, G. (1960). Dust content, radiology and pathology in simple pneumoconiosis of coal workers. Pt I. General observations. *Br. J. ind. Med.* **17**, 87.

ROBERTSON, O. H. & LOOSLI, C. G. (1938). A study of the macrophage reaction in the pulmonary lesions of dogs with experimental pneumococcus lobar pneumonia. *J. exp. Med.* **67**, 575.

ROGERS, D. E. & MELLY, M. A. (1960). Further observations on the behaviour of staphylococci within human leukocytes. *J. exp. Med.* **111**, 533.

ROGERS, D. E. & TOMPSETT, R. (1952). The survival of staphylococci within human leukocytes. *J. exp. Med.* **95**, 209.

ROOKS, R. (1939). The bacterial filtering efficiency of the human nose. *Am. J. Hyg.* **30**, 7.

ROSS, J. M. (1957). The pathogenesis of anthrax following the administration of spores by the respiratory route. *J. Path. Bact.* **73**, 485.

SCHILLER, E. (1956). Histobiologie der Lunge. Alveolar phagozyten und Staubtransport. *Anat. Anz.* **102**, 389.

SCHLIPKOTER, H. W. & COLLI, A. (1956). Elektronoptische Untersuchungen von Staubkom grössen in Staublungen. *Proc. Stockholm Conf. Electron Microscopy*, p. 251. Ed. F. Sjostrand & J. Rhodin. Stockholm: Almqvist and Wiksell.

SINCLAIR, D. & LA MER, V. K. (1949). Light scattering as a measure of particle size in aerosols. The production of monodispersed aerosols. *Chem. Rev.* **44**, 245.

STARLING, E. H. (1952). *Principles of Human Physiology*, 11th ed. Ed. by C. Lovatt Evans. London: Churchill.

TASK GROUP ON LUNG DYNAMICS (1966). Deposition and retention models for internal dosimetry of the human respiratory tract. *Hlth Phys.* **12**, 173.

TYNDALL, J. (1881). *Essays on Floating-matter of the Air in Relation to Putrefaction and Infection*. London: Longmans.

VAN WIJK, A. M. & PATTERSON, H. S. (1940). The percentage of particles of different sizes removed from dust-laden air by breathing. *J. ind. Hyg. Toxicol.* **22**, 31.

VON HAYEK, H. (1942). Über Bau und Funktion der Alveolarepithel-Zellen. *Anat. Anz.* **93**, 149.

WATKINS-PITCHFORD, W. & MOIR, J. (1916). On the nature of the doubly refracting particles seen in microscopic sections of silicotic lungs, and an improved method for disclosing siliceous particles in such sections. *Publs. S. Afr. Inst. med. Res.* **7**, 207.

WEIBEL, E. R. (1963). *Morphometry of the Human Lung*. Berlin: Springer Verlag.

WELLS, W. F. (1955). *Airborne Contagion and Air Hygiene*. Cambridge, Mass.: Harvard University Press.

WILSON, I. B. & LA MER, V. K. (1948). The retention of aerosol particles in the human respiratory tract as a function of particle radius. *J. ind. Hyg. Toxicol.* **30**, 265.

ZEBEL, G. (1956). Über die Kornverteilung von Lungenstauben. *Beitr. Silikosforsch.* **41**, 33.

MICROBIAL SURVIVAL

J. D. ANDERSON* AND C. S. COX

Microbiological Research Establishment, Porton, Salisbury, Wiltshire

INTRODUCTION

Laboratory studies of microbial survival in the aerosol have been largely concerned with bacteria, and little is known of the behaviour of viruses and fungi.

Such studies have shown that the effects of growth medium, method of growth, and metabolic state of the organism are superimposed upon that of species and strain. The nature of the atmospheric environment, including its relative humidity, composition and temperature, can be crucial. Electromagnetic radiation can reduce the survival of microbial aerosols. Results are also influenced by other conditions such as choice of spray fluid and the time and manner of collection. No simple relationship exists between the degree of survival and time of storage in the aerosol. For fragile organisms the effect of collecting device, and the nature and osmotic pressure of the collecting fluid can be of paramount importance. Owing to the large number of variables which affect survival in the aerosol, both the results and their interpretation are markedly dependent upon the precise technique employed.

LABORATORY APPARATUS AND TECHNIQUES

Organism

Table 1 lists literature on microbial survival in the aerosol other than that concerned primarily with air disinfection or studies *in vivo*. Because many factors influence survival it is not possible to make any general statement on the influence of choice of organism upon the response to any applied stress. However, the response of different strains of an organism to a given stress can show a similar pattern of behaviour, e.g. three strains of *Escherichia coli* are less stable at high than at low relative humidities (Cox, 1966*a*).

Growth methods

Few comparative studies have been made on the effect of growth methods on subsequent survival in the aerosol, apart from those of

* Present address: Department of Medicine, The University, Bristol.

Brown (1953b) who showed that at high relative humidities the survival of *Escherichia coli* grown on agar was better than when grown in broth culture. This difference was apparent only at high relative humidities.

Culture age modifies survival in the aerosol. For *Escherichia coli* death-rate is a maximum during the transition from lag to logarithmic growth (Brown, 1953b), and *Serratia marcescens* behaves similarly (Goodlow & Leonard, 1961). Re-incubation in growth medium before spraying can modify aerosol survival properties (Anderson & Dark, 1966; Cox & Baldwin, 1966). Brown (1954) found that young cultures of three psychrophilic bacteria died more rapidly than old cultures at all relative humidities, in contrast to *Escherichia coli* in which this effect of age was observed only at high relative humidities. This effect has been confirmed with *E. coli* (Cox, 1966a).

Generation of aerosols

Microbial aerosols are usually generated from aqueous suspensions but have occasionally been formed from the dry state. Green & Lane (1957) provide a useful summary of methods and mechanisms for the production of aerosols. It is not known whether there is an interaction between microbes when in the same aerosol particle. An aerosol containing one microbe per particle should therefore be used whenever possible. Particle size may also influence survival; Dunklin & Puck (1948) showed that the death-rate of pneumococci in 1·6-micron particles was lower than in 3·2-micron particles. By contrast, Goodlow & Leonard (1961) found that in solar radiation large particles of an unstated organism survived better than small particles.

Aerosols may be generated from aqueous suspensions by atomization in a jet of air, by the 'spinning top', 'vibrating reed', or ultrasonic methods. Various types of air-jet atomizers have been reviewed by Rosebury (1947) and Green & Lane (1957). Air-jet atomizers yield a heterogeneous size distribution of particles and have a large output. Some are provided with baffles, e.g. the Collison (1935) spray, to eliminate large particles. The 'spinning top' atomizer (May, 1949; Walton & Prewitt, 1949) produces homogeneous clouds of any desired droplet size in the range 20–150 microns, and has a moderately large output. The 'vibrating reed' atomizer yields aerosols of uniform and controllable particle size but at a very low output (Dimmock, 1950; W. R. Wolf, 1961; Zentner, 1961; Harris, 1964); this type of generator causes little mechanical damage to the microbe. Muromtsev & Nenashev (1960) developed an ultrasonic aerosol atomizer which is claimed to be superior to pneumatic methods for producing biological aerosols, as it does not damage bacteria and produces a concentrated aerosol with an initial size range of 1–6 microns.

Aerosols have been generated from fine dry powders by explosive means (Beebe, 1959) or by erosion of pellets with air jets (Wright, 1949; Dimmick, 1959, 1960a). Aerosols dispersed from solids may have survival properties different from those generated from suspensions (Beebe, 1959; Dimmick, 1960a; Goodlow & Leonard, 1961).

Storage

With few exceptions, experiments with microbial aerosols, prior to the middle of the last decade, were carried out in laboratory rooms and containers of various sizes. A dynamic control system developed by Henderson (1952), primarily for use in animal exposure experiments, has subsequently been modified for aerosol survival studies. Under controlled conditions the bacterial aerosol was introduced into air flowing through a metal tube. Aerosol samples could be recovered at different points along the tube so that the effect of aerosol age upon microbial survival could be determined. Only short storage times in the aerosol were possible owing to the dimensions of the apparatus and the air-flow rate. Aerosol storage times may be increased using apparatus based on a vertical wind tunnel (Druett & May, 1952). Hatch & Dimmick (1965) increased aerosol holding times simply by increasing the dimensions of the basic Henderson apparatus. An additional feature of their apparatus was that a further supply of air could be injected at a point along the length of the tube to permit study of the effects of changes of relative humidity during storage. An entirely different and ingenious system for the long-term storage of aerosols has been based on the rotating drum (Goldberg, Watkins, Boerke & Chatigny, 1958). Losses of aerosol particles in the 1 micron range from sedimentation and impaction are much less than in most other types of apparatus. Although this method has now displaced others for the storage of laboratory aerosols there is no satisfactory technique for the long-term storage of large aerosol particles. These rotating drums are generally constructed of stainless steel but the insertion of transparent panels of plastic materials allows the action of light on microbial aerosols to be investigated (e.g. Webb, 1961a). The transmission characteristics of 'plexiglass' and similar materials make them unsuitable for work with certain components of sunlight. H. A. Druett (private communication) has overcome this difficulty by the use of silica panels.

The survival of micro-organisms may be followed in comparatively large droplets supported on fine glass fibres, a method with the advantage that no mechanical damage takes place during droplet formation or collection. This technique, based on a design by Mr K. R. May, employs small numbers of micro-organisms and can provide pertinent data on death processes (Cox, 1965; Silver, 1965). Micro-organisms desiccated by freeze-drying or on cellulose fibres (McDade & Hall, 1963; Rountree, 1963; Annear, 1962), films (Maltman, Orr & Hinton, 1960; Webb, 1960 b; McDade & Hall, 1964; Maltman, 1965) and filter membranes (Webb, 1960 b) permit study of larger populations and provide useful analogies with death processes in the aerosol.

Collection of aerosols

Many different collecting devices have been designed because no single sampling method can provide all the information required for studies of aerosols. Loss of viability can occur during or after sampling, and its extent is likely to depend upon the sampling procedure.

Basic methods of sampling microbial aerosols include impingement in liquids, impaction on solid surfaces, filtration, sedimentation, centrifugation, electrostatic and thermal precipitation. Methods, and other aspects of sampling have been reviewed by Green & Lane (1957), Wolf *et al.* (1959) and Bachelor (1960). Many contributors (Brachman *et al.* 1964) at the First International Aerobiology Symposium in 1963 recommended that data obtained with any specialized sampler should be compared with those determined with a standard reference sampler. The U.S. Army Chemical Corps all-glass impinger (Wolf *et al.* 1959) which is based on the raised Porton impinger of May & Harper (1957), was chosen as the standard liquid impinger. The Andersen (1958) stacked sieve sampler was chosen as the standard apparatus for impaction on solid surfaces.

Because of the above recommendation and because these two types of sampler are in wide use, they will be described in detail. In the 'A.G.I. 30' all-glass impinger, and similar apparatus, e.g. the raised Porton impinger (May & Harper, 1957), air is drawn through a short length of capillary tubing held above a liquid surface. The air-jet strikes the base of the container and the aerosol particles become trapped in violently agitated collecting fluid. When the pressure drop across the capillary reaches about half an atmosphere, the flow in the tube attains sonic velocity. At or above this suction, the impinger operates at constant flow and once calibrated does not require a flowmeter. Although suitable for a wide range of aerosol densities, long sampling times may be required for dilute aerosols. Under such conditions, and especially at low relative humidities, cooling and evaporation of the collecting fluid occurs. The Andersen sampler is essentially a cascaded arrangement of sieve type samplers in which air is drawn through a pattern of holes in the sieves, and particles are impacted on to agar surfaces. The unit consists of six stages with smaller holes in each succeeding sieve. The bigger particles are impacted in the top stages which have large holes and the smaller particles in the lower stages. The Andersen sampler can only be used with very dilute aerosol clouds and yields the particle size distribution; it is not really suitable for viability determinations.

These two types of samplers will generally cover most experimental requirements for recovering microbial aerosols.

Since the publication of reviews by Green & Lane (1957), Wolf *et al.* (1959) and Bachelor (1960) the main developments have been with electrostatic samplers (e.g. Morris, Darlow, Peel & Wright, 1961; Langer, Pierrard & Yamate, 1964), and with modifications of the Andersen sampler which allow an improved determination of particle size distribution (May, 1964). To improve the collection of virus aerosols, Jensen (1965) has modified the medium used in the Andersen sampler.

Determination of populations recovered from microbial aerosols

Numbers of viable microbes in an aerosol fall as a result of physical and biological losses. These must be separately determined in order to study the influence upon viability of the many factors involved in aerosol experiments. The physical losses result from deposition on surfaces through settling, convective flow or diffusion, or by electrostatic attraction. On removing a sample from a storage container, dilution of the remaining aerosol occurs and if appreciable the extent of this dilution will also have to be determined.

Certain investigators calibrate a particular piece of apparatus for physical losses and assume that the rate of loss is always constant over the calibrated range. Although experimentally convenient, in our experience the rate of physical loss is variable and this method should only be used with reservation.

Physical losses in a given aerosol are seldom determined directly since a knowledge of total and viable numbers in recovered populations is sufficient to estimate survival. If necessary the extent of physical losses could then be calculated from the total microbial numbers in a sample and from the characteristics of the sampling device. In principle, total microbial numbers in a sample recovered from an aerosol may be determined by direct count under the microscope or by light-scatter measurements. In practice, such methods are difficult since dilute microbial suspensions are usually involved, lysis of organisms may occur after collection, and foreign particles may interfere. Nevertheless, with suitable precautions, modifications of the slide culture technique (Postgate, Crumpton & Hunter, 1961) have been applied to organisms recovered from aerosols either directly on a nutrient agar surface (Cox & Baldwin, 1964, 1966) or in a clarified sampling fluid (G. J. Harper, private communication).

The main methods for determining total microbial numbers in recovered aerosol samples are based on tracer techniques, in which material which does not undergo any biological loss is added to the microbial suspension. Determinations of the tracer and microbe content of aerosol spray and of collecting fluids enables calculation of the total and viable numbers of recovered microbes. Where the size of the equilibrated aerosol particle is determined by the size of the microbe, differential physical losses may occur if the tracer and test organism are of different size. Tracer methods may involve the use of dyes, spores, radioisotopes or enzymes.

In the dye tracer technique, compounds such as methylene blue (Ferry, Farr, Rose & Blau, 1951) or sodium fluorescein (Wolfe, 1961) are added to microbial suspensions before spraying. However, dyes may be toxic to the organism, especially when they are concentrated by evaporation of water from the aerosol droplet. Also, all aerosol particles are labelled with dye whilst only a proportion contain microbes, so that under certain conditions (e.g. spraying microbes suspended in dilute solutions) particles containing microbes may be larger than those with dye only. Spores of *Bacillus subtilis* var. *niger* (*Bacillus globigii*) are the main tracer used in the spore technique (Harper & Morton, 1952; Harper, Hood & Morton, 1958). Evidence that a proportion of the spores may die in the aerosol (Harper *et al.* 1958; Anderson, 1966; Cox, 1966*a*) indicates that this tracer is not as satisfactory as was once thought. This convenient tracer technique is especially suitable for dilute bacterial aerosols provided allowance is made for spore death, or where great accuracy is not required.

In the radiotracer technique, organisms should ideally be labelled directly with a suitable radiotracer which will form part of the structure of the microbe. Bacteria have been labelled by growth in media supplemented with [^{35}S] (Miller, Scherff, Piepoli & Idoine, 1961), [^{32}P] (Harper & Morton, 1952) or [^{14}C] (Anderson, 1966). The technique may have applications for other micro-organisms. Alternatively, a labelled suspension of a tracer organism may be added to a suspension of the test microbe (Miller *et al.* 1961; Harper *et al.* 1958; Anderson,

1966). This method has the advantage that growth conditions can be chosen which will yield a tracer organism of high specific activity without modifying the growth conditions for the test microbe. The tracer organism should preferably be the killed organism under test or an organism of similar physical decay properties. Instead of labelling the micro-organism, a biologically inert radioactive solution may be added to the spray fluid (e.g. Harstad, 1965). This method resembles the dye tracer technique and is open to the same criticisms. Radio tracer methods are not applicable for the assay of dilute microbial suspensions because excessively large amounts of radioactivity would have to be used which would be likely to produce biological damage. The β-galactosidase of *Escherichia coli* strain B is not damaged on aerosolization (Anderson, 1966) and the assay of this enzyme has been used for the determination of total bacterial numbers (Anderson & Crouch, 1966). The principle has application for other 'aerostable' enzyme systems and the minimum number of organisms determined would depend on the activity of the enzyme and the sensitivity of the assay method.

Numbers of airborne particles may be determined by light-scatter measurements on the aerosol. Total microbial numbers in a recovered sample may then be calculated from this data and from the characteristics of the sampling device (Ferry *et al.* 1951; Dimmick, 1960*b*). However, light scatter is influenced by changes in particle size distribution which may result from differential fallout or from changes in humidity. This technique can be used only over a limited range of aerosol densities (Harper *et al.* 1958).

FACTORS AFFECTING SURVIVAL IN THE AEROSOL

Relative humidity

It has been widely recognized that relative humidity influences the survival of viral and bacterial aerosols. Microbial survival is dependent upon many factors, and effects attributed to relative humidity may be largely due to other factors. Determination of the intrinsic effect of relative humidity on survival is not therefore a simple procedure.

Most workers have found for bacteria and viruses that the relationship of survival to relative humidity is free from abrupt changes; this suggests an absence of narrow relative humidity zones at which microbes are particularly unstable. However, in studies with *Escherichia coli* where the survival has been measured at small increments of relative humidity, such narrow zones of instability have in fact been detected in atmospheres of air and nitrogen (Anderson, 1966; Cox, 1966a,b; Cox & Baldwin, 1966). Other workers (e.g. Brown, 1953b, 1954; Webb, 1959b; Webb & Dumasia, 1964; Webb, Dumasia & Singh Bhorjee, 1965) have not detected narrow zones of instability when studying *E. coli* over smaller ranges of relative humidity and at larger increments of humidity. One cannot at present say whether these apparently different results are due to insufficient data or whether differences of technique may have modified the response of this organism to relative humidity. Although *E. coli* may differ fundamentally from other organisms there is evidence for a similar critical dependence of survival for freeze-dried *Serratia marcescens* stored at high relative humidity (Monk, Elbert, Stevens & McCaffrey, 1956; Monk & McCaffrey, 1957; Davis & Bateman, 1960; Bateman, McCaffrey, O'Connor & Monk, 1961) and *E. coli* (Davis & Bateman, 1960). This evidence implies that similar critical zones may exist for *S. marcescens* in the aerosol state.

To predict the behaviour of any organism at a given relative humidity one should therefore look for analogous examples in the available literature (Table 1), but caution is needed in view of the large number of variables which may affect survival. In general, decay rates tend to be highest at the extremes of the humidity range, 100–20 %.

Composition of atmosphere

Early studies of the effects of atmosphere on the survival of microbial aerosols were mainly concerned with air disinfection. The main bactericidal agents employed for this purpose have been epoxides, glycols, halogens, hypochlorites, lactones, ozone and phenols. Most of these studies have been of a practical nature and have not been primarily concerned with fundamental aspects of survival.

Air used in laboratory aerosol experiments is generally presumed to be free from toxic components and is not submitted to purification procedures other than, perhaps, filtration. Although Webb (1959b, 1965a) found that the survival of unstated organisms in air and in inert atmospheres was similar, and Rosebury (1947) found that an inert atmosphere did not prolong the survival of *Pasteurella tularensis* at low relative humidity, most investigators have obtained better survival in inert atmospheres. Ferry, Brown & Damon (1958b) found that replacement of air by nitrogen enhanced the survival in aerosols of *Micrococcus candidus*, *Escherichia coli* and *Serratia marcescens*. They attributed this effect to the toxic action of oxygen. Levine & Cabelli (1963) found that germination of spores of *Bacillus subtilis* (var. *niger*) collected from the aerosol was dependent upon the oxygen content of the atmosphere.

Hess (1965) showed that for low, but not high, relative humidities the survival of *S. marcescens* and *E. coli* was dependent upon the partial pressure of oxygen in nitrogen–oxygen mixtures. Cox (1966*a*) found that the survival of three strains of *E. coli* was enhanced at low, but not high, relative humidities when nitrogen replaced air. The effect, which was attributed to the toxic action of oxygen, has since been confirmed (unpublished data). Other components of laboratory air besides oxygen may affect survival and are being studied.

Temperature

The survival of microbial aerosols has not been extensively investigated as a function of temperature.

Williamson and Gotaas (1942) found that temperature changes over the range 24–30° C had no effect upon the aerosol survival of *Escherichia coli*, *Staphylococcus aureus* and *Streptococcus salivarius*. In contrast DeOme *et al.* (1944) found that the death-rate of *Salmonella pullorum* increased with rising temperature over the range 28–37° C; the death-rate of pneumococci also increased with temperature over the range 14–33° C (Dunklin & Puck, 1948). Kethley, Fincher & Cown (1957) found a similar correlation with *Serratia marcescens* over the range −40 to 32° C, and at relative humidities from 20 to 80%. Webb (1959*b*) obtained a similar result over a narrower range of conditions. Likewise, aerosols of vaccinia, influenza, Venezuelan equine encephalomyelitis and polio viruses survived better at low than at high temperatures (Harper, 1961).

These limited studies suggest that in general the death-rate of microbial aerosols increases with temperature.

Radiation

Radiation can be lethal to microbial aerosols and has been used as a method of air disinfection; this last aspect will not be discussed. Because of the techniques involved and because the response of organisms may differ, one of the main difficulties of radiation experiments is to assess the precise level of radiation which is harmful (Monaci, 1952; Wells, 1955). There are no reports of the effect of particulate radiation on the aerosol, and most interest has centred on sunlight or on discrete regions of its spectrum.

The decay rate of *P. tularensis* in artificial sunlight was directly proportional to the applied light intensity and decreased linearly with increasing humidity. *P. pestis* behaved similarly except that the increase in decay rate was not directly proportional to the light intensity (Beebe &

Pirsch, 1958). Likewise, Goodlow & Leonard (1961) found that relative humidities above 70% afforded protection against the effects of solar radiation on an unstated organism which was more stable in large, than in small particles. *Serratia marcescens* in artificial sunlight is also less stable at low than at high relative humidities but shows this change in response between relative humidities of 55 and 65%. Inositol was found to protect against radiation damage, and the degree of protection was sensitive to small changes in light intensity (Webb, 1963 *a*, 1965 *b*).

The effect of solar range ultraviolet radiation resembled that of artificial sunlight in that its lethal action on *Pasteurella tularensis* in the aerosol was proportional to the radiation intensity and that moisture protected (Beebe, 1959). Webb (1961 *a*), using wavebands of 2,800–3,200, 3,400–4,500 and 5,200–5,800 Å on aerosols of *Serratia marcescens* showed that the upper two wavebands could photoreactivate organisms which had been irradiated with the ultraviolet band of 2,800–3,200 Å. Simultaneous irradiation with the visible and ultraviolet bands had an additive lethal effect. Red dyes of the alizarin type desensitized this organism to ultraviolet radiation whilst blue and yellow dyes enhanced damage. The effect of relative humidity on the survival of aerosols of this organism exposed to these three wavebands resembled the response to artificial sunlight (Webb, 1963 *a*). Besides proving lethal, radiation has been shown to increase the rate of mutation of bacteria in aerosols. This effect has been demonstrated for *S. marcescens* in artificial sunlight (Webb, 1963 *a*) and for *Escherichia coli* in the waveband 2,800–3,200 Å (Webb, 1964).

The effects of X-rays on microbial aerosols has received little attention. Unlike the effects of light there is a sharp decrease in the sensitivity of *Escherichia coli* to irradiation by 250 kV. X-rays when the relative humidity falls below 70%. Maximum damage occurred between relative humidities of 70 and 80%. Inositol protects against this damage (Webb & Dumasia, 1964; Webb, 1965 *a*, *b*).

All these reports concern bacteria and the only virus studied is Rous sarcoma virus. When exposed to ultraviolet radiation (2,800–3,200 Å) it behaved in a similar manner to *Serratia marcescens* (Webb, 1963 *b*).

The responses so far discussed were observed with aerosols generated from liquid suspensions. When generated from the dry-state, bacteria were less sensitive to radiation (Beebe, 1959; Goodlow & Leonard, 1961). A further difference was that only the dry disseminated aerosols showed a spontaneous reactivation when held in the dark after ultraviolet irradiation (Dimmick, 1960 *c*).

Cloud age

Many workers express results as the logarithm of the number of survivors versus aerosol age, and from this treatment derive decay rates. This procedure is not altogether satisfactory since the rate of loss of viability may not follow first-order kinetics with respect to the number of survivors. In general there is a rapid initial decay followed by slower processes, the rates of which are time dependent. The decay rates obtained are sometimes expressed as a function of variables which affect survival and thus act as a measure of the susceptibility of an organism to any imposed stress. A fuller understanding of all the factors involved in aerosol experiments may eventually lead to a better system for the analysis of results. Monk & Mattuck (1956) have suggested some alternative mathematical treatments.

Additives to spray fluids

For most purposes the properties of suspensions sprayed from distilled water are taken to represent the fundamental response of microbes to stress in the aerosol. Additives to this spray fluid have been studied both to improve survival and to identify lethal mechanisms. Table 2 summarizes literature relating to such studies, most of which is for aerosols stored in the dark. Experiments have usually been carried out at a few selected relative humidities and many compounds have only a marginal effect upon survival. Additives include amino acids, antibiotics, aromatic compounds, dyes, metal chelating agents, polyhydric alcohols, salts, spent growth medium and sugars.

In practice it is difficult to select a likely protective additive merely by studying the literature since the response of a protected microbe can still be influenced by the growth conditions, relative humidity, the concentration of additive and the nature of the collecting fluid.

The literature survey indicates, however, that relatively simple compounds including inositol, and di- and tri-saccharides are good protecting agents. Spent growth medium, which is a complex mixture, often affords protection even though it may contain sodium chloride which has been shown to have a lethal effect.

Collecting media

Studies of collecting media are aimed at providing information about lethal mechanisms and ways in which microbial survival may be improved on collection and during subsequent storage.

Liquid collecting agents based on simple salt solutions and broths are most widely used. Addition of alginate prevents physical losses of certain bacteria in the impinger (Henderson, 1952). Cysteine has been incorporated into media for the collection of *Pasteurella tularensis* (Hood, 1961; Cabelli, 1962). Sugars such as sucrose (I. H. Silver, private communication; Cox, 1965, 1966*a*, *b*) and melezitose (Cabelli, 1962) can improve survival and may be used to prevent freezing when sampling at low temperatures.

For samplers of the Andersen (1958) type the solid media are often based on nutrient agar. Low-temperature sampling with such media may be carried out after addition of carboxymethylcellulose ether (Lee & Garbett, 1966). An alternative method of low-temperature sampling is to use glass slides coated with polysiloxan which is fluid down to $-60°$ C (Vlodavets, Zuikova & Motova, 1958).

MECHANISMS OF DEATH

Survival in aerosol experiments is usually estimated as ability to replicate under the chosen test conditions. Irreversible and lethal changes may take place at any stage of an aerosol experiment. Also the damage which could be induced may not be expressed until a later stage and even then only under certain conditions. A simple example of this is the production of a mutant which would appear dead on a chemically defined medium yet viable on a complex medium. It is therefore often difficult to attribute death to a particular stage of an aerosol experiment.

Causes of death during aerosol generation

There is no evidence of death during generation of aerosols of *Escherichia coli* and *Serratia marcescens* in the Collison (1935) type of air-jet atomizer, providing generation occurs under saturated conditions. Webb (1959*a*) has shown that if the humidity in the spray pot is not fully saturated, then the extent of death of *S. marcescens* is related to the saturation deficit. However, death may occur on generation of aerosols of fragile organisms such as *Pasteurella tularensis* or sensitive organisms such as spores of *Bacillus subtilis* (var. *niger*).

Aerosols generated from the dry state have different survival properties from those prepared from aqueous suspensions (Beebe, 1959; Dimmick, 1960*a*, *c*; Goodlow & Leonard, 1961). This effect could be due to differences in the method of generation, in the particle size distribution, in the factors involved in the preparation of the sample, and the manner in which the aerosol equilibrates with the atmosphere.

Death during production of aerosols has not been examined with other types of generator.

Death during storage caused by water loss

The relative humidity at which an aerosol is stored influences the rate and extent of loss of water from both the droplet and the microbe. Except at extremely high relative humidities, droplets of a typical aerosol evaporate in milliseconds. This rate may not correspond with the rate of loss of water from the microbe since the processes involved are different. One cannot therefore at the moment decide whether rate or extent of water loss influences survival in the aerosol. For dried organisms the extent of water loss is related to relative humidity (Scott, 1958; Webb, 1960*b*; Bateman, Stevens, Mercer & Carstensen, 1962).

The dehydration and rehydration processes involved in aerosol experiments are likely to have a marked effect on the structure of macromolecules such as proteins, structural elements and nucleic acids. Professor S. J. Webb has explained decreased survival in aerosols largely in terms of water movements, although data by other workers show that oxygen is involved. There is evidence that protein structure may depend on water content, e.g. Boyes-Watson, Davidson & Perutz (1947). Webb (1959*b*) suggested that movements of water molecules in and out of the organism resulted in a collapse of cellular protein structure which could account for the death of *Escherichia coli* and other organisms. Such a mechanism does not apply to the *β*-galactosidase of *E. coli*. This enzyme was chosen as a representative bacterial protein, and using activity as a criterion of structural integrity Anderson (1966) showed that loss of water in the aerosol did not damage this protein. Webb (1960*b*) proposed that changes in the tertiary structure of proteins caused by desiccation produce a breakdown of bacterial cellular membranes resulting in a loss of differentiation in *E. coli* and other bacteria. However, he later considered that mechanisms other than membrane damage were responsible for the death of *E. coli* following desiccation (Webb, 1961*b*). There is evidence that the structure of DNA *in vitro* depends upon its water content (e.g. Falk, Hartman & Lord, 1962, 1963*a,b*; Falk, 1964); RNA may also undergo structural changes (Rich & Watson, 1954). Webb and his co-workers have suggested that a structural change in nucleoproteins may cause the death of a variety of bacteria and viruses and explain increased mutation by *E. coli* and *Serratia marcescens* (Webb, 1961*b*, 1963*a,b*, 1964, 1965*a*; Webb, Bather & Hodges, 1963; Webb, Cormack & Morrison, 1964; Webb, Dumasia & Singh Bhorjee, 1965). When populations of *E. coli* infected with phage T7 were aerosolized inactivation of phage DNA occurred (Cox & Baldwin, 1966).

A further consequence of water loss is that substances may achieve toxic concentrations (Monk, McCaffrey & Davis, 1957; Bateman, McCaffrey, O'Connor & Monk, 1961) or crystallize (Silver, 1965). The formation of supersaturated solutions seems an essential property of simple solutes which behave as protecting agents (Cox, unpublished data). One would expect that compounds able to protect against freeze-drying might protect against the aerosol stress and that other parallels would exist. However, the degree of supersaturation may be different under the conditions of aerosol and freeze-drying experiments because a greater degree of cooling is involved in the latter.

Damage to metabolic processes will be a consequence of the phenomena described above. Metabolic studies on microbes recovered from aerosols have been limited to bacteria and have been concerned with protein synthesis, ion control and phage replication. The ability of *Escherichia coli* to synthesize β-galactosidase in the presence of a specific inducer was considerably impaired in the period immediately following recovery from the aerosol; loss of ability to synthesize this protein appeared to precede death (Anderson, 1966). Decreased ability to synthesize β-galactosidase was also demonstrated with *E. coli* dried on millipore filters (Webb, Dumasia & Singh Bhorjee, 1965). [^{43}K]-labelled populations of *E. coli* lost practically all radio-isotope within a very short time after recovery from bacterial clouds, except at high relative humidities and with short storage times. Loss of potassium is a sequel of aerosolization but is not in itself immediately lethal. Loss of control of potassium levels implies loss of control over other ions and substrates and also a disruption of structures and metabolic functions dependent upon this cation (Anderson & Dark, 1966). The results of these ion and protein synthesis studies suggest that even viable bacteria recovered from aerosols cannot be regarded as unchanged rehydrated forms of the original bacterium.

Webb *et al.* (1965) subjected populations of *Escherichia coli* B collected from the aerosol to phages T1, T2, T3, T4 and T7. The capacity to replicate these phages varied with the phage used and with the relative humidity at which the bacteria were stored. The capacity to replicate phages T2 and T4 was unaffected while for phages T1, T3 and T7 the capacity declined with storage relative humidity over the range 80–30%. Loss of capacity to replicate was never as great as loss of viability of the bacterium. These results suggest that at low relative humidities damage to *E. coli* B in the aerosol affects metabolic processes essential to the growth of the bacterium and to the replication of the odd-numbered phages but not of the even-numbered phages. Cox &

Baldwin (1966) subjected populations of *E. coli* B which had been collected from aerosols to phage T7 and demonstrated that different death mechanisms operated at low and at high relative humidities. At low relative humidities, oxygen was involved in the death mechanism and the results will be discussed below. At high relative humidities damage occurred to processes common to growth of *E. coli* B and replication of phage T7. At high relative humidities Webb *et al.* (1965) did not detect appreciable death of *E. coli* or impaired replication of phage T7. This difference may be related to the critical relative humidity zones mentioned previously.

Death during storage caused by oxygen

The better survival of bacterial aerosols in inert atmospheres than in air indicates that there is a toxic component in air. This evidence, and the fact that the extent of death increases with oxygen content, suggests that oxygen may be the toxic component. However, air and commercial oxygen are known to contain impurities and it has not yet been determined if these are involved in the apparent toxic action of oxygen. The finding that after collection from the aerosol the multiplication of *Escherichia coli* B is severely inhibited at low relative humidities under conditions where it replicates phage T7 has been attributed to the toxic action of oxygen. Oxygen must therefore act on a process not involved in the replication of phage T7 (Cox & Baldwin, 1966). Oxygen is not involved in the initial loss of [^{43}K] by populations of *E. coli* recovered from aerosols (Anderson & Dark, 1966).

Freeze-dried *Serratia marcescens* (Bateman, McCaffrey, O'Connor & Monk, 1961; Benedict *et al.* 1961) and *Escherichia coli* (Lion & Bergmann, 1961*a*, *b*; Lion, 1963) are also susceptible to oxygen poisoning. The free radicles formed in freeze-dried bacterial cultures in the presence of oxygen may be involved in the lethal process (Dimmick, Heckly & Hollis, 1961; Lion, Kirby-Smith & Randolph, 1961). By analogy, a similar lethal mechanism may operate in the aerosol.

Death during storage caused by irradiation

Professor S. J. Webb and his co-workers have emphasized the importance of water content in influencing the response of an organism to radiation (summarized by Webb, 1965*a*,*b*). They have drawn parallels between the lethal and mutagenic action of X-rays, ultraviolet radiation and desiccation. They suggest that ultraviolet radiation produces rupture of the H bonds between water molecules themselves or between water molecules and cellular nucleoprotein, whilst damage caused by X-irradiation results from a direct action on the water molecules themselves. Both ultraviolet and X-irradiation have been described as having a desiccating effect on essential macromolecules.

Oxygen may be involved in damage caused by radiation. Dimmick (1960c) has suggested that ultraviolet radiation may produce volatile peroxides. The added effect of oxygen, sometimes found in X-ray studies, may be due to the formation of oxygen irradiation products (Webb & Dumasia, 1964).

Only the effects of radiation on organisms in the aerosol have been considered in this review.

Death during collection

Death during collection may result from osmotic shock. Osmotic shock results from the transient rise in internal osmotic pressure when organisms rehydrate on collection. The pressure rise may cause minor damage or even be sufficient to rupture the cellular membranes. Collection into fluids of high osmotic pressure has been used to reduce the degree of osmotic shock. There are indications that the protecting action of fluids of high osmotic pressure may not always operate through the prevention of osmotic lysis (Cox, 1965, 1966a,b; Cox & Baldwin, 1966). Osmotic lysis has also been demonstrated with freeze-dried *Escherichia coli* (Record, Taylor & Miller, 1962) and may also occur with *Vibrio metchnikovi* (Leach & Scott, 1959).

The effects of osmotic shock have scarcely been investigated in the aerosol with microbes other than bacteria. The extent of osmotic damage depends on the robustness of a microbe and will obviously be influenced by the organism and growth conditions, e.g. *Pasteurella tularensis* is far more sensitive to shock than *Escherichia coli*, and aged organisms may have a greater resistance than log phase organisms.

Microbes may be adsorbed on the walls of the collecting apparatus (e.g. impingers) to produce a physical or biological loss. Few investigators seem to consider this possibility, although Henderson (1952) found that such losses did occur, and could be reduced by addition of alginate to the collecting fluid.

Shear and impaction forces during collection may damage sensitive microbes and account for possible differences in survival obtained with various sampling devices. May & Harper (1957) have discussed methods of reducing such damage. Prolonged aspiration has also been found to reduce survival on collection (George, Ward & Cabelli, 1965).

Table 1. *Summary of literature on microbial survival in the aerosol*

Phages, viruses and rickettsias

Organism	References
Coliphage	Ehrlich, Miller & Idoine, 1964; Cox & Baldwin, 1966
Colorado tick fever	Watkins, Goldberg, Deig & Leif, 1965
Encephalomyocarditis	Watkins *et al.* 1965
Influenza	Loosli, Lemon, Robertson & Appel, 1943; Lester, 1948; Shechmeister, 1950; Hemmes, Winkler & Kool, 1960; Harper, 1961, 1963; Hood, 1963
Meningopneumonitis	Rosebury, 1947
Neurovaccinia	Watkins *et al.* 1965
Ornithosis	Bolotovskii, 1959
Pigeon pox	Webb, Bather & Hodges, 1963
Polio	Hemmes, Winkler & Kool, 1960; Harper, 1961, 1963, 1965
Psittacosis	Rosebury, 1947
Rous sarcoma	Webb, 1963*b*; Webb *et al.* 1963
Vaccinia	Harper, 1961, 1963, 1965
Venezuelan equine encephalomyelitis	Harper, 1961, 1963
Vesicular stomatitis	Watkins *et al.* 1965

Bacteria and mycoplasmas

Organism	References
Achromobacter	Brown, 1953*a*, 1954
Bacillus anthrax	Henderson, 1952
Bacillus subtilis (*B. globigii*)	Henderson, 1952; Harper, Hood & Morton, 1958; Webb, 1959*b*, 1960*a*, *b*; Miller, Scherff, Piepoli & Idoine, 1961; Levine & Cabelli, 1963; Cox & Baldwin, 1964, 1966; Cox, 1965, 1966*a*, *b*; George, Ward & Cabelli, 1965; Hess, 1965; Anderson, 1966
Brucella suis	Rosebury, 1947; Harper, Hood & Morton, 1958
Corynebacterium xerose	Ferry, Brown & Damon, 1958*a*
Escherichia coli	Williamson & Gotaas, 1942; Ferry, Farr, Rose & Blau, 1951; Brown, 1953*b*, 1954; Ferry, Brown & Damon, 1958*a*, *b*; Webb, 1959*a*, *b*, 1960*a*, *b*, 1961*b*, 1964, 1965*a*; Webb, Cormack & Morrison, 1964; Webb & Dumasia, 1964; Webb, Dumasia & Singh Bhorjee 1965; Cox, 1965, 1966*a*, *b*; Cox & Baldwin, 1964, 1966; Hayakawa & Poon, 1965; Hess, 1965; Anderson, 1966; Anderson & Dark, 1966
Klebsiella pneumonia	Goldberg, Watkins, Boerke & Chatigny, 1958
Malleomyces	Rosebury, 1947
Micrococcus	Ferry, Farr, Rose & Blau, 1951; Brown, 1953*a*, 1954; Ferry & Maple, 1954; Ferry *et al.* 1958*a*, *b*.
Mycobacterium	Ferry *et al.* 1958*a*, *b*.
Mycoplasma	Kundsin, 1966
Pasteurella pestis	Beebe & Pirsch, 1958
P. tularensis	Rosebury, 1947; Beebe & Pirsch, 1958; Beebe, 1959; Hood, 1961; Miller *et al.* 1961; Cabelli, 1962; Hayes, Bamesberger & Cabelli, 1965; George *et al.* 1965
Pneumococcus	Dunklin & Puck, 1948.
Pseudomonas	Brown, 1953*a*, 1954; Webb, Cormack & Morrison, 1964
Salmonella pullorum	DeOme *et al.* 1944
Sarcina lutea	Hatch & Dimmick, 1965

Table 1 (*cont.*)

Organism	References
Serratia marcescens (*Chromobacter prodigiosum*)	Rosebury, 1947; Henderson, 1952; Kethley, Cown & Fincher, 1957; Kethley, Fincher & Cown, 1957; Kuehne & Decker, 1957; Ferry et al. 1958a, b; Webb, 1959a, b, 1960a, b, 1961a, 1963a, c, 1965a, b; Dimmick, 1960a, c; Goodlow & Leonard, 1961; Miller et al. 1961; Zimmerman, 1962, 1965; Webb et al. 1964; Hatch & Dimmick, 1965; Hess, 1965; Cox, 1965, 1966a
Staphylococcus	Williamson & Gotaas, 1942; Dunklin & Puck, 1948; Webb, 1959a,b, 1960a
Streptococcus	Wells & Zapposodi, 1942; Williamson & Gotaas, 1942; Dunklin & Puck, 1948; Shechmeister & Goldberg, 1950

Fungi

Aspergillus	Mazur & Weston, 1955
Pestalotia	Mazur & Weston, 1955

Table 2. *Survey of studies on additives to spray fluids*

Bacteria

Organism	References
Bacillus subtilis	Webb, 1960a, 1965a
Escherichia coli	Brown, 1954; Webb, 1959a, 1960a, 1961b, 1964, 1965a; Webb, Cormack & Morrison, 1964; Webb & Dumasia, 1964; Webb, Dumasia & Singh Bhorjee, 1965; Cox, 1965, 1966a, b; Silver 1965.
Pasteurella tularensis	Hood, 1961
Pseudomonas aeruginosa	Webb et al. 1964
Serratia marcescens	Webb, 1959a, 1960a, 1961a, 1963a, c, 1965a, b; Webb. et al. 1964; Zimmerman, 1962, 1965; Cox, 1965, 1966a; Hess, 1965
Staphylococcus	Webb, 1959a, 1960a, 1965a; Vlodavets, 1964

Phages and viruses

Coliphage	Ehrlich, Miller & Idoine, 1964
Influenza	Lester, 1948; Harper, 1963
Pigeon pox	Webb, Bather & Hodges, 1963
Polio	Harper, 1963, 1965
Rous sarcoma	Webb, 1963b; Webb et al. 1963
Vaccinia	Harper, 1963, 1965
Venezuelan equine encephalomyelitis	Harper, 1963

ACKNOWLEDGEMENTS

We thank Dr C. E. Gordon Smith, Dr D. W. Henderson, F.R.S., and Mr I. H. Silver for advice during preparation of this article.

REFERENCES

ANDERSEN, A. A. (1958). New sampler for the collection, sizing and enumeration of viable airborne particles. *J. Bact.* **76**, 471.

ANDERSON, J. D. (1966). Biochemical studies of lethal processes in aerosols of *Escherichia coli. J. gen. Microbiol.* **15**, 303.

ANDERSON, J. D. & CROUCH, G. T. (1966). A new principle for the determination of total bacterial numbers in populations recovered from aerosols. *J. gen. Microbiol.* (in the Press).

ANDERSON, J. D. & DARK, F. A. (1966). Studies on the effects of aerosolization on the rates of efflux of ions from populations of *Escherichia coli* strain B. *J. gen. Microbiol.* (in the Press).

ANNEAR, D. I. (1962). Recoveries of bacteria after drying on cellulose fibres. A method for the routine preservation of bacteria. *Aust. J. exp. Biol. med. Sci.* **40**, 1.

BACHELOR, H. W. (1960). Aerosol samplers. *Adv. appl. Microbiol.* **2**, 31.

BATEMAN, J. B., McCAFFREY, P. A., O'CONNOR, R. J. & MONK, G. W. (1961). Relative humidity and the killing of bacteria. The survival of damp *Serratia marcescens* in air. *Appl. Microbiol.* **9**, 567.

BATEMAN, J. B., STEVENS, C. L., MERCER, W. B. & CARSTENSEN, E. L. (1962). Relative humidity and the killing of bacteria: the variation of cellular water content with external relative humidity or osmolality. *J. gen. Microbiol.* **29**, 207.

BEEBE, J. M. (1959). Stability of disseminated aerosols of *Pasteurella tularensis* subjected to simulated solar radiations at various humidities. *J. Bact.* **78**, 18.

BEEBE, J. M. & PIRSCH, G. W. (1958). Response of air-borne species of *Pasteurella* to artificial radiation simulating sunlight under different conditions of relative humidity. *Appl. Microbiol.* **6**, 127.

BENEDICT, R. G., SHARPE, E. S., CORMAN, J., MEYERS, G. B., BAER, E. F., HALL, H. H. & JACKSON, R. W. (1961). Preservation of microorganisms by freeze-drying. II. The destructive action of oxygen. Additional stabilizers for *Serratia marcescens*. Experiments with other organisms. *Appl. Microbiol.* **9**, 256.

BOLOTOVSKII, V. M. (1959). Necessary conditions for the successful production of experimental infection with Ornithosis virus aerosol. *Probl. Virol.* **4**, 103, *Biol. Abstr.* (1961), **36**, 7985.

BOYES-WATSON, J., DAVIDSON, E. & PERUTZ, M. F. (1947). An X-ray study of horse methaemoglobin. I. *Proc. R. Soc.* A, **191**, 83.

BRACHMAN, P. S., EHRLICH, R., EICHENWALD, H. F., GABELLI, V. J., KETHLEY, T. W., MADIN, S. H., MALTMAN, J. R., MIDDLEBROOK, G., MORTON, J. D., SILVER, I. H. & WOLFE, E. K. (1964). Standard sampler for assay of airborne microorganisms. *Science*, **144**, 1295.

BROWN, A. D. (1953 *a*). The survival of airborne microorganisms. I. Experiments near 0° with some psychrophilic bacteria. *Aust. J. biol. Sci.* **6**, 463.

BROWN, A. D. (1953 *b*). The survival of airborne microorganisms. II. Experiments with *Escherichia coli* near 0°. *Aust. J. biol. Sci.* **6**, 470.

BROWN, A. D. (1954). The survival of airborne microorganisms. III. Effects of temperature. *Aust. J. biol. Sci.* **7**, 444.

CABELLI, V. J. (1962). The rehydration of dried bacteria. *Bact. Proc.* p. 125.

COLLISON, W. E. (1935). *Inhalation Therapy Technique*. London: William Heinemann. (Medical Books.)

COX, C. S. (1965). Protecting agents and their mode of action. *1st Int. Symp. on Aerobiol.* p. 345. Published by Naval Biological Laboratory, Naval Supply Center, Oakland, California.

Cox, C. S. (1966 a). The survival of *Escherichia coli* atomized into air and into nitrogen from distilled water and from solutions of protecting agents, as a function of relative humidity. *J. gen. Microbiol.* **43**, 383.

Cox, C. S. (1966 b). The survival of *Escherichia coli* in nitrogen under changing conditions of relative humidity. *J. gen. Microbiol.* **45**, 283.

Cox, C. S. & Baldwin, F. (1964). A method for investigating the cause of death of airborne bacteria. *Nature, Lond.* **202**, 1135.

Cox, C. S. & Baldwin, F. (1966). The use of phage to study causes of loss of viability of *Escherichia coli* in aerosols. *J. gen. Microbiol.* **44**, 15.

Davis, M. S. & Bateman, J. B. (1960). Relative humidity and the killing of bacteria. I. Observations on *Escherichia coli* and *Micrococcus lysodeikticus.* *J. Bact.* **80**, 577.

DeOme *et al.* (and 20 others) (1944). The effect of temperature, humidity and glycol vapour on the viability of airborne bacteria. *Am. J. Hyg.* **40**, 239.

Dimmick, R. L. (1959). Jet disperser for compacted powders in the one to ten micron range. *Archs ind. Health*, **20**, 8.

Dimmick, R. L. (1960 a). Characteristics of dried *Serratia marcescens* in the airborne state. *J. Bact.* **80**, 289.

Dimmick, R. L. (1960 b). Measurement of the physical decay of aerosols by a light scatter method compared to a radioactive tracer method. *J. Hyg., Camb.* **58**, 373.

Dimmick, R. L. (1960 c). Delayed recovery of airborne *Serratia marcescens* after short-time exposure to ultraviolet irradiation. *Nature, Lond.* **187**, 251.

Dimmick, R. L., Heckley, R. S. & Hollis, D. P. (1961). Free-radicle formation during storage of freeze-dried *Serratia marcescens. Nature, Lond.* **192**, 776.

Dimmock, N. A. (1950). Production of uniform droplets. *Nature, Lond.* **166**, 686.

Druett, H. A. & May, K. R. (1952). A wind tunnel for the study of airborne infections. *J. Hyg., Camb.* **50**, 69.

Dunklin, E. W. & Puck, T. T. (1948). The lethal effects of relative humidity on air-borne bacteria. *J. exp. Med.* **87**, 87.

Ehrlich, R., Miller, S. & Idoine, L. S. (1964). Effect of environmental factors on the survival of airborne T-3 coliphage. *Appl. Microbiol.* **12**, 479.

Falk, M. (1964). The ultraviolet spectra of native and denatured deoxyribonucleic acid. *J. Am. chem. Soc.* **86**, 1226.

Falk, M., Hartman, Jr., K. A. & Lord, R. C. (1962). Hydration of deoxyribonucleic acid. I. A gravimetric study. *J. Am. chem. Soc.* **84**, 3843.

Falk, M., Hartman, Jr, K. A. & Lord, R. C. (1963 a). Hydration of deoxyribonucleic acid. II. An infra-red study. *J. Am. chem. Soc.* **85**, 387.

Falk, M., Hartman, Jr, K. A. & Lord, R. C. (1963 b). Hydration of deoxyribonucleic acid. III. A spectroscopic study of the effect of hydration on the structure of deoxyribonucleic acid. *J. Am. chem. Soc.* **85**, 391.

Ferry, R. M., Brown, W. F. & Damon, E. B. (1958 a). Studies of the loss of viability of stored bacterial aerosols. II. Death rate of several non-pathogenic organisms in relation to biological and structural characteristics. *J. Hyg., Camb.* **56**, 125.

Ferry, R. M., Brown, W. F. & Damon, E. B. (1958 b). Studies of the loss of viability of bacterial aerosols. III. Factors affecting death rates of certain non-pathogens. *J. Hyg., Camb.* **56**, 389.

Ferry, R. M., Farr, L. E., Rose, J. & Blau, M. R. (1951). A study of freshly generated aerosols of *Micrococcus candidus* and *Escherichia coli. J. infect. Dis.* **88**, 256.

Ferry, R. M. & Maple, T. G. (1954). Studies of the loss of viability of stored bacterial aerosols. I. *Micrococcus candidus. J. infect. Dis.* **95**, 142.

GEORGE, E. S., WARD, C. B. & CABELLI, V. J. (1965). The development of the multiple orifice impinger (MOI) as an answer to the problem of prolonged operation (aspiration) in the all glass impinger. *1st Int. Symp. on Aerobiol.* p. 201. Published by Naval Biological Laboratory, Naval Supply Center, Oakland, California.

GOLDBERG, L. J., WATKINS, H. M. S., BOERKE, E. E. & CHATIGNY, M. A. (1958). The use of a rotating drum for the study of aerosols over extended periods of time. *Am. J. Hyg.* **68**, 85.

GOODLOW, R. J. & LEONARD, F. A. (1961). Viability and infectivity of micro-organisms in experimental airborne infection. *Bact. Rev.* **25**, 182.

GREEN, H. L. & LANE, W. R. (1957). *Particulate Clouds: Dusts, Smokes, and Mists.* London: E. and F. N. Spon Ltd.

HARPER, G. J. (1961). Airborne microorganisms: survival tests with four viruses. *J. Hyg., Camb.* **59**, 479.

HARPER, G. J. (1963). The influence of environment on the survival of airborne virus particles in the laboratory. *Arch. ges. Virusforsch.* **13**, 64.

HARPER, G. J. (1965). Some observations on the influence of suspending fluids on the survival of airborne viruses. *1st Int. Symp. on Aerobiol.* p. 335. Published by Naval Biological Laboratory, Naval Supply Center, Oakland, California.

HARPER, G. J., HOOD, A. M. & MORTON, J. D. (1958). Airborne microorganisms: A technique for studying their survival. *J. Hyg., Camb.* **56**, 364.

HARPER, G. J. & MORTON, J. D. (1952). *Bacillus subtilis* spores labelled with radiophosphorus. *J. gen. Microbiol.* **7**, 98.

HARRIS, W. J. (1964). Device for producing droplet samples of suspensions for electron microscopy and especially for quantitative particle assay. *J. sci. Instrum.* **41**, 636.

HARSTAD, J. B. (1965). Sampling submicron T1 bacteriophage aerosols. *Appl. Microbiol.* **13**, 899.

HATCH, M. T. & DIMMICK, R. L. (1965). A study of dynamic aerosols of bacteria subjected to rapid changes in relative humidity. *1st Int. Symp. on Aerobiol.* p. 265. Published by Naval Biological Laboratory, Naval Supply Center, Oakland, California.

HAYAKAWA, I. & POON, C. P. (1965). Short storage studies on effects of temperature and relative humidity on the viability of airborne bacteria. *Am. ind. Hyg. Ass. J.* **26**, 150.

HAYES, D. K., BAMESBERGER, W. L. & CABELLI, V. J. (1965). The influence of storage, aerosolization and rehydration on the permeability of *Pasteurella tularensis* to phosphate ions. *1st Int. Symp. on Aerobiol.* p. 389. Published by Naval Biological Laboratory, Naval Supply Center, Oakland, California.

HEMMES, J. H., WINKLER, K. C. & KOOL, S. M. (1960). Virus survival as a seasonal factor in influenza and poliomyelitis. *Nature, Lond.* **188**, 430.

HENDERSON, D. W. (1952). An apparatus for the study of airborne infection. *J. Hyg., Camb.* **50**, 53.

HESS, G. E. (1965). Effects of oxygen on aerosolized *Serratia marcescens*. *Appl. Microbiol.* **13**, 781.

HOOD, A. M. (1961). Infectivity of *Pasteurella tularensis* clouds. *J. Hyg., Camb.* **59**, 497.

HOOD, A. M. (1963). Infectivity of influenza virus aerosols. *J. Hyg., Camb.* **61**, 331.

JENSEN, M. M. (1965). Inactivation of virus aerosols by ultraviolet light in a helical baffle chamber. *1st Int. Symp. on Aerobiol.* p. 219. Published by Naval Biological Laboratory, Naval Supply Center, Oakland, California.

KETHLEY, T. W., COWN, W. B. & FINCHER, E. L. (1957). The nature and composition of experimental bacterial aerosols. *Appl. Microbiol.* **5**, 1.

KETHLEY, T. W., FINCHER, E. L. & COWN, W. B. (1957). The effect of sampling method upon the apparent response of airborne bacteria to temperature and relative humidity. *J. infect. Dis.* **100**, 97.

KUEHNE, R. W. & DECKER, H. M. (1957). Studies on the continuous sampling of *Serratia marcescens* using a slit sampler. *Appl. Microbiol.* **5**, 321.

KUNDSIN, R. B. (1966). Characteristics of mycoplasma aerosols as to viability, particle size and lethality of ultraviolet irradiation. *J. Bact.* **91**, 942.

LANGER, G., PIERRARD, P. & YAMATE, G. (1964). Further development of an electrostatic classifier for submicron air-borne particles. *Int. J. Air Wat. Pollut.* **8**, 167.

LEACH, R. H. & SCOTT, W. J. (1959). The influence of rehydration on the viability of dried microorganisms. *J. gen. Microbiol.* **21**, 295.

LEE, R. E. & GARBETT, M. (1966). Carboxymethylcellulose ether media for cold-weather aerosol sampling. *Appl. Microbiol.* **14**, 133.

LESTER, W. (1948). The influence of relative humidity on the infectivity of airborne influenza A virus (PR8 strain). *J. exp. Med.* **88**, 361.

LEVIN, M. A. & CABELLI, V. J. (1963). Germination of spores as a consequence of aerosolization and collection. *Bact. Proc.* p. 26.

LION, M. B. (1963). Quantitative aspects of the protection of freeze-dried *Escherichia coli* against the toxic effect of oxygen. *J. gen. Microbiol.* **32**, 321.

LION, M. B. & BERGMANN, E. D. (1961a). The effect of oxygen on freeze-dried *Escherichia coli*. *J. gen. Microbiol.* **24**, 191.

LION, M. B. & BERGMANN, E. D. (1961b). Substances which protect lyophilized *Escherichia coli* against the lethal effect of oxygen. *J. gen. Microbiol.* **25**, 291.

LION, M. B., KIRBY-SMITH, J. S. & RANDOLPH, M. L. (1961). Electron spin resonance signals from lyophilized cells exposed to oxygen. *Nature, Lond.* **192**, 34.

LOOSLI, C. G., LEMON, H. M., ROBERTSON, O. H. & APPEL, E. (1943). Experimental airborne influenza infection. Influence of humidity on survival of virus in air. *Proc. Soc. exp. Biol. Med.* **53**, 205.

MALTMAN, J. R. (1965). Bacterial responses to desiccation and rehydration. *1st Int. Symp. on Aerobiol.* p. 291. Published by Naval Biological Laboratory, Naval Supply Center, Oakland, California.

MALTMAN, J. R., ORR, J. H. & HINTON, N. A. (1960). The effect of desiccation on *Staphylococcus pyogenes* with special reference to implications concerning virulence. *Am. J. Hyg.* **72**, 335.

MAY, K. R. (1949). An improved spinning top homogeneous spray apparatus. *J. appl. Phys.* **20**, 932.

MAY, K. R. (1964). Calibration of a modified Andersen bacterial aerosol sampler. *Appl. Microbiol.* **12**, 37.

MAY, K. R. & HARPER, G. J. (1957). The efficiency of various liquid impinger samplers in bacterial aerosols. *Br. J. ind. Med.* **14**, 287.

MAZUR, P. & WESTON, W. H. (1955). Effects of spray drying on the viability of fungous spores. *J. Bact.* **71**, 257.

MCDADE, J. J. & HALL, L. B. (1963). An experimental method to measure the influence of environmental factors on the viability and pathogenicity of *Staphylococcus aureus*. *Am. J. Hyg.* **77**, 98.

MCDADE, J. J. & HALL, L. B. (1964). Survival of Gram-negative bacteria in the environment. I. The effect of relative humidity on surface exposed organisms. *Am. J. Hyg.* **80**, 192.

MILLER, W. S., SCHERFF, R. A., PIEPOLI, C. R. & IDOINE, L. S. (1961). Physical tracers for bacterial aerosols. *Appl. Microbiol.* **9**, 248.

MONACI, V. (1952). Studies on air disinfections with ultraviolet rays. *Boll. Ist. sieroter. milan.* **31**, 301, *Biol. Abstr.* (1954), **28**, 16590.

MONK, G. W., ELBERT, M. L., STEVENS, C. L. & McCAFFREY, P. A. (1956). The effect of water on the death rate of *Serratia marcescens*. *J. Bact.* **72**, 368.

MONK, G. W. & MATTUCK, R. D. (1956). Biological cloud dynamics. *Bull. math. Biophys.* **18**, 57.

MONK, G. W. & McCAFFREY, P. A. (1957). Effect of sorbed water on the death rate of washed *Serratia marcescens*. *J. Bact.* **73**, 85.

MONK, G. W., McCAFFREY, P. A. & DAVIS, M. S. (1957). Studies on the mechanism of sorbed water killing of bacteria. *J. Bact.* **73**, 661.

MORRIS, E. J., DARLOW, H. M., PEEL, J. F. H. & WRIGHT, W. C. (1961). The quantitative assay of mono-dispersed aerosols of bacteria and bacteriophage by electrostatic precipitation. *J. Hyg., Camb.* **59**, 487.

MUROMTSEV, S. N. & NENASHEV, V. P. (1960). The study of aerosols. III. An ultrasonic aerosol atomizer. *Zh. Microbiol. Immunobiol.* **31**, 50, *Biol. Abstr.* (1962), **37**, 6505.

POSTGATE, J. R., CRUMPTON, J. E. & HUNTER, J. R. (1961). The measurement of bacterial viabilities by slide culture. *J. gen. Microbiol.* **24**, 15.

RECORD, B. R., TAYLOR, R. & MILLER, D. S. (1962). The survival of *Escherichia coli* on drying and rehydration. *J. gen. Microbiol.* **28**, 585.

RICH, A. & WATSON, J. D. (1954). Some relations between R.N.A. and D.N.A. *Proc. natn. Acad. Sci. U.S.A.* **40**, 759.

ROSEBURY, T. (1947). *Experimental Airborne Infection*. Baltimore: Williams and Wilkins Co.

ROUNTREE, P. M. (1963). The effect of desiccation on the viability of *Staphylococcus aureus*. *J. Hyg., Camb.* **61**, 265.

SCOTT, W. J. (1958). The effect of residual water on the survival of dried bacteria during storage. *J. gen. Microbiol.* **19**, 624.

SHECHMEISTER, I. L. (1950). Studies on the experimental epidemiology of respiratory infections. III. Certain aspects of the behaviour of type A influenza virus as an air-borne cloud. *J. infect. Dis.* **87**, 128.

SHECHMEISTER, I. L. & GOLDBERG, L. J. (1950). Studies on the experimental epidemiology of respiratory infections. II. Observations on the behaviour of aerosols of *Streptococcus zooepidermicus*. *J. infect. Dis.* **87**, 117.

SILVER, I. H. (1965). Viability of microbes using a suspended droplet technique. *1st Int. Symp. on Aerobiol.* p. 319. Published by Naval Biological Laboratory, Naval Supply Center, Oakland, California.

VLODAVETS, V. V. (1964). Dynamics of the bacterial aerosol in dust and drop phases. *Mikrobiologiya*, **33**, 91.

VLODAVETS, V. V., ZUIKOVA, E. I. & MOTOVA, M. A. (1958). A comparative evaluation of the methods of bacteriologic investigation of air at negative temperatures. *Microbiologiya*, **27**, 632, *Biol. Abstr.* (1959), **34**, 13,726.

WALTON, W. H. & PREWITT, W. C. (1949). The production of sprays and mists of uniform drop size by means of spinning disc type sprayers. *Proc. phys. Soc.* **62**B, 341.

WATKINS, H. M. S., GOLDBERG, L. J., DEIG, E. F. & LEIF, W. R. (1965). Behavior of Colorado tick fever, vesicular stomatitis, neurovaccinia and equine encephalomyocarditis viruses in the airborne state. *1st Int. Symp. on Aerobiol.* p. 381. Published by Naval Biological Laboratory, Naval Supply Center, Oakland, California.

WEBB, S. J. (1959a). Chloramphenicol and the survival of airborne bacteria. *Nature, Lond.* **183**, 1072.

WEBB, S. J. (1959b). Factors affecting the viability of airborne bacteria. I. Bacteria aerosolized from distilled water. *Can. J. Microbiol.* **5**, 649.

WEBB, S. J. (1960a). Factors affecting the viability of air-borne bacteria. II. The effect of chemical additives on the behaviour of air-borne cells. *Can. J. Microbiol.* **6**, 71.

WEBB, S. J. (1960b). Factors affecting the viability of air-borne bacteria. III. The role of bonded water and protein structure in the death of air-borne cells. *Can. J. Microbiol.* **6**, 89.

WEBB, S. J. (1961a). Factors affecting the viability of air-borne bacteria. IV. The inactivation and reactivation of air-borne *Serratia marcescens* by ultraviolet and visible light. *Can. J. Microbiol.* **7**, 607.

WEBB, S. J. (1961b). Factors affecting the viability of airborne bacteria. V. The effect of desiccation on some metabolic systems of *Escherichia coli*. *Can. J. Microbiol.* **7**, 621.

WEBB, S. J. (1963a). The effect of relative humidity and light on air-dried organisms. *J. appl. Bact.* **26**, 307.

WEBB, S. J. (1963b). Possible role of water and inositol in the structure of nucleoproteins. *Nature, Lond.* **198**, 785.

WEBB, S. J. (1963c). Factors affecting the viability of airborne bacteria. VII. The relationship between the structure of chemical additives and their action on airborne cells. *Can. J. Biochem. Physiol.* **41**, 867.

WEBB, S. J. (1964). Bound water, metabolites and genetic continuity. *Nature, Lond.* **203**, 374.

WEBB, S. J. (1965a). *Bound Water in Biological Integrity*. Springfield, Illinois: Charles C. Thomas.

WEBB, S. J. (1965b). Radiation, relative humidity and the mechanism of microbial death in aerosols. *1st Int. Symp. on Aerobiol.* p. 369. Published by Naval Biological Laboratory, Naval Supply Center, Oakland, California.

WEBB, S. J., BATHER, R. & HODGES, R. W. (1963). The effect of relative humidity and inositol on air-borne viruses. *Can. J. Microbiol.* **9**, 87.

WEBB, S. J., CORMACK, D. V. & MORRISON, H. G. (1964). Relative humidity, inositol and the effect of radiation on air-dried microorganisms. *Nature, Lond.* **201**, 1103.

WEBB, S. J. & DUMASIA, M. D. (1964). Bound water, inositol and the effect of X-rays on *Escherichia coli*. *Can. J. Microbiol.* **10**, 877.

WEBB, S. J., DUMASIA, M. D. & SINGH BHORJEE, J. (1965). Bound water, inositol and the biosynthesis of temperate and virulent bacteriophages by air-dried *Escherichia coli*. *Can. J. Microbiol.* **11**, 141.

WELLS, W. F. (1955). *Airborne Contagion and Air Hygiene*. Cambridge, Massachusetts: Harvard University Press.

WELLS, W. F. & ZAPPOSODI, P. (1942). The effect of humidity on β Streptococci (group C) atomized into air. *Science*, **96**, 277.

WILLIAMSON, A. E. & GOTAAS, H. B. (1942). Aerosol sterilization of airborne bacteria. *Ind. Med. Surg.* **11**, *Ind. Hygiene Section*, **3**, Section **1**, 40.

WOLF, H. W., SKALIY, P., HALL, L. B., HARRIS, M. M., DECKER, H. M., BUCHANAN, L. M. & DAHLGREN, C. M. (1959). Sampling microbiological aerosols. *Publ. Hlth Serv. Publs, Wash.* no. 60.

WOLF, W. R. (1961). Study of the vibrating reed in the production of small droplets and solid particles of uniform size. *Rev. sci. Instrum.* **32**, 1124.

WOLFE, E. K. (1961). Quantitative characterisation of aerosols. *Bact. Rev.* **25**, 194.

WRIGHT, B. M. (1949). A new dust feed mechanism. *J. sci. Instrum.* **27**, 12.

ZENTNER, R. J. (1961). Techniques of aerosol formation. *Bact. Rev.* **25**, 188.

ZIMMERMAN, L. (1962). Survival of *Serratia marcescens* after freeze-drying or aerosolization at unfavourable humidity. I. Effects of sugars. *J. Bact.* **84**, 1297.

ZIMMERMAN, L. (1965). Additives to increase aerosol stability. *1st Int. Symp. on Aerobiol.* p. 285. Published by Naval Biological Laboratory, Naval Supply Center, Oakland, California.

SPREAD OF PLANT PATHOGENS IN SPACE AND TIME

J. E. VAN DER PLANK

Plant Protection Research Institute, Pretoria, South Africa

INTRODUCTION

Before we consider the spread of a pathogen in space and time, some preliminary comments are needed on two topics: (1) spread in relation to a great number of factors associated with the host plants, the pathogen itself, and the environment; and (2) definitions of spread and dispersal.

The spread of a pathogen in relation to the disease triangle: host, pathogen and environment

How do pathogens spread?

Consider a foliage disease of an annual crop. Suppose it is caused by a spore-forming fungus. A spore settles on a healthy leaf and germinates. Mycelium grows through the leaf tissue, and after a while begins to form spores. The spores disperse and settle on other leaves, where they germinate. The mycelium grows through the leaf tissue, and after a while begins to form a new generation of spores. And so the process continues, sometimes for many generations.

Suppose conditions favour infection and disease. The variety of the host plants is susceptible. The pathogen is virulent. The weather is 'disease weather': it is wet, if wetness favours the disease; it is warm, if warmth favours the disease. Because conditions favour disease, an epidemic starts. The fungus increases fast. It spreads from field to field, from plant to plant, and from leaf to leaf. Eventually, in a severe epidemic, it reaches almost every leaf of every plant of every field in the epidemic area.

But suppose that, at the other extreme, circumstances are so unfavourable to disease that the threshold condition for an epidemic is not met. There will be practically no spread of the pathogen at all.

Conditions that favour disease favour the spread of the pathogen. Consider two examples.

Puccinia graminis tritici, the cause of stem rust, spreads in a few months from the wheat fields of Texas northwards to those of the Canadian prairies. The fungus cannot survive the northern winters (except on barberry bushes which do not enter our story); but in epidemic years it spreads northward in amounts enough to devastate the fields of spring wheat on both sides of the Canadian border.

Stakman & Harrar (1957) have described what happened in 1935. *Puccinia graminis tritici* survived the winter of 1934/35 in Texas in a relatively small area. There was very little rust in early spring, and no portent then of the great epidemic to come. But the spring was late and May very wet—the rainfall in northern Texas was more than twice the normal. Rust developed quickly. Spores were blown northward, and encountered very favourable conditions for rust development in the late crops of Kansas and Nebraska. Farther north too, in the southern part of the spring-wheat area of Minnesota and neighbouring States, circumstances favoured rust. Cold, wet weather in May and June had delayed the wheat crop and made it late. The first half of July was still wet—abnormally wet—but hot; and the stands were heavy. Into these heavy stands great masses of spores were blown from Kansas and Nebraska. Rust developed quickly, and by 5 July the epidemic was on its way. It destroyed 135 million bushels of wheat in Minnesota, South Dakota and North Dakota alone.

The conditions that favoured the spread of the pathogen in 1935 were thus varied: late springs, delayed crops, abnormally high rainfall, dense stands, warm weather in the spring-wheat area at the critical time, and opportune south winds. To this list we must also add a very susceptible spring-wheat variety, Ceres, which faded into history as a result of the 1935 epidemic, and a virulent race of the fungus, race 56, which first reached devastating proportions that year.

Our other example is *Phytophthora infestans*, the cause of blight in potato crops. This fungus survives the winter in diseased tubers. The quantity that survives is relatively small, but in 'blight weather' in summer the fungus spreads fast from leaf to leaf, plant to plant, and field to field. Many countries now have a warning service, to tell farmers when they must spray with fungicides and curb the spread of the fungus. Mainly, warnings are based on records of temperature and humidity or rainfall; details vary locally, but in essence the selected criteria indicate that leaves will stay warm and wet long enough for infection. In addition, the age of the crop, how far the canopy has developed in the fields, and the susceptibility of the variety are factors often also taken into account.

Those then are the usual limiting factors in the spread of *P. infestans*.

In Britain *P. infestans*, if unchecked by fungicides, spreads to most susceptible plants and fields sooner or later almost every year. But in many countries blight appears only occasionally over the years. The pathogen is commonly stopped from spreading by dry weather, and many fields remain free from blight.

What holds for *Puccinia graminis* and *Phytophthora infestans* holds for every plant pathogen: conditions that favour disease favour the spread of the pathogen. Both *Puccinia graminis* and *Phytophthora infestans* are spore-forming fungi that primarily infect stems and leaves. But those are details which are irrelevant to the general thesis: whatever promotes disease promotes the spread of the pathogen, whether the pathogen be a fungus, bacterium or virus, however it reproduces itself, whatever parts of the host plant it attacks, in short, whatever its properties may be.

Consider now more closely the various factors involved in promoting disease and the spread of the pathogen. There is a multiplicity of them, some associated with the host plants, some with the pathogen, some with the environment, some with the host plants and the pathogen and the environment together, some perhaps acting singly but many interacting with one another. Here are a few examples. The host plants may be susceptible, because they belong to a genetically susceptible cultivar, because they are of an age that makes them susceptible, or because their nutrition makes them susceptible. The plants may form a dense canopy, which makes the ecoclimate dank and temperatures even. The plants may be hairy or have cupped leaves or other features that cause water to be trapped and so suit water-loving pathogens. The pathogen may be of a virulent race, and specially adapted to the environment. Its spores may be of a size and shape that allow efficient dispersal. The environment may favour disease. Temperatures and humidities may be optimal. The soil may be wet or dry, cold or hot, acid or alkaline, sandy or clayey, rich or poor in organic residues, whatever favours the particular disease. Cultivation may be semi-urban and in smallholdings, which encourages diseases such as wart disease of potatoes. It is doubtful whether it will ever be possible to name all the factors; deeper delving is likely always to unearth new ones.

To avoid naming separate factors and to emphasize that factors act and interact in great numbers, it is convenient to refer to the disease triangle: host, pathogen and environment.

The spread of a pathogen depends on the disease triangle.

Spread and dispersal

We distinguish sharply between spread and dispersal.

As we define *spread*, a pathogen spreads where it goes and infects. The whole disease triangle is involved, and the spread during any given time may involve a succession of generations. Thus when we say that *Peronospora tabacina*, the cause of blue mould in tobacco, spread in a few years from its point of escape in Western Europe to Asia and North Africa, we do not imply that a few spores escaped and, in a single act of dispersal, crossed Europe and the Mediterranean. We imply only that conditions were suitable for disease—there were susceptible host plants, the climate permitted infection, and so on—and the pathogen made its way by means of an unspecified number of acts of dispersal until it reached Asia and North Africa.

But spread has not only a geographical sense. One can also talk, for example, of *Puccinia graminis* spreading over the stems of wheat plants.

Dispersal (to consider just spores for a start) is here defined as the process from take-off to deposition. It does not include spore formation at the one end or spore germination at the other. This meaning is clear from the fact that spores of mosses and puffballs, not pathogenic to plants, have been used to study dispersal, and that deposition has been studied on sticky cylinders of glass or other inorganic material. (It well illustrates the difference between dispersal and spread, as defined here, that although moss spores and sticky glass cylinders are useful and apt tools for studying dispersal they are inept for studying spread apart from the constituent process of dispersal).

More generally, and not just for spores in particular, dispersal is the movement of propagules from a lesion to healthy, susceptible tissue, if the pathogen causes local lesions, or from infected plants to healthy susceptible plants, if the pathogen infects systemically. This definition covers most dispersal by fungi, bacteria and viruses, with or without vectors. But special cases demand elaboration. The pathogen of wart disease of potatoes is carried by man in infected tubers—this is only one of the several ways it disperses—and to cover dispersal in tubers we would have to think in terms of movement from infected rooted (or stationary) plants to healthy rooted plants. To cover the dispersal of *Penicillium italicum* between oranges packed in cases on a moving train, we would have to elaborate still further. But we need not concern ourselves overmuch with elaborations here.

THE SPREAD OF THE PATHOGEN IN SPACE

Following the order in the title we proceed to discuss spread in space, and leave spread in time to the next section.

The most conspicuous feature of spread in space is that it is not uniform. As the pathogen spreads from plant to plant and field to field it leaves an irregular pattern of disease, with more disease in some areas than others. The pattern is associated largely with different mechanisms of dispersal; and diversity in dispersal is a common feature of pathogens. We shall use *Phytophthora infestans* as an example most of the time; the spread of other fungi may differ in detail, but not, it seems from the general literature, in broad pattern.

Foci are local areas of higher than average disease. To give in full the definition adopted by the British Mycological Society (Anonymous, 1953), a focus is the site of local concentrations of diseased plants or disease lesions, either about a primary source of infection or coinciding with an area originally favourable to establishment, and tending to influence the pattern of further transmission of disease.

The uneven distribution of disease has long been known from observations on the ground, and now photography from the air is making the patterns clearer.

Foci of potato blight caused by Phytophthora infestans

Plate 1 is reproduced from a paper by Brenchley & Dadd (1962). It is an infra-red photograph of blight in crops of potatoes. It was taken on 16 July. On the lower right is a focus, probably the initial focus, which had been discovered on 4 July, when it was already 2 yd. in diameter. By 16 July, there were a number of daughter (and, perhaps, grand-daughter) foci in the field and in a field to the north above a strip of wheat about 60 yd. wide. On the evidence this spread to establish daughter foci had occurred on 8 June when the wind was in the right quarter and the temperature and humidity was favourable. The photograph gives the picture after blight was established and had begun to spread but before it became general and obscured the pattern of its spread.

There are two features of this pattern which need comment.

Phytophthora infestans was not uniformly distributed through the fields, but occurred in foci. The foci stand out fairly clearly against the background of the rest of the field.

The daughter foci are not markedly clustered near the initial focus. They are well dispersed through the crops. (We accept here the evidence that what we call the initial focus was indeed the initial focus and the parent of the other foci. The search for initial foci has been continued (Brenchley, 1964), and the feature now being discussed—that daughter foci are not closely clustered about the parent focus—is general.)

These features tell us that *P. infestans* disperses in at least two ways. It disperses along a steep gradient; disease decreases quickly as distance from the source of inoculum increases. In this way it enlarges existing foci. It also disperses along a shallow gradient; disease decreases slowly as distance from the source increases. In this way it establishes new foci. And it disperses much more often along a steep than a shallow gradient.

Let us consider how *P. infestans* disperses in more detail.

Observed dispersal of Phytophthora infestans along steep gradients from the source of the inoculum

Figure 1 analyses various records of potato blight. It shows the amount of disease at various distances from the source of the inoculum. Limasset's (1939) data, shown in curves 1 and 2, were taken from Gregory (1945). The data of Bonde & Schultz (1943) were for a field about 100 ft. away from a diseased pile of culled potatoes, which was the source of inoculum for the field. Blight was found in the pile on 12 June and was general through the pile by 25 June. The readings in the field, on which curve 3 is based, were made on 12 July. It is possible that there had been some secondary dispersal before then, so the gradient, steep as it is, may underestimate the true steepness. Waggoner's (1952) results shown in curve 4 are for *Phytophthora infestans* dispersed from a focus established 9 days previously by artificial inoculation; and those shown in curve 5 are for the gradient as it existed a further 9 days later. Curve 3 was drawn from actual records of the number of lesions per 100 plants. The other curves were compiled from data to which the multiple-infection transformation (Gregory, 1948) had to be applied. It is known that in practice this transformation invariably under-corrects, especially at high proportions of disease, so that the true gradients were probably even steeper than they are represented to be in Fig. 1.

The sources of *P. infestans* in these experiments are regarded as point sources. It is assumed, possibly somewhat wrongly for curve 3, that there was no secondary spread—no second generation of the fungus—from lesions along the gradient established from the initial point source. In this way we can equate the spread of disease with the dispersal of propagules, and assume that the disease gradients in Fig. 1 tell how *P. infestans* dispersed.

Curve *A*, added to Fig. 1, shows a gradient in which disease varies inversely as the fifth power of distance from the source of inoculum. This is a very steep gradient. Yet as far as any single straight line can do, it gives a fair representation of the steepness of the five experimental curves in Fig. 1 at the low levels of disease which are the most relevant to our discussion.

To Fig. 1 we have also added two curves, marked G, to represent Gregory's (1945) equation for dispersal under conditions of low atmospheric turbulence. For convenience we have kept to the parameters that Gregory himself used.

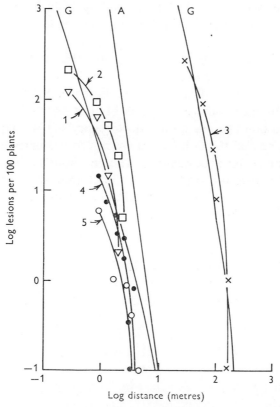

Fig. 1. Amount of potato blight caused by *Phytophthora infestans* at varying distances from the source of inoculum. Curves 1 and 2 are from Limasset (1939); curve 3 from Bonde & Schultz (1943); and curves 4 and 5 from Waggoner (1952). Curve A is for disease varying inversely as the fifth power of distance. The curves marked G are calculated from Gregory's (1945) equation for dispersal in conditions of low turbulence.

Two G curves are drawn, for this reason: Gregory's equations demand that the gradient varies with distance from the source, and not with the amount of inoculum (and hence the amount of disease). As the distance increases, the gradient becomes steeper. This being so, one can draw a series of G lines, which increase in steepness as the distance from the source increases. But in Fig. 1 the observations are so grouped that two G lines are enough for the purpose of reference.

The five experimental curves in Fig. 1 are reasonably consistent.

At high levels of disease they are less steep than the G lines. One must not attach too much importance to this difference. In curves 1, 2, 4 and 5 at least some of this difference must be due to the inevitable under-correction by the multiple-infection transformation. As to curve 3, it is not unlikely that there had been some secondary spread in the field before Bonde and Schultz took their readings, which could explain the difference between curve 3 and the corresponding G line at high disease levels.

At low levels of disease—the levels more relevant to our narrative—the experimental curves are steeper than the G lines. Here too one must not attach too much significance to the difference. Steeper G lines could be obtained by using other, and probably just as realistic, parameters.

There is no point to our doing so. Gregory's (1945) equations have been introduced and the G lines drawn, not to evaluate their accuracy, but as a vehicle for a calculation we are about to make. For this calculation it is relevant to know that the G lines, steep as they are, do not exaggerate the actual steepness so far as we can ascertain it from five experimental sets of observations.

Dispersal along a very steep gradient can enlarge existing foci. And the steepness means that the foci stand out clearly defined against the background of the rest of the field. The steeper the gradient, the clearer is the definition. But dispersal along a very steep gradient cannot easily start daughter foci widely separate from their parents.

The dispersal of Phytophthora infestans along shallow gradients

First consider negative evidence that *Phytophthora infestans* disperses along shallow as well as steep gradients. This evidence is that steep gradients, such as those shown in Fig. 1, cannot explain the observed pattern on which foci occur.

As an example, take the first blight outbreak photographed by Brenchley (1964): an outbreak near Lakenheath, west Suffolk. A blighted dump of potatoes in a ditch separating two fields of King Edward potatoes started it. From this focus, four new foci were established, as daughter and granddaughter foci, at different dates before 27 July. They were 30, 150, 25 and 40 yd. from their respective sources, all in an apparently uniform field. There were no other sources of blight in the neighbourhood. (In the whole survey area of 70 square miles only seven outbreak centres were found. Outbreak centres were rare, which tallies with the general literature.)

The problem is this: there were four new foci, 30, 150, 25 and 40 yd.

and no nearer the sources of infection. What is the probability of this occurring on Gregory's equations for low-turbulence dispersal, exemplified by the G lines in Fig. 1? The answer is, less than 10^{-8}. (For this calculation we assume the field was uniform; the parent foci were circular and 2 m. in diameter when the spores were dispersed; and the spores came from the centre of the foci. These assumptions are probably realistic enough.) If one allows for the observation that, at the low levels of disease relevant to a lesion starting far from any other, the gradients in Fig. 1 were still steeper than the G lines, the real probability is even less.

Clearly, steep gradients, which mean sharp edges to foci, are the antithesis of stray daughter foci all far from these edges. For such daughter foci to start, shallow gradients are necessary.

There is other evidence for shallow gradients. *P. infestans* is known to disperse far. Schrödter (1960) summarized evidence in the literature about this, and quoted observations by various workers which suggest that sporangia of *P. infestans* have a flight range of more than 60 km.

Schrödter's purpose in summarizing this evidence was to support his equations on the effect of various conditions of wind and turbulence on dispersal. His equations demand very shallow gradients of disease: gradients less steep than those in which disease varies inversely as the square of the distance from the source of propagules. What concerns us here is that these shallow gradients could well establish daughter foci far from the parent, because there would be no horizon to the distance propagules could disperse (Van der Plank, 1960).

Schrödter's are not the only equations compatible with foci formed far from the parent. Gregory's, too, both as he originally derived them (Gregory, 1945) and later presented them (Gregory, 1961), provide for shallow gradients given appropriate parameters.

The comparative rarity of dispersal along shallow gradients to start new foci

Phytophthora infestans disperses along steep gradients to enlarge existing foci without destroying their identity as foci. It disperses along shallow gradients to start new foci. What is the relative frequency of these two methods?

If we assume that each daughter focus starts from a single lesion, the average number of lesions in a focus is also the ratio of the number of acts of infection which enlarge existing foci to the number which start new foci. There may be up to 1,000 lesions on a single, heavily infected plant, and many infected plants in a single focus, so we infer that dispersal along a shallow gradient to start a new focus is a relatively rare act.

This relative rarity does not make the act any less important in the spread of *P. infestans.*

Diversity the key to the dispersal of Phytophthora infestans

Purely to emphasize the contrast, I have talked as though *Phytophthora infestans* disperses along only two gradients: one steep to enlarge old lesions, one shallow to start new lesions. This oversimplifies the picture.

P. infestans disperses in many ways. Sporangia are carried by water. They are carried in air. These statements are themselves oversimplifications. As regards dispersal in water, propagules may be carried by dew on a still night. They may be splashed about by sprinkler irrigation on a calm day. They may be carried in driving rain in a gale. As regards dispersal by air, Hirst (1958) trapped sporangia in the morning, noon and afternoon (usually with a peak near noon), on wet days and on days without rain; to choose just one factor, the turbulence of the air must have varied greatly and the gradient with it. And air and water are not the only agents. One of Brenchley & Dadd's (1962) aerial photographs shows blight strongly developed along wheelings made by the sprayer. *P. infestans* is regularly carried from Scotland to South Africa in diseased seed potatoes. . . .

Many different gradients are possible, perhaps an infinitude of them, some steep, some shallow, some intermediate. And with them are many focal patterns. Foci can be nearly round or irregular with clear edges; or vaguely defined, widely scattered or clustered. There is no typical gradient, typical focus or typical distribution of foci. We can select data or photographs to illustrate some particular point; but we cannot call them typical. All that is typical of the patterns we know is their diversity.

Foci when the epidemic has advanced far

Large, conspicuous foci are common early in an epidemic. Later, when disease becomes general it appears more uniformly distributed; foci are then inconspicuous, small and overlapping. But there is no reason to believe that dispersal has changed in essentials—though it may change in many details, as when increasing disease opens up the foliage, changes the ecoclimate, and allows freer movement of the air—or become less diverse.

Comment about some other pathogens

What has been said about *Phytophthora infestans* holds for many other pathogens: they disperse in diverse ways and produce foci of various patterns.

Among the first to connect a particular pattern of foci with diverse ways of dispersion were Heald & Studhalter (1914). *Endothia parasitica* destroyed most of the indigenous chestnut trees of the eastern United States. There was an advance of the epidemic along a broad front. In addition there were 'spot' infections—new foci—miles ahead of the main front. Heald & Studhalter, and Leach (1940) ascribed the new distant foci to sticky pycnospores carried on the beaks of migratory birds. Closer dispersal was ascribed to airborne ascospores which the fungus produces abundantly.

Rust of coffee is caused by the fungus *Hemileia vastatrix*. Nutman, Roberts & Bock (1960) showed that uredospores are dispersed by rain splash, but only over short distances. Yet there has long been evidence that *H. vastatrix* does in fact also disperse far. Although it has no other host than coffee, it soon appears in new plantations grown from seed, far from any other coffee. Crowe (1963) has given evidence, necessarily circumstantial but nevertheless convincing, that distant dispersal is by insects. The larvae of two species of midge eat the spores of *H. vastatrix* in the rust pustules. In turn, the larvae are parasitized by two species of Hymenoptera which Crowe regards as vectors of the fungus. When rust is abundant, so are the midge larvae and their winged parasites. Crowe trapped parasites away from infected coffee and found spores of *H. vastatrix* on them.

For the third and last example we shall consider a virus. Swollen shoot disease of cacao is caused by a virus transmitted by mealy bugs. Workers agree that vectors crawling through the canopy enlarge existing foci, and that vectors blown by wind start daughter foci.

What we wish these examples to show—and many more could be quoted—is that pathogens commonly disperse in more than one way. Diversity characterizes dispersal.

THE SPREAD OF THE PATHOGEN IN SPACE AND TIME

We have been concerned with the pattern of disease in space, with only passing allusion to the effect of time: to changes in disease between successive dates. Bringing in time means bringing in the rate of spread of disease; and we shall now be concerned primarily with rates.

We shall consider the rate of spread of the pathogen as being practically the same as the rate of increase of disease. Consider an example.

The increase of potato blight and the spread of Phytophthora infestans

Figure 2 shows the spread of *Phytophthora infestans* through fields of the potato variety Bintje in the sand areas of the Netherlands in 1953 (Anonymous, 1954). A field was taken to be infected as soon as any blight, however little, was found there. We are here considering just spread over a wider area, fields being the units of area.

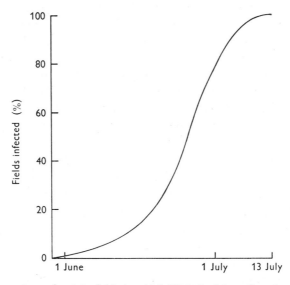

Fig. 2. The percentage of potato fields in which blight had been found at various dates. The data are for the variety Bintje in the sand areas of the Netherlands in 1953 (Anonymous, 1954).

Blight was first noticed—the first field was recorded as infected—at the end of May. By the middle of July, blight had been found in all fields. *P. infestans* took about 1½ months to spread to all the fields.

Figure 3 continues the story of the same disease in the same fields in the same year. But now the increase of disease and the spread of the pathogen are followed by expressing diseased foliage as a percentage of the total foliage. Here we take the spread of the pathogen to be not just from field to field, but also from plant to plant in the same field and from leaf (or stem) to leaf (or stem) of the same plant.

Note the difference in dates between Figs. 2 and 3. Figure 2 starts at the end of May when the first field was found infected. There was presumably little disease in that field, and none in the others, so the overall percentage of disease was then very small: too small to be recorded in Fig. 3. (We could, of course, have recorded disease early in the epidemic if we had used a logarithmic scale.) The last field found infected was in the middle of July. But this field and many others were then still only lightly infected. It was not until the beginning of August that disease in all fields was practically complete. In other words, it was not until the beginning of August that *P. infestans* practically stopped spreading in the fields of Bintje potatoes in the sand areas of the Netherlands in 1953.

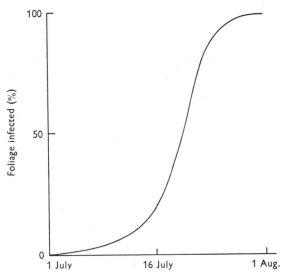

Fig. 3. The increase of blight in potato fields of the variety Bintje in the sand areas of the Netherlands in 1953 (Anonymous, 1954).

Figure 3 rather than Fig. 2 indicates what we mean by the spread of the pathogen: it is the spread from field to field, from plant to plant, and from one part of a plant to another throughout its whole susceptible tissue. Wherever a new lesion appears, whether on the same plant as its source or in some other field, there the pathogen has spread. This spread is practically indistinguishable from the increase of blight.

Further, to turn to rates, the rate of spread of the pathogen is also practically the same as the rate of increase of disease. The increase of disease between successive dates in Fig. 3 measures not only the rate of increase of disease but also the rate of spread of *P. infestans*.

The spread of the pathogen and the number of acts of dispersal

Figure 3 shows the spread of *Phytophthora infestans* through fields of potatoes. It does not record the countless acts of dispersal that made this spread possible.

Dispersal is the only process in spread that, like spread itself, is concerned with the movement of the pathogen.

Dispersal provides the motion in spread. But fast spread does not mean longer motions or faster motions; it means more motions. The difference between an epidemic season and a season of little disease is essentially that in the epidemic season there are many more acts of dispersal.

When we say that in an epidemic season there are more acts of dispersal, we are in fact discussing a rate, with the season as the unit of time: more acts per season. We could also talk of more acts of dispersal per month (or per week or per day) during an epidemic, if this were more convenient.

Our thesis then is that fast spread of the pathogen means frequent acts of dispersal. Consider two diseases.

P. infestans spreads faster in a very susceptible variety. The manifestations of susceptibility have been studied by many workers. The lesions sporulate more freely and for a longer time. The proportion of spores that manage to start new lesions is greater. The period needed before newly infected tissue can start sporulating is less. All these manifestations lead to more frequent acts of dispersal, increased sporulation directly, the other manifestations indirectly. But the manifestations do not affect the act of dispersal itself: how the propagules move.

Further, to leave the factor of susceptible varieties, there is at least some evidence that fast spread of *P. infestans* can at times be associated with shorter than usual acts of dispersal (but of course more of them). Hirst & Stedman (1960) found that blight increases fastest in fields when the rows close up and the canopy becomes close and dense. Because lesions are almost all below the canopy, we infer that *P. infestans* spreads fastest while individual acts of dispersal are most restricted. But because the relative humidity under the dense canopy is higher than in fields with open rows, sporulation is greater and a higher proportion of spores are able to infect: there are therefore more acts of dispersal.

Consider now *Puccinia graminis*. Uredospores blown long distances by winds along the wheat belt from Texas to the red spring-wheat areas have been carefully studied. The results have shown the importance of long-distance dispersal; short-distance dispersal, on the other hand, has had much less attention.

Consider the two years 1925 and 1935. The stem rust epidemics in both these years have been described by Stakman & Harrar (1957). Both were years of widespread, long-distance dispersal—classic text-book examples of how far this pathogen can disperse. In the first few days of June 1925 uredospores of *P. graminis* dispersed over a vast rust-free area 600 miles long and more than 400 miles broad: a quarter of a million square miles. In 1935 uredospores dispersed from northern Texas 350 miles northward to Kansas and Nebraska, with a later extension of 360 miles to the southern part of the spring-wheat area.

There the similarity between 1925 and 1935 ends. 1935 was the year of a great epidemic that destroyed 135 million bushels of grain in Minnesota, South Dakota and North Dakota (Stakman & Harrar, 1957). 1925 was a year of relatively mild losses, totalling about 12 million bushels in Minnesota, South Dakota, North Dakota and the other ten States of the barberry-eradication area (Stakman & Fletcher, 1930), despite the fact that there were still many millions of barberry bushes left in 1925.

The purpose of this comparison is not to belittle long-distance dispersal; obviously, it is important. But if we look for reasons why 1935 differed so much from 1925, we shall not find the difference in long-distance dispersal. We shall find it in the untold millions of acts of short-distance dispersal made possible by the combination of climatic and other features of 1935 which we described in our introductory remarks.

An equation for rate of spread of the pathogen

Let us look more closely at the element of time: at the rate of increase of disease which (on what we have said) is also the rate of spread of the pathogen.

We measure the rate of increase of disease as the rate of increase of the proportion x of infected tissue. If t stands for time, our concern is with the rate dx/dt. To be more precise and show that we mean the rate at the particular time t, we write $dx(t)/dt$, where $x(t)$ is x at time t.

To be clear on another detail, the proportion x of infected tissue is, for local lesion disease, the amount of infected foliage (to consider just foliage diseases) as a proportion of the total foliage (so that the percentage of disease recorded in Fig. 3 is $100x$), or, for systemic disease, the number of infected plants as a proportion of the total number of plants.

Infected tissue is of three kinds: (i) infected tissue that has not yet had time to become infectious; (ii) infectious tissue; and (iii) tissue that was infectious but has ceased to be so. Newly infected tissue needs a period p to become infectious (for example, to start to form spores). This is called the period of latency. Thereafter it remains infectious only for a period i, after which it is 'removed' from the epidemic.

If $x(t)$ is the proportion of tissue infected (whether infectious or not) at time t, then $x(t-p)$ is the proportion infected at time $t-p$ and, at time t, is the proportion that has passed through the period of latency and is either infectious or removed. So too $x(t-i-p)$ is the proportion infected at time $t-i-p$ and, at time t, the proportion that has been removed. Hence $x(t-p)-x(t-i-p)$ is the proportion of infectious tissue.

The proportion of healthy tissue at time t is $1-x(t)$.

We define a relative infection rate R, in which the absolute rate $dx(t)/dt$ is related both to the proportion of infectious tissue (the tissue that supplies the spores, for example) and of healthy tissue (the tissue on which these spores can germinate and start new infections). Thus

$$\frac{dx(t)}{dt} = R[x(t-p)-x(t-i-p)]\,[1-x(t)].$$

With a spore-forming pathogen for example, R measures the efficiency with which spores are produced on infectious tissue, dispersed to healthy tissue, germinate there and start new infections.

Some properties of the equation have been discussed elsewhere (Van der Plank, 1963, 1965). We need not go into complications here. What primarily concerns us is that all factors of the disease triangle—the susceptibility of the host plants, temperature, rainfall, etc.—affect $dx(t)/dt$, the rate of spread of the pathogen, by affecting i, R or p, singly or together, directly or indirectly.

The rate of spread of the pathogen, the number of daughter lesions
per lesion, and the frequency of dispersal: a self-evident relation

We came to the conclusion earlier that the rate of spread of the pathogen was the frequency of acts of dispersal. What does our equation say about this?

To answer this, we change the unit of time. Instead of using days or years as units, we make i, the period of infectiousness, the unit. Then the equation becomes

$$\frac{dx(t)}{dt} = iR\left[x\left(t-\frac{p}{i}\right)-x\left(t-1-\frac{p}{i}\right)\right]\left[1-x(t)\right].$$

In this equation iR is the new relative infection rate. It is still the rate $dx(t)/dt$ relative both to the amount of infectious tissue that produces the spores (or other propagules) and to the amount of healthy tissue which the spores can infect. But now this relative rate is not expressed per day or per year, but is dimensionless so far as these units are concerned.

What is iR numerically? Early in an epidemic when $x(t)$ is small and $1 - x(t)$ near enough to 1 to be ignored as a factor, iR is the average number of daughter lesions produced by a parent lesion during its whole existence (literally, while it is infectious). As disease increases and $1 - x(t)$ can no longer be ignored as a factor, the average number of daughter lesions per parent is less than iR but still proportional to it at any given level of disease.[†]

In these relations the period of latency p determines how many parent–daughter generations there are, say, per season. But for simplicity we shall leave p out of the argument.

Previously we related the rate of spread to the frequency of acts of dispersal. Now we relate it to iR and the average number of daughter lesions per parent. It comes to the same thing, because, other things being equal, the number of daughter lesions per parent is proportional to the number of acts of dispersal per parent (i.e. for spore-bearing pathogens, to the number of spores dispersed from a lesion and falling on healthy susceptible tissue).

Indeed the whole relation we are considering—the rate of spread of a pathogen related to the frequency of dispersals or the number of daughter lesions in the lifetime of the parent—is self-evident, provided that we accept Fig. 3 rather than Fig. 2 as defining spread. On our definition, which Fig. 3 illustrates, the pathogen spreads where it goes; it spreads when a new lesion is formed, irrespective of whether that new lesion is on the leaf next to the source of inoculum or in the next field. The rate of spread is then clearly determined by the number of daughter lesions in the lifetime of the parent or by the frequency of dispersal.

Fast spread is more dispersals, rather than longer dispersal. This is why fast spread, as shown, for example, by *Phytophthora infestans* in a blight epidemic, is so closely related to conditions that favour disease: susceptible host plants, a suitable ecoclimate, etc.

[†] Suppose $1 - x(t)$ is not negligible as a factor, and we wish to compare the numbers of daughter lesions per parent lesion in two fields of different varieties and different values of iR. We cannot compare them at the same levels of disease over the whole interval i, because the value of $1 - x$ will change during that interval, and will change differently in the two fields. We can only relate the number of daughter lesion per parent lesion to iR by comparing the rates of increase of the number at some instant when the fields are at the same level of disease.

Diversity in the manner of dispersal

It will be objected that we have oversimplified spread. We have not specially related it to distance in a geographical sense. We give spread from leaf to leaf on a plant the same weight as spread from field to field. We think of spread in terms of Fig. 3 and not Fig. 2.

But really what is the objection about? Figures 2 and 3 are for the same epidemic: the epidemic of blight in Bintje potatoes in the sand areas of the Netherlands in 1953. Figure 3 shows spread both within fields and between fields; Fig. 2 shows only spread between fields. To choose Fig. 2 and stress long-distance dispersal—or at any rate dispersal over distances long enough to spread disease from field to field—instead of choosing Fig. 3 is to choose to study a part of the process of dispersal instead of the whole of it.

Long-distance dispersal and short-distance dispersal are all part of the diverse process of dispersal. Long-distance dispersal promotes short-distance dispersal, and vice versa.

In the early stages of an epidemic, when most plants are still healthy, short-distance dispersal is relatively efficient. Lesions are closely surrounded by susceptible tissue, which spores (to consider a spore-bearing pathogen) can reach by short flights and settle on. There is little immediate, direct advantage in long flights. But as disease increases (as it does, for example, in the centre of a focus) lesions become increasingly surrounded by lesions, and short flights are increasingly likely to end on tissue already diseased. Then long-distance dispersal is needed to start new colonies and allow easy dispersal over short distances to begin anew.

An efficient pathogen must be able to disperse over long as well as short distances. The problem facing the pathogen, if we may put it so, is like the problem of a player who must place his shots not just to the best advantage during his immediate turn, but also during his next turn, and the turn after that. . . . He needs a variety of shots. So does a pathogen.

DISCUSSION

The essence of our argument is that we distinguish between the spread of the pathogen and the dispersal of its propagules.

Within reasonable limits we can take a word to mean what we define it to mean. Thus in physics work, energy, power, force—familiar words in common speech—are used with restricted meanings clearly defined.

The definition of spread should give little difficulty. A pathogen spreads where it goes and infects. And 'where it goes' we interpret directly: along a stem or across a continent, as the case may be. A new lesion anywhere means the pathogen has spread. We have already argued that it is unrealistic to confine the meaning of spread to the covering of larger distances and invading new geographical territory. This is just one of the sorts of spread that occur concurrently and are all parts of one process and of equal weight.

Dispersal is the movement of the propagule from a lesion to healthy susceptible tissue (or, for systemic disease, from an infected to a healthy susceptible plant). The restriction on the meaning here is that the destination of the propagule must be healthy susceptible tissue. This restriction is not absolutely necessary; we could develop the argument without it. But it is convenient, because dispersal to healthy, susceptible tissue is the only dispersal relevant to spread.

REFERENCES

ANONYMOUS (1953). Some further definitions of terms used in plant pathology. *Trans. Br. mycol. Soc.* **36**, 267.

ANONYMOUS (1954). Verslag van de enquete over het optreden van de aardappelziekte, *Phytophthora infestans* (Mont.) de Bary in 1953. *Jaar. plziektenk. Dienst*, 1953, p. 34.

BONDE, R. & SCHULTZ, E. S. (1943). Potato refuse piles as a factor in the dissemination of late blight. *Bull. Me. agric. Exp. Sta.* no. 416, 230.

BRENCHLEY, G. H. (1964). Aerial photography for the study of potato blight epidemics. *World Rev. Pest Control*, **3**, 68.

BRENCHLEY, G. H. & DADD, C. V. (1962). Potato blight recording by aerial photography. *N.A.A.S. q. Rev.* **14**, 21.

CROWE, T. J. (1963). Possible insect vectors of the uredospores of *Hemileia vastatrix* in Kenya. *Trans. Br. mycol. Soc.* **46**, 24.

GREGORY, P. H. (1945). The dispersion of air-borne spores. *Trans. Br. mycol. Soc.* **28**, 26.

GREGORY, P. H. (1948). The multiple-infection transformation. *Ann. appl. Biol.* **35**, 412.

GREGORY, P. H. (1961). *The Microbiology of the Atmosphere*, 251 pp. London: Leonard Hill.

HEALD, F. D. & STUDHALTER, R. A. (1914). Birds as carriers of the chestnut blight fungus. *J. agric. Res.* **2**, 405.

HIRST, J. M. (1958). New methods for studying plant epidemics. *Outl. Agric.* **2**, 16.

HIRST, J. M. & STEDMAN, O. J. (1960). The epidemiology of *Phytophthora infestans*. I. Climate, ecoclimate and the phenology of disease outbreak. *Ann. appl. Biol.* **48**, 471.

LEACH, J. G. (1940). *Insect Transmission of Plant Diseases*, 615 pp. New York: McGraw-Hill.

LIMASSET, P. (1939). Recherches sur le *Phytophthora infestans* (Mont.) de Bary. *Ann. épiphyt.* **5**, 21.

NUTMAN, F. J., ROBERTS, F. M. & BOCK, K. R. (1960). Method of uredospore dispersal of the coffee leaf-rust fungus, *Hemileia vastatrix*. *Trans. Br. mycol. Soc.* **43**, 509.

SCHRÖDTER, H. (1960). Dispersal by air and water—the flight and landing. In *Plant Pathology*, vol. III, p. 169. Ed. by J. G. Horsfall & A. E. Dimond. New York: Academic Press.

STAKMAN, E. C. & FLETCHER, D. G. (1930). The common barberry and black stem rust. *Fmrs' Bull. U.S. Dep. Agric.* 1544, 28 pp.

STAKMAN, E. C. & HARRAR, J. G. (1957). *Principles of Plant Pathology*, 581 pp. New York: Ronald Press.

VAN DER PLANK, J. E. (1960). Analysis of epidemics. In *Plant Pathology*, vol. III, 229. Ed. by J. G. Horsfall & A. E. Dimond. New York: Academic Press.

VAN DER PLANK, J. E. (1963). *Plant Diseases: Epidemics and Control*, 349 pp. New York: Academic Press.

VAN DER PLANK, J. E. (1965). Dynamics of epidemics of plant disease. *Science*, **147**, 120.

WAGGONER, P. E. (1952). Distribution of potato late blight around inoculum sources. *Phytopathology*, **42**, 323.

EXPLANATION OF PLATE

Plate 1. Initial focus (*lower right*) and daughter foci in crops of potatoes in west Suffolk, 16 July 1960. The strip in the centre is wheat. From Brenchley & Dadd (1962), by permission of the Controller of Her Majesty's Stationery Office.

PLATE 1

SPREAD OF PATHOGENS WITHIN CROPS AS AFFECTED BY LIFE CYCLE AND ENVIRONMENT

J. M. OGAWA, D. H. HALL AND P. A. KOEPSELL

Department of Plant Pathology, University of California, Davis, California, U.S.A.

INTRODUCTION

Failure to control a plant disease often results from incomplete knowledge of the annual life cycle of the pathogen and the effects upon it of the fluctuating environment. The least obvious, but very important, phase of the life cycle of certain pathogens is dispersal of their spores by air. And lack of knowledge of this phase often hinders the development of effective control measures for the disease.

The infection potential of a pathogen in an individual crop is largely dependent on the total quantity of inoculum present on the surface of the susceptible host plants, and this is determined by many factors including: (1) the number of inoculum sources; (2) the quantity of inoculum produced on those sources; (3) the quantity of inoculum from these sources reaching the susceptible host; (4) the proportion of deposited inoculum remaining viable when conditions favourable for infection occur; and (5) the incubation period for development of more inoculum. The spread of the pathogen depends on the suitability of environmental conditions for dissemination of spores and subsequently for infection during the period when the host is susceptible.

Three common plant diseases are chosen to illustrate how the life cycle of airborne pathogens, and conditions in the immediate environment interact to affect the spread of the pathogen within a field. Information on these effects can make control of spread possible. The diseases discussed are: brown-rot blossom-blight of almond (*Prunus amygdalus* Batsch.) caused by *Monilinia laxa* (Aderh. & Ruhl.) Honey; powdery mildew of plum (*Prunus salicina* Lindl.) probably caused by *Sphaerotheca pannosa* Wallr.; and downy mildew of hops (*Humulus lupulus* L.) caused by *Pseudoperonospora humuli* (Miy. & Tak.) Wilson.

BROWN-ROT BLOSSOM-BLIGHT ON ALMOND

The basic problem

The most important disease on almond in California is the blossom- and twig-blight caused by the fungus *Monilinia laxa*. This disease is also important in other stone-fruit producing areas throughout the world, and requires periodic applications of fungicides for satisfactory control.

The life cycle of the pathogen on almond under California conditions is shown in Table 1. The fungus overwinters primarily on the previous

Table 1. *Seasonal cycle of the almond brown-rot fungus, Monilinia laxa*

MONTH	ENVIRONMENT FOR INFECTION	TREE	
December to March		Blighted blossoms and twigs of previous year ⟶	Conidia
		Mummies and peduncles of previous year ⟶	
February	Favourable	Blossoms ⟵	
March to August		Blighted blossoms ⟶	
		twigs	
	Generally unfavourable	Fruit ⟵ — — — — — — ⟶	
September		Fruit harvested	
October to November		Blighted blossoms ⟶	
		twigs	
		⟶ Mummies ⟶	

year's blighted blossoms and twigs, and produces sporulating cushions (sporodochia, see Pl. 1, fig. 1) after the rains and fogs of early winter. These sporodochia continue to develop throughout the flowering period, producing lemon-shaped spores about 8×12 microns when moist (Pl. 1, fig. 2), but these shrivel under dry conditions (Pl. 1, fig. 3). The blossoms become infected as soon as they emerge from the bud scales, and are most susceptible when their stigmas and anthers are exposed (Ogawa & English, 1960) (Pl. 2, fig. 1). Although no data are available for almonds, with sweet cherries Calavan & Keitt (1948) found that stigmas are less likely to become infected by *M. laxa* after fertilization. Almond blossoms are susceptible only for about 2 weeks during the flowering period.

Cultivars of almond differ in their susceptibility to infection, the most important commercial almond, 'Nonpareil', being more resistant than 'Ne Plus Ultra', 'Peerless', or 'Drake'. Because almonds are self-sterile these more susceptible cultivars must be interplanted among

'Nonpareil' as pollinators to ensure a good commercial crop, and thus a proportion of susceptible trees occurs in all commercial orchards. Sporodochia of *M. laxa* on these more susceptible hosts cultivars can provide airborne inoculum for the 'Nonpareil' blossoms, from which blossom- and twig-blighting develop during the latter part of the flowering period (Pl. 2, fig. 2), but spores are rarely produced on infected blossoms early enough for other blossoms to become infected secondarily from airborne spores.

The environment during December and January is critical because free moisture is necessary for sporodochial production. As a source of moisture during flowering, rain favours the development of epiphytotics more than do fog or dew. This is because the temperature during rain more closely approaches the spore germination optimum of $21°C$, whereas in fog or dew, temperature tends to be below the optimum.

Protective fungicide spraying is difficult with spray applicators moving over the ground because the orchard floor is wet, and in many years wind and rain make it almost impossible to spray satisfactorily. In addition the whole orchard needs to be sprayed within a few days.

Research on control

Keitt & Palmiter (1937) decreased the amount of apple scab (*Venturia inaequalis*) inoculum surviving from the previous season by applying eradicant sprays to fallen leaves on the orchard floor. Wilson (1943), with knowledge of this fact, made a careful study of the life cycle of the apricot and almond blossom-blight pathogen (*Monilinia laxa*), but found no apothecial stage of the fungus on the orchard floor, such as Hewitt & Leach (1939) found in the spring for another pathogen on stone fruit, *M. fructicola*. In the absence of such an overwintering source that might have been controlled by eradicant sprays on the orchard floor, the only inoculum for infection of almond was the spores (conidia) produced on remains of the previous year's infected blossoms and twigs on the tree itself. Arsenites were therefore tested as winter sprays in attempts to eradicate the sporodochia-producing conidia on the apricot and almond twigs several weeks before the blossoms emerged. On apricots the chemical eradicated the fungus even within the infected twigs, with subsequent reduction of blossom infection by as much as 98%, but on almonds the arsenites caused severe phytotoxicity and had to be abandoned. Wilson (1942) then tried sodium dinitro-*o*-cresylate and sodium pentachlorophenoxide (SPCP) on a few almond trees to test phytotoxicity and effectiveness. He showed that even a 53% reduction in viable conidia by sodium dinitro-*o*-cresylate gave only a 12% reduction in blossom blight. The mycelium in the twigs was not killed by these chemicals and new sporodochia developed. He therefore concluded that these materials would not be successful as eradicant sprays against this disease unless they were rendered more capable of penetrating the conidial masses on the sporodochia.

Wilson & Baker (1946a) reported a detailed study on aerial dissemination of spores, with special reference to conidia of *Monilinia laxa*, and later (1946b) showed how the incidence of infection decreased with increasing distance from the source. This information laid the foundation for better understanding of the spread of the brown-rot pathogen. Conidia of *M. laxa* were found to disseminate under wind velocities as low as 2·4 m.p.h. and were readily transported in air currents. The disease incidence decreased outward from the conidial source trees in approximately direct proportion to the aerial concentration of conidia. For example, when 36% of the twigs of the source tree were infected, blossom blight averaged 16, 5, 2 and 1% on apricot trees 22, 44, 66 and 88 ft. away, respectively. This relationship with distance from the source gave confirmatory evidence that *M. laxa* spores are transported by air to other trees in the orchard, and also explained the poor control of the disease obtained in previous tests when eradicants were tested on small plots of trees which would receive inoculum from surrounding untreated parts of the orchard.

Applying this knowledge of airborne spread to additional tests with eradicant fungicides, Wilson (1950) took special precautions to use large plots, locating them on the south side of the orchard adjacent to an open field, since southerly winds prevailed during rains. Blossom infections were recorded only on trees near the centre of the plots. In these new tests, 8 lb. of 37% SPCP in 100 gal. of water applied in January reduced sporodochia in a range from 37 to 87%, and reduced twig blight by 31–73% of the amount on unsprayed plots.

Ogawa & Wilson (1960) made further studies attempting to improve the eradicatory action of SPCP, to extend the periods of sporodochial suppression, and to decrease the viability of the conidia on new sporodochia which develop after the winter spray. Yamada & Kishi (1955) had shown that a mixture of liquid lime-sulphur and SPCP was more effective on the black spot disease caused by *Alternaria kikuchiana* Tanaka, of Japanese pears than either compound alone. Preliminary laboratory studies showed that *Monilinia fructicola* was affected similarly when mixtures of liquid lime-sulphur (LLS) and SPCP were incorporated into agar inoculated with mycelial plugs. Similar results were obtained with bioassay of *M. laxa* spores. When almond twigs in the orchard were sprayed with the same chemicals and collected after 2 months, initial and final sporodochial counts per blighted twig averaged 14 and 7 for SPCP, 5 and 5 for LLS, 8 and 0 for the mixture, and 25 and 37 for the control. When spores collected from twigs were dusted on water agar germination after 24 hr. was 73% for the control, 50 for SPCP, 1 for LLS and 0·3 for the mixture.

Table 2. *Effect of eradicant fungicides on sporodochial production, conidial germination, and blossom blight caused by Monilinia laxa on Drake almond, 1958*

Fungicide	Dates of application	Average number of sporodochia per twig	Twigs with sporodochia (%)	Conidial germination on agar (%)	Amount blossom blight per 100 20 in. shoots inspected
		Orchard no. 1			
SPCP†	12 Dec. 1957	0·58	18	94‡	21·2
SPCP plus					
LLS†	12 Dec. 1957	0·94	16	26	15·7
SPCP	22 Jan. 1958	0·28	20	34	42·4
Untreated		2·04	74	78	93·1
		Orchard no. 2			
SPCP	13 Dec. 1957	4·6	100	46§	60·9
SPCP plus					
LLS	13 Dec. 1957	1·7	48	1	37·8
SPCP	9 Jan. 1958	8·8	76	3	78·1
Untreated		14·7	96	60	232·0

† SPCP is 8·0 lb. of 37% sodium pentachlorophenoxide in 100 gal. of water applied at the rate of 400 gal./acre with an airblast sprayer and LLS is 11·2 gal. of 32 degrees Baumé calcium polysulphide combined with SPCP.

‡ Potato dextrose agar.

§ Water agar.

In field-scale experiments 8 lb. of 37% SPCP and 11·2 gal. of LLS in 100 gal. of water (hereafter designated as 'combination spray') was applied in December and January by an air-blast sprayer to large plots, in which trees of the cultivar 'Drake' were always included because of their extreme susceptibility. The combination spray applied in December drastically reduced the numbers of sporodochia per twig, the percentage of blighted twigs with sporodochia, and the percentage of blighted blossoms (Table 2). In addition viability of conidia was reduced when tested on agar plates. Note that in Table 3 more spores from treated plots germinated when exposed to anthers and stigmas in water, than in water alone or on water agar; nevertheless the viability of treated spores was much less than that of untreated spores exposed to anthers and stigmas.

Because blossom blight was reduced, even though considerable numbers of sporodochia with viable spores were present, the effect of SPCP treatment on conidial release was studied at various air velocities. Apricot trees with sporodochia were sprayed with 2, 4, and 8 lb. of 37% SPCP on 17 February 1964, and infected twigs were collected on 4 March (early in the blossom period), and again on 13 March (at the end of the blossom period) when the orchard relative humidity was 68%. The twigs were brought into the laboratory where the temperature was 21° C and the relative humidity ranged from 31 to 26% during the

Table 3. *Germination and infectivity of Monilinia laxa conidia collected from orchard no. 2, on blossom parts, 1958*

| | | Percentage germination | | | | | Percentage blossoms |
Fungicides	Dates of application	On water agar	In water (control)	In water + petal	In water + stigma	In water + anther	blighted in laboratory tests†
SPCP‡	13 Dec. 1957	69	—	—	—	—	65
SPCP plus LLS‡	13 Dec. 1957	7·5	10	6	13	34	25
SPCP	9 Jan. 1958	0·5	—	—	—	—	25
Untreated		42	18	44	91	87	65

† Incubated at 22° C and 80% R.H.

‡ SPCP is 8·0 lb. of 37% sodium pentachlorophenate in 100 gal. of water applied at the rate of 400 gal./acre with an airblast sprayer and LLS is 11·2 gal. of 32 degrees Baumé calcium polysulphide combined with SPCP.

experiment. Twigs with sporodochia were taped across the entrance of the cyclone spore collector described by Ogawa & English (1955), and in successive collections air velocities of 10, 18 and 25 m.p.h. were passed over the twigs for 30 sec. After each collection the spore trap was washed with water and with 70% alcohol, and then dried by air. Spores were collected at each velocity on a glass cover slip mounted at the base of the spore trap.

Very few spores were collected at 10 mi./hr. compared with 18 mi./hr. (Table 4). At 25 mi./hr. the number of spores released from the sporodochia greatly increased. SPCP reduced the numbers of spores released by more than sixfold, and reduced the viability of spores from 100% in the untreated to 36·6% when treated with 8 lb. of SPCP. Phase microscopic observations of scrapings of sporodochia of treated twigs revealed atypical, spore-like bodies with little or no cytoplasm, and also conidiophore-like structures producing chains of undelimited bodies resembling spores (Pl. 2, fig. 4).

These data confirm the view that the spread of *Monilinia laxa* in the field depends on the inoculum level as determined by numbers of viable conidia surviving and the wind velocity available to remove conidia from the sporodochia. The occurrence of new infections depends on the viability of spores. Because, although locally distributed by air, *M. laxa* conidia do not spread extensively from orchard to orchard, and because secondary infection seldom occurs, SPCP applied in the winter effectively reduces the number of blossom infections in the spring. The combination fungicide offered more striking results; in some years, however, phytotoxicity was observed.

Table 4. *Dispersal by air currents of Monilinia laxa spores from apricot twigs treated with sodium pentachlorophenoxide*

Average number of spores collected per twig in 30 sec.†

Fungicide	Lb. per 100 gal. of water	Expt. 1 (4 March) Wind speed (mi./hr.)			Expt. 2 (13 March) Wind speed (mi./hr.)			Spore viability‡ (%)
		10	18	25	10	18	25	
Untreated	—	0·4	0·8	62·8	3·3	155·5	818·2	100·0
SPCP§	2	0·2	1·0	10·7	1·2	2·5	22·5	81·0
SPCP	4	0·4	0·4	7·5	0·2	1·0	6·5	66·2
SPCP	8	0·2	1·6	11·1	1·6	15·5	149·6	36·6

† Average number of spores from one twig in Expt. 1, and five twigs in Expt. 2 for each treatment. The number of spores in ten fields were averaged for Expt. 1 and in four fields in Expt. 2.

‡ Spores germinated on water agar.

§ SPCP is 37% sodium pentachlorophenoxide.

POWDERY MILDEW OF PLUM

The basic problem

Powdery mildew of plum in California may be caused by either of two fungi. *Podosphaera oxyacanthae* (DC.) de Bary is reported by Anderson (1956) to be of little economic importance. In California, the fungus causes infection on the leaves of plum only in late fall after the harvest of the fruit. The second mildew fungus was identified by Weigle & French (1956) as *Sphaerotheca pannosa* Wallr. In California, it was found only on plum cultivars 'Kelsey', 'Gaviota', and 'Wickson'.

In 1960 powdery mildew was found on fruit of 'Kelsey' plum growing in the lower San Joaquin Valley near Arvin, and in the foothills of the lower Sacramento Valley near Newcastle. On some trees all fruit were infected. Protective applications of sulphur and other compounds by growers gave unsatisfactory control.

On peach Weinhold (1961) found *Sphaerotheca pannosa* overwintering in the scales of terminal buds and infecting new shoots, but Yarwood (1952) found that the *S. pannosa* inoculum for the mildew on apricot fruit came from particular cultivars of roses.

Research on control on plum

A study of the life cycle of *Sphaerotheca pannosa* showed that the fungus infected the plum fruit shortly after flowering. In one plum orchard a gradient of increasing mildew infections led towards the source of

Table 5. *Survey of powdery mildew on plum varieties near Newcastle, California, in 1961, 1962 and 1963*

Plum cultivar and orchard	Amount of mildew on plums during			Distance from rose to plum orchard (m.)
	1961 (%)	1962 (%)	1963 (%)	
	'Kelsey'			
A	100†	50‡	5§	40
B	100†	40‡	1§	100
C	—	50	0	50
D	—	10‡	2	500
E	—	—	30	400
F	—	—	10	200
G	—	—	5	100
H	—	—	10	200
	'Gaviota'			
B	—	30	0§	300
	'Wickson'			
I	—	—	1	75

† Large rose bush killed back with weed killer after infections on plums had become established.
‡ New growth of rose with mildew was not eradicated until infection on plum occurred.
§ Eradication of rose before infection occurred.

mildew spores, a 'Dorothy Perkins' rose bush covering a ground area of about 8×15 m., and standing about 4 m. high. The rose bush was severely mildewed, and sporulation was especially heavy on surfaces of rapidly growing shoots (Pl. 2, fig. 3); upon flowering, however, sporulation decreased (Pl. 2, fig. 4).

The incidence of infection on plum fruit showed a gradient, and ranged from 100 % at 9 m. from the source of inoculum, to almost none at 90 m. away. Other orchards were surveyed, and the association between mildew on plums and proximity to rose bushes is given in Table 5. 'Dorothy Perkins' rose was the most common source of inoculum for fruit infection, but other cultivars with heavy sporulation also provided mildew inoculum.

In the spring, about 5% of the new growth on rose was severely infected with mildew, while other shoots had little or no infection, suggesting that the fungus overwinters in a small proportion of the buds. Thereafter mildew continued to develop on the roses throughout the growing season, and evidently provided the primary source of airborne inoculum for the orchard nearby, as the fungus does not overwinter on plum.

Table 6. *Seasonal cycle of the plum fruit powdery mildew*

Month	Environment for infection	Rose		Kelsey and Gaviota plum
January to February	Favourable	Dormant buds		None
March		Sporulation on shoots ——→ Conidia Leaves Stems Shoots		Blossoms Leaves
April		Shoots ←——→	←——→	Fruits Leaves
May to July		Shoots ←——→	← — →	Fruits Leaves
August		Shoots ←——→		Fruit harvested Leaves
September to December		Shoots ←——→		Leaves

Wind dissemination of spores from rose sources was demonstrated by placing Rotorod spore samplers (Perkins & Leighton, 1957) at a series of distances from an infected rose bush. Approximately 24,000 l. of air was sampled at each position during a 3 hr. period from 2 to 5 p.m. The numbers of spores collected per litre of air downwind was: 29·5 at the inoculum source; 0·63 at 15 m.; 0·23 at 30 m.; 0·40 at 45 m.; and 0·58 at 52·5 m. The spores varied in appearance from barrel-shaped to those that were collapsed and probably not viable (Pl. 3, fig. 1) (see Longrée, 1939).

When mildew spores from different orchards and different rose cultivars were inoculated by rubbing sporulating rose leaves on fruits and leaves of plum, mildew developed only on the fruit (plum leaves are susceptible to *Podosphaera* only in late fall), and success was achieved with inoculum from a wide variety of rose cultivars. Six days after inoculating fruit a microscopic fine, web-like growth of mildew appeared, and slight sporulation was visible in 14 days. Spores from the

14-day-old infections were able to infect and produce the disease on other fruit. Mildew spreads very quickly on the fruit surface (Pl. 3, fig. 2), causing chlorotic areas which later turn into scabby lesions with no sign of the fungus. Fruit at the pit-hardening stage of growth started to show the scabby texture, indicating the development of hyper-sensitivity to mildew, and after this no further fruit infection occurs.

The seasonal cycle of the plum mildew is shown in Table 6. Effective reduction of fruit mildew (complete in some instances) has been possible by eradicating the infected rose source, utilizing the knowledge that the primary source of airborne inoculum is the rose, and that secondary infections from fruit take place for only a limited period.

DOWNY MILDEW OF HOPS

The basic problem

The production of hops can be limited by the fungus *Pseudoperonospora humuli*. In California, severe losses amounting to over one-half of the crop have been experienced during the last decade, and the fungus is present in all the commercial hop yards.

Hops are grown on hills about 2 m. apart on squares, with approximately 1,000 plants per acre. Each winter, the hop crowns are exposed for pruning, and unthrifty plants are removed. New rhizomes are obtained from crowns during the pruning operation and are used to replace plants removed. Buds begin to grow during the first week in April; shoots are cut back during the latter part of April; and four shoots of the regrowth are trained in May, two on each string. Trained shoots that become infected with mildew may require cutting back, and new shoots must be trained to take their place.

In attempts to develop a control programme more effective than repeated applications of fungicides, information was sought on the life cycle of the pathogen and its significance for spread within the fields under the semi-arid environment of California.

Research on control

Two hop fields were selected for further detailed study in 1958. Field no. 1 was 12 acres of established yard on the south-western portion of a large acreage of hops on the American river near Sacramento. During rain, prevailing winds were from an open area of field crops to the south or south-west. Field no. 2 was 8 acres of established hops on Deer Creek, 15 miles east of field no. 1. Field no. 2 was bounded by hop yards on all sides but the west. A third field of 20 acres planted in 1962 adjacent to the Consumnes River just 5 miles east of field no. 2 was added to the programme later. Field no. 3 was bordered on the north-west corner by an established yard.

Table 7. *Percentage hills with hop downy mildew in yards as related to precipitation for years 1958, 1960 and 1961† in California*

1958		Field		1960		Field		1961		Field	
Date	Rain‡ (in.)	1 (%)	2 (%)	Date	Rain (in.)	1 (%)	2 (%)	Date	Rain (in.)	1 (%)	2 (%)
April				April				April			
1–4	4·53	—	—	7	—	0·29	0·26	5	—	0·68	—
5	0·47	—	—	11	0·21	—	—	12	0·02	—	—
10	0·04	—	—	20	—	1·06§	—	14	—	0·36	0·22
22	0·70	—	—	22	0·02	—	—	19	—	0·09	0·07
24	—	1·93	—	23	0·04	—	—	21	0·24	—	—
29	—	—	1·35	26	0·84	—	—	22	0·20	—	—
				27	0·21	—	—	28	—	0·27§	0·22
May				May				May			
5	1·17	—	—	1	0·02	—	—	1	0·11	—	—
11	0·04	—	—	3	—	6·85	0·57	4	—	0·27	0·60§
12	0·02	—	—	11	—	10·60	2·85§	6	0·01	—	—
15	—	0·84	—	21	0·01	—	—	10	0·01	—	—
22	0·70	—	—	23	0·48	—	—	11	0·04	0·88	1·14
	—	—	—	24	0·04	—	—	19	—	1·18	5·08
	—	—	—		—	—	—	22	—	—	10·43
	—	—	—		—	—	—	31	0·01	—	—
June				June				June			
2	0·02	0·17	17·69	11	—	2·22	—	1	0·01	—	—
8	0·17	—	—		—	—	—		—	—	—
12	0·04	—	—		—	—	—		—	—	—
July											
16	—	—	0·09		—	—	—		—	—	—

† In 1959, only 0·21 in. of rain fell from April to June and disease incidence in three observations of each field showed less than 0·89 % disease.

‡ Data obtained from the U.S. Weather Bureau, Airport Station, Sacramento, California. Trace of rain not recorded.

§ Secondary infections observed for first time.

A survey of the pattern of mildew spread in fields nos. 1 and 2 was started in 1958. A record was kept of each plant in each experimental area. Infected shoots originating directly from systemically infected crowns were recorded as primary spikes; all other types of infections were recorded as secondary infections (Pl. 3, fig. 3; Pl. 4, figs. 1, 2). The primary spikes were removed during the surveys in 1960 and 1961. Table 7 shows the incidence of mildew in fields nos. 1 and 2 from 1958 to 1961. During the initial examinations in early April each year, primary infections were found on less than 1 % of the hills. Secondary infections were never found before the occurrence of primary spikes. In the presence of primary spikes after rain, secondary infections were found within 4–6 days. Only occasionally were secondary infections found on plants with primary spikes during periods without rain, owing to heavy dews, as noted by Skotland (1961) in the State of Washington. Rain in late April and in May is more conducive to secondary spread of mildew than in any other time of year because there are more susceptible shoots and the temperature is closer to the optimum for mildew infection (about 18 °C).

Removal of diseased shoots and parts of the hop crown did not prevent the recurrence of primary spikes on the same plant. The possibility of removing the whole plant was therefore considered, as hop plants are the only host of hop downy mildew in California. In fields severely affected with mildew more hop plants die during the winter, and as many as 25% may need replanting in the spring. (Some loss may be caused by other decay-producing organisms, as in yards where mildew is not a serious problem about 5% of crowns still decayed.) Plants with primary infections produced 25% less cones than healthy plants in 1959, and 48% less in 1960. As hops planted in April produce 43% of the normal yield, removal and replanting in April will not noticeably decrease hop yields below those of diseased plants left in the field.

Spread in field no. 3

As removal and replanting in April appeared a promising control measure, the effect on secondary spread of removing mildew-infected plants was studied next. Hop crowns taken from a yard with a high incidence of mildew, and that had provided hop cuttings for a new field, were examined for downy mildew fungus in the fall of 1961. Of 100 hop crowns examined at random, 36% had typical symptoms of mildew infections and contained haustoria similar to those of hop downy mildew fungus as described by Skotland (1961). It was therefore assumed that some of the rhizomes for the new plantings were infected with the mildew fungus.

1962. The new field (no. 3) previously planted to alfalfa, was bordered by an established hop yard on the north-west corner, and showed mildew-infected plants on 12 April 1962. On 25 April, four primary spikes were found. On 27 April 0·14 in. of rain fell and on 11 May four additional primary spikes were noted, and ten secondary infections on leaves of ten plants. Infected plants were removed immediately and carried out of the field in sacks. Mildew was not found in the yard during the remainder of the season, although mildew was present in the adjacent hop field. Precipitation was 0·03 in. during May, and 0·01 in. during June.

1963. Rainfall was unusually high in April 1963, but by 15 April no mildew had developed in field no. 3. By the end of April 2·29 in. of rain had fallen intermittently during 15 days, but on 2 May only three primary spikes were found and the plants removed. Ten more primary spikes were found on 9 May, and the plants also removed. Total rainfall for 8, 10 and 11 May was 0·61 in., and on 17 May three more primary spikes and 33 plants with secondary infections were noted.

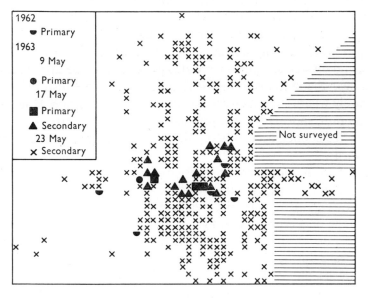

Fig. 1. Pattern of hop mildew spread in field no. 3.

Fifteen of these were adjacent to or near the three hills with primary spikes removed on 17 May. On 23 May the secondary infections had spread as far away as thirty-seven plants distant from the initial location of the primary inoculum of 9 May (Text-fig. 1). (In 1962 five diseased plants had been found and removed from this same area.) On 17 May three hills near the site of one diseased plant, which was removed on 9 May, showed plants with primary spikes (these evidently had not been visible during the 9 May survey). The initial source of inoculum was established as the three primary spikes. Secondary infections were common only in this area, and no secondary spread occurred in the same yard in ten other locations where mildewed plants had been removed on 2 and 9 May.

1964. In 1964 the grower carefully removed the plants with primary spikes at weekly intervals (on 28 April six primary spikes were recorded in the area of secondary spread of the previous year), and although significant amounts of rain occurred for secondary spread of mildew in April, May and June, no secondary infections were observed, showing that under the semi-arid California environment, removing plants with primary spikes will effectively reduce mildew inoculum.

Studies on spores

The formation, liberation, viability and dispersal of spores, and the mode of infection by the fungus were studied to explain the pattern of spread observed in the fields surveyed (Ogawa & Hall, 1964). Spores were produced on both surfaces of the stipules, on the undersides of leaves, and on stems. Spores were also produced on the upper surface of leaves near the margins in areas where stomata were also present, but only rarely where stomata were absent (Ogawa, Mathre & Hoed, 1966). With no rain, sporulation was restricted to the lower leaves of systemically infected shoots, occurring on higher leaves only if curved or cupped downwards.

Liberation of spores under the semi-arid environment in California was continuous even in calm weather, and the dispersed spores were collapsed (Ogawa & McCain, 1960), even though they regained their usual shape on wetting (Pl. 4, figs. 3, 4). During and immediately after rain, the rate of spore liberation increased. This sudden increase in spore release during rain is probably explained by the vibration caused by raindrops on sporulating leaves (Hirst & Stedman, 1963). Wind movement, greater relative humidity, and the presence of free moisture on the sporulating leaf surface also play a role in spore release. With an increase in humidity, sporangiophores untwist in a clockwise direction, and with a slight decrease in humidity they twist back counterclockwise. The twisting and twirling movements of the interlaced sporangiophores rub off spores, and in addition spore release may occur by an unknown mechanism as reported by Pinckard (1942). Placing water on the sporulating leaves also caused a sudden release of dry spores.

When spores were obtained from sporulating leaves from the field they were viable for less than a day in direct sunlight on upper leaf surfaces, and for about 3 days on lower leaf surfaces (Table 8). Their ability to produce zoospores decreased with increasing time and temperature.

The dispersal patterns of spores were determined by three methods: (1) in 1962 Vaseline-coated microscope slides placed at various distances from the sporulating sites; (2) in 1963, the preceding method plus Roto-rod Samplers (Metronics Inc., Palo Alto, California); and (3) in 1964, both the preceding methods plus Hirst Automatic Volumetric Spore Traps (Hirst, 1952). Representative data for methods (1) and (2) for four successive 1 hr. periods are given in Table 9. Both these methods collected more spores during rain than during dry weather.

Table 8. *Longevity of Pseudoperonospora humuli spores after dispersal on dry hop leaves, measured at various intervals*

Time and date of sampling†	Temperature °C		Percentage germination of spores	
	Min.	Max.	Upper surface	Lower surface
4 July, 3 p.m., initial	13 to 22		66	66
5 July, 3 p.m., 2nd	13 to 34		14	49
6 July, 3 p.m., 3rd	13 to 32		4	23
7 July, 6 p.m., 4th	14 to 32		0	8

† Five leaves were each inoculated on the upper surface, and five more inoculated on the lower surface on 4 July at 3 p.m. One-third of each leaf was removed for examination starting from 5 July. The initial germination percentage was based on spores obtained from the inoculum source.

Table 9. *Number of Pseudoperonospora humuli spores collected near sporulating hop plants during successive 1 hr. periods*, 28 *May* 1963

	1 hr. collection period			
	1st	2nd	3rd	4th
Horizontal slide				
Directly under leaf	590	17	90	1
1 m. downwind	1	0	0	0
2 m. downwind	0	1	0	1
Rotorod sampler				
2 m. downwind	21	4	11	2

Three Hirst spore traps were installed in a hop yard in 1964. Two traps were 36 m. distant from the nearest sporulating plant, one on the ground, and the other 5·8 m. above ground level. The third trap was placed 198 m. downwind from the edge of the hop yard. These traps operated from 23 April to 21 June (data through 21 May shown in Table 10). No mildew spores were collected in any of the traps until after a trace of rain, and significant numbers were first collected on 3 May when 0·02 in. of rain were recorded. Large numbers were again collected on 16 May after 0·03 in. of rain, and again on 17 May. Numbers of spores collected declined very quickly after the rain. The fact that the trap located outside the hop yard collected spores at the same time as traps in the hop yard illustrates the fact that spores can spread from field to field.

For infection to occur, spores must land on specific areas of the plant, and moisture must be deposited and retained for a period. Secondary infections in the yards were found on leaves, nodes, and growing points. Observations made during rain showed large droplets of water collected

Table 10. *Field collection of hop downy mildew spores with Hirst spore traps during* 1964

Date	Rain (in.)†	Number of spores collected by traps‡		
		A	B	C
23–30 April	Trace	0	0	0
1 May	Trace	0	0	0
2	Trace	4	3	1
3	0·02	12	33	15
4	0·01	4	5	0
5	Trace	0	1	2
6	—	1	0	0
7	—	1	5	0
8	—	4	1	0
9	—	0	1	0
10	—	8	7	0
11	—	12	6	2
12	—	0	3	0
13	—	1	4	0
14	—	3	0	0
15	—	0	0	0
16	0·03	38	35	No data
17	—	20	23	51
18	—	7	4	5
19	—	2	1	No data
20	—	0	1	2
21	—	4	6	2

† U.S. Weather Bureau, Airport Station, Sacramento, California.
‡ Trap A, 36 m. from the nearest diseased plant. Trap B, same location as trap A, but 5·8 m. high. Trap C, 198 m. downwind from the edge of the hop field.

especially between the stem and upward cupped stipules. Immediately after rain, water droplets on under surfaces of leaves were more numerous closer to the ground than on leaves higher up the trained shoots. During rain deposition of spores appeared more likely to occur on the upper surface of leaves than on the lower, and inoculations show that upper surfaces are readily infected (Sonoda & Ogawa, 1966), subsequently sporulating on the lower surface. This finding appears to be most significant in correlating the occurrence of rain with the spread of a pathogen to the leaves.

A seasonal life cycle of the hop mildew fungus under a semi-arid climate was drawn from these findings (Table 11). The environment is favourable to the fungus during only part of the growth period of the hop plants. The only source of primary inoculum in the spring is spores produced on diseased shoots that develop on infected crowns. Removing infected crowns before or after shoot development eliminated the fungus, but removing all of them is practically impossible. With the information that dispersed spores are viable for a short period of about 3 days, it appears feasible to examine the yards weekly and remove diseased plants before the occurrence of rain. Roguing diseased plants gives effective control only if adjacent fields are relatively free of mildew.

Table 11. *Seasonal cycle of the hop downy mildew fungus*

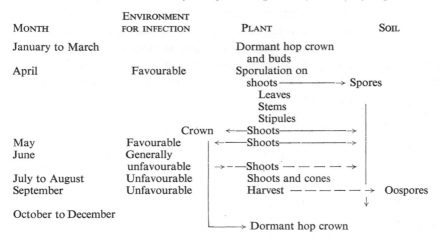

MONTH	ENVIRONMENT FOR INFECTION	PLANT	SOIL
January to March		Dormant hop crown and buds	
April	Favourable	Sporulation on shoots ————————→ Spores Leaves Stems Stipules	
		Crown ←——Shoots——————→	
May	Favourable	←——Shoots——————→	
June	Generally unfavourable	→— —Shoots — — — — →	
July to August	Unfavourable	Shoots and cones	
September	Unfavourable	Harvest — — — — — → Oospores	
October to December		——→ Dormant hop crown	

DISCUSSION AND CONCLUSIONS

The spread of the three pathogens described here is related to complex factors in their life cycles, and to the unpredictable environment directly affecting each process from sporulation to infection. The semi-arid climate in California is such that a thorough knowledge of the spread of a pathogen can implement a system of control measures not possible in areas of more rain. The investigations on apple scab development, as influenced by temperature and rain, is summarized by Post, Allison, Burckhardt & Preece (1963), and patterns of spread of pathogens as studied by van der Plank (1947, 1963) support the type of control measures developed for crops grown under semi-arid climate. The information on the dispersal of airborne spores by Gregory (1945), Wilson & Baker (1946 *a*, *b*), and Ingold (1953), and the studies on eradicant fungicides by Keitt & Palmiter (1937), and Wilson (1942, 1943), was basic in planning this research.

The diseases illustrated as examples show how the severity of an epiphytotic is greatly increased by the occurrence of secondary spread of a pathogen. In brown-rot blossom blight, secondary infection is not important; in plum powdery mildew limited secondary infections occur, whereas in hop downy mildew secondary infections can result in epiphytotics. The features of the life cycle of the pathogens which most directly affected the development of control measures are as follows.

The source of inoculum in brown-rot blossom blight comes only from the holdover infection sites on the tree. Airborne spores are produced during the winter after the rain begins. These spores spread for limited distances during the flowering time, which is the only period the blossoms are susceptible to infection. An eradicant fungicide applied to the trees in winter largely eliminates the spore pustules, so only a limited number of spores develop and these are low in viability and are released abnormally. Because the total area of the infection-sites on the blossoms is small satisfactory control of the disease is obtained by reducing the inoculum.

Sphaerotheca pannosa does not overwinter on the plum tree and infection occurs only when the fruit is in early stages of development. Sporulation on the fruit is limited because the tissue becomes hypersensitive at about the pit-hardening stage. Inoculum must therefore come from the roses adjacent to plum orchards. Abundant inoculum must be available to spread through commercial orchards which are in blocks of 10 to 50 acres or occasionally larger. The highly susceptible rose cultivars contribute to plum mildew epiphytotics. On these roses the fungus sporulates profusely on young rapidly growing shoots, but as the roses bloom the amount of inoculum is considerably reduced, and at the same time the viability of older spores declines. Based on the information that released spores are viable for short periods only, eradication of roses near plum orchards results in the elimination of most of the primary source of inoculum occurring during periods of fruit susceptibility and gives almost complete control.

With the hop downy mildew fungus the only source of primary inoculum is the perennial mycelium in the hop crowns. Less than 1% of crowns produce diseased shoots in spring. The fungus sporulates readily, and spores are released continuously in small numbers. Chances for secondary infections are limited because dispersed spores die within a few days and the environment is unfavourable for infection during the major portion of the growing season. The spores are dispersed extensively only during rain, and this is the only time extensive secondary spread is observed. Thus the removal of hop plants as soon as the diseased shoots appear assures relative freedom from inoculum. Careful removal of diseased plants results in almost complete control of mildew even during years when considerable rain occurs during the growing season.

Spores of powdery mildew when released retain their shape under a dry climate, but spores of the brown-rot fungus and downy mildew fungus collapse almost immediately. The collapsed spores, being more tolerant to heat can probably remain viable for longer periods in the field. The shape of the spores may play a significant role in the distribution pattern, as well as the ability to deposit on specific host parts.

With detailed knowledge of the life cycle of these pathogens, and especially the manner of their aerial dissemination, one can conclude that reduction or elimination of the primary inoculum will afford almost complete control of these diseases in the semi-arid environment in California.

ACKNOWLEDGEMENTS

We acknowledge the technical assistance of Judith H. Mathre, James L. Sandeno and Ronald M. Sonoda, and of Jeff Hall for preparation of illustrations.

REFERENCES

ANDERSON, H. W. (1956). *Diseases of Fruit Crops*. 501 pp. New York: McGraw-Hill Book Company, Inc.

CALAVAN, E. C. & KEITT, G. W. (1948). Blossom and spur blight (*Sclerotinia laxa*) of sour cherry. *Phytopathology*, **38**, 857.

GREGORY, P. H. (1945). The dispersion of air-borne spores. *Trans. Br. mycol. Soc.* **28**, 26.

HEWITT, W. B. & LEACH, L. D. (1939). Brown-rot sclerotinias occurring in California and their distribution on stone fruits. *Phytopathology*, **29**, 337.

HIRST, J. M. (1952). An automatic volumetric spore trap. *Ann. appl. Biol.* **39**, 257.

HIRST, J. M. & STEDMAN, O. J. (1963). Dry liberation of fungus spores by rain drops. *J. gen. Microbiol.* **33**, 335.

INGOLD, C. T. (1953). *Dispersal in Fungi*. 197 pp. Oxford: Clarendon Press.

KEITT, G. W. & PALMITER, D. H. (1937). Potentialities of eradicant fungicides for combating apple scab and some other plant diseases. *J. agric. Res.* **55**, 397.

LONGRÉE, K. (1939). The effect of temperature and relative humidity on the powdery mildew of roses. *Mem. Cornell Univ. agric. Exp. Stn*, no. 223, 43 pp.

OGAWA, J. M. & ENGLISH, H. (1955). The efficiency of a quantitative spore collector using the cyclone method. *Phytopathology*, **45**, 239.

OGAWA, J. M. & ENGLISH, H. (1960). Relative pathogenicity of two brown-rot fungi, *Sclerotinia laxa* and *Sclerotinia fructicola* on twigs and blossoms. *Phytopathology*, **50**, 550.

OGAWA, J. M. & HALL, D. H. (1964). Production, liberation and dispersal of hop downy mildew sporangia in relation to the pattern of disease development. *Abst. Xth International Botanical Congress, Edinburgh, Scotland*, p. 42.

OGAWA, J. M., MATHRE, J. H. & HOED, J. (1966). Sporulation of *Pseudoperonospora humuli* on areas of hop leaves lacking stomata. *Phytopathology*, **56**, 150 (Abstr.).

OGAWA, J. M. & McCAIN, A. H. (1960). Relations of spore moisture content to spore shape and germination reaction to temperature. *Phytopathology*, **50**, 85 (Abstr.).

OGAWA, J. M. & WILSON, E. E. (1960). Effects of the combination of sodium pentachlorophenoxide and liquid lime-sulfur on the brown-rot fungi. *Phytopathology*, **50**, 649 (Abstr.).

PERKINS, W. A. & LEIGHTON, P. A. (1957). The Rotorod sampler. *Second semi-annual report CML* 186. *Aerosol Lab., Dep. Chemistry and Chemical Engineering, Stanford University, California*. 66 pp.

PINCKARD, J. A. (1942). The mechanism of spore dispersal in *Peronospora tabacina* and certain other downy mildew fungi. *Phytopathology*, **32**, 505.

POST, J. J., ALLISON, C. C., BURCKHARDT, H. & PREECE, T. F. (1963). The influence of weather conditions on the occurrence of apple scab. *Tech. Notes Wld met. Org.* no. 55, 41 pp.

SKOTLAND, C. B. (1961). Infection of hop crowns and roots by *Pseudoperonospora humuli* and its relation to crown and root rot and overwintering of the pathogen. *Phytopathology*, **51**, 241.

SONODA, R. M. & OGAWA, J. M. Unpublished data. Department of Plant Pathology, University of California, Davis.

VAN DER PLANK, J. E. (1947). The relation between size of plant and the spread of systemic diseases. I. A discussion of ideal cases and a new approach to the problems of control. *Ann. appl. Biol.* **34**, 376.

VAN DER PLANK, J. E. (1963). *Plant Diseases: Epidemics and Control*, 349 pp. London: Academic Press.

WEIGLE, C. G. & FRENCH, A. M. (1956). Laboratory diagnosis. *Bull. Calif. Dep. Agric.* **45**, 186.

WEINHOLD, A. R. (1961). The orchard development of peach powdery mildew. *Phytopathology*, **51**, 478.

WILSON, E. E. (1942). Experiments with arsenite sprays to eradicate *Sclerotinia laxa* in stone-fruit trees as a means of controlling the brown rot disease in blossoms. *J. agric. Res.* **64**, 561.

WILSON, E. E. (1943). Tests of eradicant sprays for use against *Sclerotinia laxa* and *Coryneum beijerinckii* in apricots and almonds. *Phytopathology*, **33**, 506.

WILSON, E. E. (1950). Sodium pentachlorophenate and other materials as eradicative fungicides against *Sclerotinia laxa*. *Phytopathology*, **40**, 567.

WILSON, E. E. & BAKER, G. A. (1946 a). Some features of the spread of the plant diseases by air-borne and insect-borne inoculum. *Phytopathology*, **36**, 418.

WILSON, E. E. & BAKER, G. A. (1946 b). Some aspects of the aerial dissemination of spores, with special reference to conidia of *Sclerotinia laxa*. *J. agric. Res.* **72**, 301.

YAMADA, S. & KISHI, K. (1955). Studies on the chemical control in dormant state of diseases of fruit trees. Preliminary Report I. Effect of dormant sprays against the black spot disease of Japanese pears caused by *Alternaria kikuchiana* Tanaka. *J. hort. Ass. Japan*, **24**, 41.

YARWOOD, C. E. (1952). Apricot powdery mildew from rose and peach. *Bull. Calif. Dep. Agric.* **41**, 19.

PLATE 1

Fig. 1

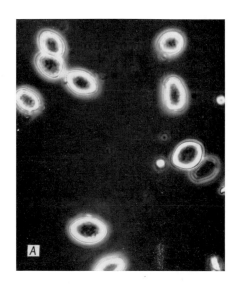

Fig. 2

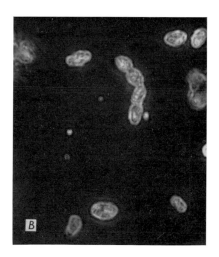

Fig. 3

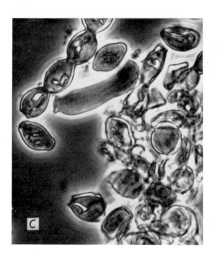

Fig. 4

(*Facing p.* 266)

PLATE 2

Fig. 1

Fig. 2

Fig. 3

Fig. 4

PLATE 3

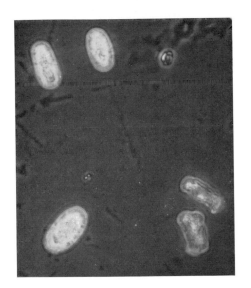

Fig. 1

Fig. 3

Fig. 2

PLATE 4

Fig. 1

Fig. 2

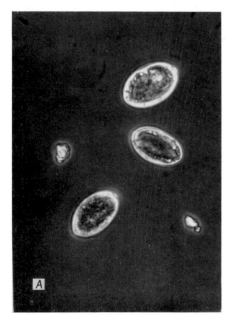

Fig. 3

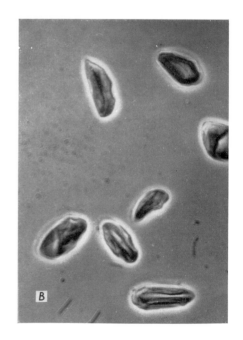

Fig. 4

EXPLANATION OF PLATES

PLATE 1

Fig. 1. Sporodochia of *Monilinia laxa* on previous year's blighted twig (mag. × 6).

Fig. 2. The shape of wet spores of *M. laxa* (phase microscopy, mag. × 550).

Fig. 3. The shape of dry spores of *M. laxa* (mag. × 550).

Fig. 4. The appearance of *M. laxa* spores in spring after treatment with sodium penta-chlorophenoxide during winter (phase microscopy, mag. × 550).

PLATE 2

Fig. 1. The most susceptible parts of an almond blossom to infection are the stigma *A* and anther *B* (mag. × 2).

Fig. 2. Current year's blighted blossoms and twig, showing sporulation only on infected blossom *A* (mag. × 3).

Fig. 3. 'Dorothy Perkins' rose with abundant sporulation on rapidly growing shoot (mag. × ½).

Fig. 4. 'Dorothy Perkins' rose with little sporulation after blossoming (mag. × ½).

PLATE 3

Fig. 1. Spores of powdery mildew of rose with barrel-shaped spores and collapsed spores (mag. × 550).

Fig. 2. 'Kelsey' plum showing initial developmental phases of mildew *A* and healthy plum *B* (mag. × 1).

Fig. 3. A diseased hop shoot *A* with sporulation on the undersurface of leaves compared with a healthy rapidly growing shoot *B* (mag. × ⅓).

PLATE 4

Fig. 1. The appearance of secondary infections on leaves from the adaxial surface (mag. × 1).

Fig. 2. The appearance of secondary infections on leaves from the abaxial surface (mag. × 1).

Fig. 3. The shape of wet spores of *Pseudoperonospora humuli* photographed under phase microscopy (mag. × 550).

Fig. 4. The shape of dry spores of *P. humuli* photographed in oil (mag. × 550).

SPREAD OF AIRBORNE BACTERIA PATHOGENIC FOR MAN

R. E. O. WILLIAMS

Department of Bacteriology, Wright-Fleming Institute, St Mary's Hospital Medical School, London, W.2

INTRODUCTION

Almost all the microbes that cause disease in man or animals are obligate parasites: although many of them can survive in the inanimate environment, very few can multiply there. For the most part, therefore, the spread of pathogens is from man to man or animal to animal (and very commonly the spread is confined within one species). For airborne spread one further limitation is apparent. The number of pathogens dispersed by infected men or animals is usually very limited, compared with the number dispersed from an infected plant crop, and if liberated in the open air they are rapidly diluted to a level at which new infections do not occur, or at least become too rare to be detected. Airborne spread of animal pathogens is, therefore, effectively confined to indoor spaces. The only exceptions to this are the fungal diseases, such as histoplasmosis or coccidioidomycosis, which are also exceptions to the generalization that the reservoir is within an animal body, for these pathogens multiply in soil.

Previous contributors to this Symposium have discussed laboratory studies concerned with the mechanism of dispersal of bacteria from 'carrier' sites, their survival in air, and the factors governing their entry into the body by the respiratory tract. It is now necessary to consider how these laboratory investigations relate to the natural behaviour of the microbes causing disease. This is not easy, for the air is rarely the only route by which a given pathogen is spread and it is generally very difficult to decide, in any particular case, just how a man or an animal acquired the infection. The epidemiological approach, coupled with various extrapolations from clinical medicine and experimental pathology, have therefore to be relied upon.

We can obtain evidence for airborne spread from:

(*a*) the primary site of implantation in the recipient host;

(*b*) demonstration of a relation between the occurrence of infection and the presence or numbers of the microbe in the air;

(*c*) epidemiological studies of the spread of the infection in relation to such factors as season, location, or propinquity of source and recipient;

(*d*) the results of measures specifically designed to limit the spread of airborne infection.

None of these lines of evidence is unequivocal: the site of implantation is usually a matter of surmise rather than demonstration; the dose–effect relationship is commonly influenced by numerous factors in the host, and in any case the incidents of infection are generally so spaced in time that we are rarely able to measure the concentration of airborne pathogens at the time the infection takes place; and the methods of control of airborne microbes that are tolerable for use in occupied places are generally very inefficient.

Airborne spread may deposit the microbes somewhere in the respiratory tract, on an exposed surface such as a surgical wound, or on a 'depot' surface from which they may later reach a susceptible target area.

It is tempting to try to classify the inhalation infections on the basis of the presumed site of implantation of the microbes in the respiratory tract (Druett, p. 165). On this basis we can recognize three patterns. First, the microbes may be deposited in the lung and set up infection there, as with pulmonary tuberculosis. Second, they may be deposited in the nose or throat, and cause upper respiratory tract disease. And third, the site of deposition may differ widely from the site in which invasion and disease occurs. This phenomenon is certainly exemplified by pulmonary anthrax and meningococcal meningitis, and probably also by pneumococcal pneumonia.

INHALATION INFECTIONS

Pulmonary tuberculosis

In man, the primary lesion in pulmonary tuberculosis is a small focus, commonly detectable only by X-rays, in the periphery of the lung. The pathogenesis of inhalation infection was studied by Ratcliffe (1952) who found that in rabbits exposed to a cloud of *Mycobacterium tuberculosis* the number of infective foci ('tubercles') corresponded closely to the number expected on the assumption that the cloud inhaled by the animal consisted of single bacillary cells each of which set up an infective lesion; the primary sites of deposition were the peripheral alveoli of the lungs. This work was confirmed by Nyka (1962) who exposed mice to a cloud of *M. tuberculosis* and examined their lungs microscopically soon after exposure. Single bacilli were seen in the subpleural alveoli, and it was noted that these bacilli were only 2–3 microns long compared with the normal 8–12 microns. This suggested that the smaller bacilli, which are able to penetrate to the alveoli, may therefore be the most infective. From the studies of both Ratcliffe and Nyka, it appears that a single bacillus can set up an infective lesion, and it seemed that, in the susceptible experimental animals, virtually all those that reached the alveoli did so.

There have been numerous attempts to estimate the numbers of tubercle bacilli discharged by infective patients; the earlier work was usefully reviewed by Arnould (1942). Because of the difficulties of cultivation *in vitro*, the air has generally been sampled by exposure of guinea-pigs. Some indication of the state of the air in hospitals at the turn of the century is given by the observation of Le Noir & Camus (1909), who exposed twelve guinea-pigs in a hospital room containing infected patients; four of the animals developed tuberculosis. A more sophisticated form of the same experiment has been reported by Riley *et al.* (1962). The air from a series of single-bed rooms, in which patients known to have *M. tuberculosis* in their sputum were nursed, was drawn through a chamber in which guinea-pigs were housed. From the numbers of animals infected, and from a comparison of the cultural characteristics of the strains isolated from the guinea-pigs with those from patients, it was possible to determine the source of most of the air strains. It was apparent that patients varied considerably in the numbers of bacilli dispersed into the air: fifty-three of sixty-one patients generated no case of infection in a guinea-pig, but the remaining eight were probably responsible for a total of 134 infections.

This variability in the rate of dispersal of microbes by infected patients is a general phenomenon, and will be referred to again when we deal with streptococcal and staphylococcal infections. Although there is probably a continuous distribution in the numbers dispersed by different individuals, those in the upper part of the distribution may well be recognized as 'dangerous dispersers', evidently responsible for epidemics, while the less active dispersers are responsible for sporadic infections. Many epidemics of tuberculosis in closed communities have been reported (Lincoln, 1965), often resulting from the exposure of a number of susceptible subjects, especially school children, to a particularly active disperser. There is also some evidence for particular danger from special activities; an epidemic among people who sing together may well be attributable both to the vigorous expiratory movements involved and also to the need for repeated deep inhalation, which gives the greatest opportunity for by-passing the protective mechanisms of the upper respiratory tract (Proctor, 1966).

Riley *et al.* (1962) estimated that one exceptionally infectious patient disseminated *M. tuberculosis* into the air to give a concentration of one infective particle per 200 ft.⁹ (about 6 m.⁹), this represented the dispersal of some sixty infective particles per hour. The particles recognized in these experiments were certainly small, since they were carried some distance through the air-exhaust ducts and penetrated to the lungs of the guinea-pigs. The patient must certainly have disseminated in total a far greater number of infective particles, most of which were too large to reach the guinea-pig chamber, or in which the bacteria died before arrival there.

It is thus clear that infected patients do distribute tubercle bacilli into the air in small particles (corresponding at least in size to the 'droplet nuclei' of Wells & Wells (1936)) and all the evidence suggests that infection probably results from the inhalation of infected particles small enough to reach the furthest depths of the lung. Such small particles can remain airborne for long periods of time so that a single carrier might well be able to infect susceptibles at some distance. Some evidence for such transfer was obtained in factories by Stewart & Hughes (1951), whose epidemiological study suggested that a single infected person was a risk to all the people working in the same room, no matter how large the room.

The campaign against spitting in public places had its origin in hygiene as well as aesthetics and a great deal of work was published in the early part of the century on the survival of *M. tuberculosis* in dust (Lange, 1926; Augustine, 1929). There seems no doubt that, qualitatively at least, the organism can survive and remain infective for considerable periods, but it is not clear whether the residual contamination of the environment is a significant hazard after the removal of an infected individual; Chapman & Dyerly (1964) could find no evidence of such contamination from tuberculin-sensitivity conversion tests in a rather limited study of 209 children living in premises from which an infective patient had been removed.

Pulmonary or inhalation anthrax

Anthrax is an infection that has been the subject of much careful experimental study in animals and it has been shown that the minimum dose for inhalation infection is obtained when the bacilli are administered as single spores, and so in a size that can penetrate to the lung alveoli (Druett, Henderson, Packman & Peacock, 1953). The pulmonary form of anthrax is not a pneumonia; the bacilli are apparently taken up into the lymphatic channels in the lungs and conveyed to lymph glands in the mediastinum where they multiply to produce the characteristic haemorrhagic mediastinitis (Plotkin *et al.* 1960; see also Ross, 1957).

Sporadic cases of pulmonary anthrax have occurred for many years among workers in factories handling raw wool and hair, chiefly from goats and horses (Min. Labour Report, 1959). An epidemic involving five cases in a mill processing goat hair in New Hampshire in 1957 has been the subject of very intensive study (Brachman, Plotkin, Bumford & Atchison, 1960; Dahlgren *et al.* 1960; Norman *et al.* 1960). Air sampling with an Andersen sampler, carried out some months after the epidemic, indicated that the numbers of particles containing *Bacillus anthracis* that might be inhaled during an 8 hr. shift by a worker in the card room of the mill was between 600 and 2,150; 25–30 % of these were found to be less than 5 microns in diameter.

Bacillus anthracis was found in the anterior nares of 15% of the men in another plant, but none of these carriers became ill.

In subsequent experiments (Brachman, Kaufmann & Dalldorf, 1966) the effluent air from around the 'picking machine' in the factory was drawn into a chamber in which a number of monkeys were housed and in which the air could be sampled with impingers. No precise estimate could be made of the average dose inhaled by the monkeys before they became ill, but, in one experiment, inhalation of some 5,000–6,000 particles less than 5 microns in diameter apparently infected six of thirty-seven monkeys. This dose is of the same order of magnitude as that found for direct experimental infection of monkeys in the laboratory.

Airborne transfer of *Bacillus anthracis* is thus one of the ways by which man can be infected, the immediate source being dust from wool collected from infected animals. The microbes are doubtless present in the form of spores, but whether the spores are generally associated with organic matter or not is unknown. Noble, Lidwell & Kingston (1963) found that the only bacterial species present in the air largely in the form of very small particles was *B. subtilis*, presumably also in spore form. The observations were, however, very limited in extent.

Workers in goat-hair mills very rarely develop pulmonary anthrax, even though they must inhale considerable numbers of bacilli; the factors that predispose some of the men to disease are not known. In animals, and indeed for most cases of anthrax in man, airborne spread is not concerned, the organisms being conveyed by direct contact or by ingestion.

For these two bacterial infections, pulmonary tuberculosis and pulmonary anthrax, it seems certain that the infection is transferred by small airborne particles penetrating to the depths of the lungs and there is some direct evidence that infective particles of the right size are present in the air when infections occur. Nevertheless, these small particles probably represent only a minority of the total number of infective particles distributed into the air from the source, be it patient or bale of goat hair. Presumably the greater effectiveness of the small particles reflects the different susceptibilities of the different parts of the respiratory tract, or—in a microbiologically oriented symposium—the different nutritional opportunities offered to the parasite.

The next group of infections to be discussed are those which are characterized by upper respiratory tract disease or colonization.

Staphylococcal nasal carriage

The area of skin just inside the anterior orifice of the nose is well known as a site in which *Staphylococcus aureus* can very commonly be found in normal healthy people in all parts of the world. The carrier state is not constant, and in any defined community it can generally be shown that there is a continuous exchange of strains (Williams, 1963). This has been particularly studied in hospital because the establishment of the healthy carrier state seems to be the method by which antibiotic-resistant staphylococci maintain themselves in the ever-changing community of patients within a hospital.

Both the dispersal of staphylococci by infected persons, especially healthy carriers, and their acquisition have been studied in some detail (Williams, 1966; and Lidwell, p. 121). Present evidence indicates that carriers disperse their staphylococci into the air from the skin, which is itself contaminated or colonized from the principal reservoir in the anterior nares (Davies & Noble, 1962; Solberg, 1965). Carriers differ greatly in the number of staphylococci that they shed, the differences probably being related to the numbers of cocci present on the skin (Noble & Davies, 1965). In hospital the heavy dispersers can be recognized by the large numbers of their staphylococci that can be found in the air.

In the air of hospital wards the numbers of particles containing viable *S. aureus* commonly varies between 1 and 10 per 100 ft.^{3} (or about 3 m.^{3}), with occasional peaks up to 100 per 100 ft.^{3} or more. About half the particles have equivalent diameters in the region 8–16 microns (Noble *et al.* 1963), presumably because they are generally associated with epithelial squames (Davies & Noble, 1962). They are thus too large to penetrate to the depths of the lungs, and indeed it seems common sense that they should be trapped in the nose where there is evidently a surface on which they can often flourish. This may be too glib a picture, for the site of colonization is restricted to the area within about 1–2 cm. of the anterior nares. It is not clear whether the airborne particles actually get trapped here, or further back on the mucous membrane covering the convoluted turbinate cartilages.

In our studies in a surgical ward we found no great difference in the rate at which patients in beds at various distances from a carrier acquired staphylococci, suggesting that a disperser in one part of an open ward was able to contaminate the whole space. This is not inconsistent with the observation that the median equivalent particle diameter is in the region of 12 microns because such particles have a settling rate of only 1–2 ft. per minute.

The most dramatic example of acquisition of staphylococci in hospital is that of the newborn infant: 60–80% of infants commonly become nasal carriers of *S. aureus* within the first week of life. The infant's skin is actually colonized even sooner than the nose and there is good evidence that the greater part of the transfer is by contact, presumably by way of the nurses' hands (Mortimer *et al.* 1962). But some carefully controlled studies (Mortimer, Wolinsky, Gonzaga & Rammelkamp, 1966) have demonstrated clearly that airborne transfer of staphylococci can certainly occur, for even when the possibility of contact transfer was completely excluded, 6–10% of the infants became colonized.

In wards for adult patients the evidence for airborne transfer is much less direct, but there is some indication that the rate at which patients acquire staphylococci in the nose may be related to the average number of staphylococci in the ward air (Williams, 1966; Lidwell *et al.* 1966). In my own studies, staphylococci of the relevant phage type were found in the air prior to 64% of the acquisitions observed. The rate of acquisition is, however, determined by the variety (e.g. as indicated by phage type) of staphylococcus as well as the number inhaled.

One implication of the studies on nasal acquisition concerns the size of the effective dose of staphylococci. Some rather indirect calculations (Williams, 1966) suggest that the median dose inhaled to give an acquisition rate of nasal carriage of about 1% per day must be less than twenty particles containing staphylococci (each of which may harbour an average of about four viable cocci (Lidwell, Noble & Dolphin, 1959).

The more detailed observations of Lidwell *et al.* (1966) indicated that the frequency of nasal acquisition after inhalation of ten airborne particles of a single strain of *S. aureus* was about 1 in 300–800 and that the acquisition rate was not related linearly to the inhaled dose.

These estimates are all derived somewhat indirectly. It has not yet been possible to relate acquisition to exposure on a precise short-term basis for we can only estimate the exposure by air sampling over rather prolonged periods, and the number of patients exposed at any one time is small. But the figures are consistent with extrapolation of the data from experimental inoculation of infants observed by Shinefield, Ribble, Boris & Eichenwald (1963) and analysed by Williams (1966): in newborn infants an acquisition rate of 1 % might have been achieved by the inoculation of about eighteen cocci.

The nose is not, of course, the only part of the human body colonized by *S. aureus*. The skin is another very common site, but for adults there is some evidence that skin carriage is very often secondary to nasal carriage. Contamination of skin from the nose, and subsequent desquamation of the contaminated skin, is thought to be the route of dispersal of staphylococci (see Lidwell, p. 122).

In hospital, there is often widespread contamination of bedding and floordust with *S. aureus* derived from the dispersers in the environment. These staphylococci remain viable, in blankets at least, for some time and must be redispersed into the air. There is conflicting experimental evidence on the effect of desiccation on virulence but this in itself suggests that the effect may not be great. For a time it was thought that dissemination from contaminated bedding and other fabrics might constitute a major pathway of spread of staphylococci in hospitals, and methods were devised to control this route by disinfection of blankets as well as other bedding between use by successive patients. No one has demonstrated that such disinfection has any effect on the incidence of infection or on the rate of acquisition of staphylococci in the nose. However, this may be because bedding becomes so rapidly recontaminated during use that disinfection can have only the most transient effect (Williams *et al.* 1962). However, some evidence (p. 129) indicates that carriers disseminate skin bacteria even when clothed in sterile garments, so that fabric reservoirs may well be truly of minor importance.

Throat infection with Streptococcus pyogenes

During the Second World War there was very great interest in the spread of infection by *Streptococcus pyogenes*, especially in military installations in the United States, and it was easy to show that the streptococci were abundant in the air in the hospital wards and barracks in which clinical infections were occurring. Much of the transfer between men was assumed to be by the airborne route and for a time there was an implied assumption that the infective particles were the small 'droplet nuclei' described by Wells & Wells (1936). No one appears to have returned to the study of streptococcal infection recently to make the direct determination of particle size, which would now be possible. However, it was also shown that the streptococci could be recovered, often in enormous numbers from bedclothes and floor dust in places where infection was spreading and these depots were also held to be of great importance. The extensive studies of Hamburger and his colleagues (e.g. Hamburger, Green & Hamburger, 1945) demonstrated that the nasal carrier of the streptococci was a far more dangerous source for spread than the throat carrier (see also Holmes & Williams, 1958). In the light of subsequent work on staphylococcal dispersal, one is tempted to think that the special activity of the streptococcal nasal carrier might be related to his ability to contaminate his skin and shed his organisms by desquamation as well as by mouth spray, although normally streptococci are rather rapidly killed by the fatty acids of the skin (Ricketts, Squire & Topley, 1951). It is recognized that patients with skin lesions infected with streptococci may be very potent dispersers (Loosli, Smith, Cline & Nelson, 1950).

The importance of the environmental depots of streptococci has been minimized in later studies, partly because several attempts to control the spread of infection by control of dust were rather ineffective, and partly because Rammelkamp et al. (1958) produced more direct evidence that dried streptococci may often be lacking in the ability to infect. Some evidence suggests that fairly close contact is necessary for the infection to spread (e.g. Holmes & Williams, 1958), and this may point to the involvement of the larger short-range droplets or epithelial squames rather than droplet nuclei as the vehicle of spread. Wannamaker (1954) studying the spread of streptococci in military barracks obtained evidence suggesting that the acquisition rate declined with increasing separation between infected carrier and potential recipient, from sixty-five to sixty-eight acquisitions per 100 man weeks' exposure with separation of 0–10 ft., to twenty-two with separations of more than 30 ft. However, other factors made these results difficult to assess precisely.

The characteristic sites in which the haemolytic streptococcus produces disease are the tonsils and pharynx. One of the gaps in our knowledge seems to be on the extent to which inhaled bacteria-carrying particles may impinge on the pharyngeal wall. But the primary site of invasion need not be the same as the site of deposition. Indeed particles deposited in the nasal fossa will land on the mucous blanket that covers the whole of the epithelium and which is being continually carried back towards the pharynx and tonsils by the cilia of the epithelium. So it is reasonable to postulate that infection is generally conveyed by streptococcus-carrying particles of a size that are retained in the nose and that they reach the pharynx by transfer over the surface of the epithelium.

Other infections doubtless have an analogous mechanism of implantation; diphtheria is the most obvious example among bacterial diseases, and the viral infections of the pharynx must behave similarly (Tyrrell, p. 290).

The next group of infections comprise those where the obvious focus of disease is remote from the presumed site of entry of the bacteria to the body, either in a different part of the respiratory tract, or in a different part of the body altogether. Meningococcal meningitis is a good example of the latter. Pneumococcal pneumonia may well be an example of the former, although there can be no guarantee that the pneumonia does not—at least in some cases—result from direct pulmonary implantation.

Meningococcal infection

Although the characteristic disease produced by *Neisseria meningitidis* is cerebrospinal meningitis, the primary site of implantation is probably the nasopharynx. In epidemics, and to a less extent at other times, the organism can be found as a commensal on the tonsillar and naso-pharyngeal mucosa. The method of spread to the meninges is not really known; and there has been considerable discussion whether this is by direct invasion or by the blood-stream, as is suggested by the fact that a bacteraemia can commonly be demonstrated at the onset of illness in severe cases.

Epidemics of meningococcal meningitis have been observed in Britain and the United States in circumstances of unusual crowding—classically in army barracks during the two world wars. During the 1914–18 war, indeed, Glover (1920) suggested that the spread of the disease could be directly related to the closeness of the bunks in dormitories and claimed that increasing the spacing between bunks diminished the spread of infection. But the bunks were originally no more than 6 in. or so apart and the improved spacing was no more than 18–24 in., achieved by reducing the number of men in the barracks. Other workers have failed to observe the association between bed spacing and the spread of infection but perhaps none has started with such a degree of 'overcrowding'. Indeed it seems rather unlikely that the simple manoeuvre of spacing beds would control the spread of infection in a confined service population, in which there must be so many other opportunities for the spread of infection. In any case an army barracks in which the beds are especially close together is likely to be overcrowded in other areas as well as in the dormitories.

Epidemics of meningitis are a regular phenomenon in parts of West Africa (Waddy, 1957). The epidemics occur especially in areas where the dwelling houses are large and interconnected, so providing especially good opportunities for indoor spread. There is a dramatic relation between the incidence of the disease and the weather: epidemics build up during the dry season and terminate promptly at the start of the wet season when the ambient humidity rises very steeply (Lapeysonnie, 1963). The mechanism of this effect—like that of season on other respiratory infections (e.g. Lidwell, Morgan & Williams, 1965)—is unknown.

Pneumococcal pneumonia

In man, pneumonia due to *Streptococcus pneumoniae* is often a disease of very acute onset; the infection commonly spreads rapidly to involve the whole of one lobe of the lung, hence the name lobar pneumonia. Much work was done in the years up till about 1945 on the pathogenesis of the disease, which, it was shown, could be reproduced in animals by the implantation of pneumococci into the lung alveoli and terminal bronchioles, provided that the cocci were suspended in mucin or a viscous starch solution (Robertson, 1938). Nungester & Klepser (1938) also produced the disease by introducing the mucous material into the bronchioles first and subsequently exposing the animals to a spray of pneumococci. These experiments suggest, therefore, that pneumoccal pneumonia might result from the inhalation of the bacteria in small particles that penetrate to the alveoli.

However, other investigations made around the same time suggest an alternative mode of infection. It was shown that mucous material deposited in the upper respiratory tract of animals could, in some circumstances, be drawn into the depths of the lung (Nungester & Klepser, 1938). Typical provoking factors were ether anaesthesia, alcohol intoxication and exposure to cold. These were all conditions that interfered with closure of the glottis, which normally acts as a mechanical protective to the lower respiratory tract; they may also interfere with the ciliary activity of the bronchial mucous membrane, and with the cough reflex, which normally act to clear the bronchial tree of inhaled particles. The same predisposing factors are recognized as aetiologically important in human pneumonia. Nungester, Klepser &

Kempf (1943) showed that, in addition, very deep inspiration could draw mucous material from the upper respiratory tract into the lungs in rats. It is thus entirely possible that the lung disease results from the accidental drawing into the lungs of infected mucus from the upper respiratory tract, in which case there would be no need to postulate that the disease had to be spread by small airborne particles.

Remarkably few studies have been published that give any direct evidence on the mode of transmission in man. In studies of a large epidemic in a U.S. Army Air Force camp (Hodges & MacLeod, 1946; Hodges, MacLeod & Bernhard, 1946), spread was thought to result from airborne dissemination in school rooms and it was noted that pneumococci were commonly found in floor dust. The incidence of pneumonia in different groups was closely related to the nasopharyngeal carrier rate among healthy men but there do not seem to be any studies to show whether nasopharyngeal carriage of a pneumococcus precedes the lung infection; the correlation of a high carrier rate with a high pneumonia rate in a group might merely indicate that spread was greater in some environments than others and that such spread might result either in pneumonia or upper respiratory tract carriage.

Pulmonary plague

Pulmonary infections with *Pasteurella pestis* have been extensively studied in the laboratory (Druett *et al.* 1956) and it has been shown that 1 micron particles initiate broncho-pneumonia in guinea-pigs, while inhalation of particles 10–12 microns in diameter leads to the rapid onset of septicaemia, presumably from invasion through the upper respiratory tract.

The human disease, plague, is ordinarily spread by the bite of infected fleas but there is a pulmonary form which is certainly spread through the air from man to man. Whether there is direct implantation in the lungs or spread from the upper respiratory tract is not known. Plague bacilli were recovered, often in very large numbers, in 'cough plates' exposed in air near patients with the pulmonary disease by Strong & Teague (1912) but as the plates were held open in front of the coughing patients, it is unlikely that many of the particles recognized were small enough to penetrate to the lung alveoli.

The epidemiology of the pulmonary disease is of great interest, though not fully understood. It seems to be related to weather conditions (Teague & Barber, 1912; Meyer, 1961); a particularly virulent epidemic occurred in Manchuria in 1910–11 at a time of especially cold weather. It is not known whether the association with cold is related to the overcrowding and lack of ventilation of dwellings in which the people stay to keep warm, or whether there is some direct action either on the respiratory tract or on the microbe. There is some experimental evidence for depression of the respiratory tract clearance mechanisms by exposure to cold (Green & Kass, 1964); and, under conditions of extreme cold, airborne droplets may persist much longer than they do in more temperate conditions. In parentheses it may be noted that the same problem of how cold weather may affect the spread of respiratory infections is seen with several virus diseases, especially the common cold (Lidwell *et al.* 1965). Although the association of pulmonary plague with cold weather has been observed in Kashmir and Japan as well as in Manchuria, it is not absolute; an outbreak in Oakland, California, occurred in April (Kellogg, 1920).

SEDIMENTATION INFECTION

Staphylococcal wound infection

During a surgical operation, the patient's tissues are exposed to the risk of infection from bacteria that settle from the air. Such bacteria may be derived from the members of the surgical team working in the operating room or, in some circumstances, they may be carried into the operating room on air currents. The second of these possibilities has received the greater precise study because of the difficulty, with infection transferred from the occupants of the room, of distinguishing between airborne infection and transfer by other routes.

Bourdillon & Colebrook (1946), studying the cross-infection of patients with extensive burns, laid the foundations for the modern study of air hygiene in surgical operating rooms; they stressed the importance of ventilating these rooms under a slight positive pressure to ensure that air from more contaminated parts of the hospital did not enter the dressing room. Later Shooter, Taylor, Ellis & Ross (1956) demonstrated the value of this type of ventilation in controlling staphylococcal infection of surgical wounds. Subsequently a great deal of thought has been given to the mechanics of hygienic ventilation in operating rooms (Report, 1962) but there have been no very satisfactory investigations that show just what proportion of the infections that occur are attributable to airborne spread. There are some reports suggesting that they do not occur (e.g. Howe & Marston, 1963) but these are based on failure to find staphylococci in the air during the operation on a patient who subsequently developed infection. These studies are difficult to interpret because the infection rate is ordinarily very low and because the numbers of staphylococci in the air are also low. Staphylococcal particles may fall into the wound or on to the culture plate, but generally there are probably too few to do both. Evidence for the importance of airborne spread is perhaps more likely to come from epidemiological studies and from the introduction of specific control methods, in either case on a rather large scale. One such attempt, using air disinfection with ultraviolet radiation, has been reported recently (Nat. Res. Council, 1964); there was some suggestion that the treatment may have reduced the infection rate in the clean incised wounds, that is, those for which alternative routes of infection were fewest. The difference was not very great. It seems likely that the contribution of airborne transfer to surgical wound infection is ordinarily small but may be substantial in some cases (Shooter *et al.* 1956; Blowers, Mason, Wallace & Walton, 1955).

DISCUSSION

Most standard medical text-books state that respiratory tract infections are spread by 'droplets', and sometimes by 'dust'. In much of the more specialist epidemiological literature the spread of respiratory infections has been attributed to 'droplet nuclei', and the term airborne infection has been reserved for this transfer by small particles which, it is often tacitly assumed, penetrate to the depths of the lungs (Riley & O'Grady, 1961).

There is virtually only one study of the size of the airborne bacteria-carrying particles as they actually exist in occupied places (Noble *et al.* 1963) and this was confined to very few species, mostly non-pathogenic. But the study does show that there is a continuous distribution in the sizes of airborne particles carrying bacteria and that the greatest number are in the 8–16 microns size range. This is larger than the traditional 'droplet nuclei' and too large to penetrate to the lung alveoli, but 12-micron particles have a settling rate in normally turbulent air of only 1·2 ft./min. and so can be carried considerable distances in air currents. The smaller particles that penetrate to the alveoli seem to be relatively rare among the infected particles discharged from the upper respiratory tract during talking, coughing and sneezing, and they are probably very rare indeed among the infected epithelial squames shed from the skin. Most diseases of respiratory entry thus probably result from upper respiratory tract deposition, with, in some cases, subsequent spread to other parts of the tract. Tuberculosis is the outstanding exception, and this presumably because the bacilli are unable to establish themselves with ease after deposition in the upper respiratory tract.

So far there seems to have been very little attempt to determine what factors determine the different areas of preference in the respiratory tract of the various pathogenic (or commensal) bacteria; it seems very improbable that this is determined by differences in the areas in which primary deposition takes place. Since each of the different parts of the respiratory tract has a characteristic epithelial covering, and often a quite characteristic commensal microbial flora, the development of methods to study this problem might be of great value. Associated with this is a need to discover more precisely the methods by which bacteria from the upper respiratory tract can reach the lower part of the tract, in the face of all the mechanical and physiological defences.

The latest hey-day of airborne infection was ushered in by Wells, in the 1930's, who looked to a development of 'sanitary ventilation' that would eliminate respiratory tract infections in the way that purification of drinking water has virtually eliminated the enteric fevers. That this hope remains unrealized is presumably because so few of the respiratory diseases are like tuberculosis in apparently requiring deposition of the microbe in the lung alveoli, and which, therefore, can be conveyed only by the very small proportion of 2–3 micron particles that are liberated during coughing and other expiratory activities. No dramatic control of the spread of the larger, shorter-range droplets could be expected from any of the methods of air sanitation in common use, and none has been observed. Some effect might be expected with the particles of intermediate size and there are some hints that streptococcal infections (Med. Res. Council, 1954) and staphylococcal infection (see Williams, 1966) may be affected to some extent. But it appears that with most of the infections we encounter, transfer by routes susceptible to 'sanitary ventilation' constitutes only a small part of all the transfer that takes place and the reduction in dosage that we can achieve in practice is often too small to have a detectable effect on the incidence of infection.

REFERENCES

ARNOULD, E. (1942). Contagion tuberculeuse et produits d'expectoration. *Presse méd.* **50**, 613.

AUGUSTINE, A. E. (1929). The transfer of tuberculosis by dust and other agents. *J. prevent. Med.* 3, 121.

BLOWERS, R., MASON, G. A., WALLACE, K. R. & WALTON, M. (1955). Control of wound infection in a thoracic surgery unit. *Lancet*, ii, 786.

BOURDILLON, R. B. & COLEBROOK, L. (1946). Air hygiene in dressing rooms for burns and major wounds. *Lancet*, i, 561, 601.

BRACHMAN, P. S., KAUFMANN, A. F. & DALLDORF, F. G. (1966). Industrial inhalation anthrax. *Bact. Rev.* **30**, 646.

BRACHMAN, P. S., PLOTKIN, S. A., BUMFORD, F. H. & ATCHISON, M. M. (1960). An epidemic of inhalation anthrax: the first in the twentieth century. II. Epidemiology. *Am. J. Hyg.* **72**, 6.

CHAPMAN, J. S. & DYERLY, M. D. (1964). Presumably infected premises with respect to conversion of the tuberculin test. *Am. Rev. resp. Dis.* **89**, 197.

DAHLGREN, C. M., BUCHANAN, L. M., DECKER, H. M., FREED, S. W., PHILLIPS, C. R. & BRACHMAN, P. S. (1960). *Bacillus anthracis* aerosols in goat hair processing mills. *Am. J. Hyg.* **72**, 24.

DAVIES, R. R. & NOBLE, W. C. (1962). Dispersal of microorganisms on desquamated skin. *Lancet*, ii, 1295.

DRUETT, H. A., HENDERSON, D. W., PACKMAN, L. & PEACOCK, S. (1953). Studies on respiratory infection. I. The influence of particle size on respiratory infection with anthrax spores. *J. Hyg., Camb.* **51**, 359.

DRUETT, H. A., ROBINSON, J. M., HENDERSON, D. W., PACKMAN, L. & PEACOCK, S. (1956). Studies on respiratory infection. II. The influence of aerosol particle size on infection of the guinea-pig with *Pasteurella pestis*. *J. Hyg., Camb.* **54**, 37.

GLOVER, J. A. (1920). Observations of the meningococcus carrier rate, and their application to the prevention of cerebrospinal fever. *Spec. Rep. Ser. med. Res. Counc.* no. 50, 133.

GREEN, G. M. & KASS, E. H. (1964). Factors influencing the clearance of bacteria by the lung. *J. clin. Invest.* **43**, 769.

HAMBURGER, M. JR, GREEN, M. J. & HAMBURGER, V. G. (1945). The problem of the 'dangerous carrier' of Hemolytic streptococci. I. Number of Hemolytic streptococci expelled by carriers with positive and negative nose cultures. *J. infect. Dis.* **77**, 68.

HODGES, R. G. & MACLEOD, C. M. (1946). Epidemic pneumococcal pneumonia. II. The influence of population characteristics and environment. *Am. J. Hyg.* **44**, 193.

HODGES, R. G., MACLEOD, C. M. & BERNHARD, W. G. (1946). Epidemic pneumococcal pneumonia. III. Pneumococcal carrier studies. *Am. J. Hyg.* **44**, 207.

HOLMES, M. C. & WILLIAMS, R. E. O. (1958). Streptococcal infection among children in a residential home. IV. Outbreaks of infection. *J. Hyg., Camb.* **56**, 211.

HOWE, C. W. & MARSTON, A. T. (1963). Qualitative and quantitative bacteriologic studies on hospital air as related to postoperative wound sepsis. *J. Lab. clin. Med.* **61**, 808.

KELLOGG, W. H. (1920). An epidemic of pneumonic plague. *Am. J. publ. Hlth*, **10**, 599.

LANGE, B. (1926). Weitere Untersuchungen über die Bedeutung der Staubinfektion bei der Tuberkulose. *Z. Hyg. InfektKrankhr.* **106**, 1.

LAPEYSSONNIE, L. (1963). La méningite cérébro-spinale en Afrique. *Bull. World Hlth Org.* **28** (Suppl.).

LE NOIR, P. & CAMUS, J. (1909). Recherches sur la contagion de la tuberculose par l'air. *C. r. hebd. Séanc. Acad. Sci., Paris*, **148**, 309.

LIDWELL, O. M., MORGAN, R. W. & WILLIAMS, R. E. O. (1965). The epidemiology of the common cold. IV. The effect of weather. *J. Hyg., Camb.* **63**, 427.

LIDWELL, O. M., NOBLE, W. C. & DOLPHIN, G. W. (1959). The use of radiation to estimate the numbers of micro-organisms in air-borne particles. *J. Hyg., Camb.* **57**, 299.

LIDWELL, O. M., POLAKOFF, S., JEVONS, M. P., PARKER, M. T., SHOOTER, R. A., FRENCH, V. I. & DUNKERLEY, D. R. (1966). Staphylococcal infection in thoracic surgery: experience in a subdivided ward. *J. Hyg., Camb.* **64**, 321.

LINCOLN, E. M. (1965). Epidemics of tuberculosis. *Fortschr. TuberkForsch.* **14**, 157.

LOOSLI, C. G., SMITH, M. H. D., CLINE, J. & NELSON, L. (1950). The transmission of hemolytic streptococcal infections in infant wards with special reference to 'skin dispersers'. *J. Lab. clin. Med.* **36**, 342.

MEDICAL RESEARCH COUNCIL AIR HYGIENE COMMITTEE (1954). Air disinfection with ultra-violet irradiation. *Spec. rep. Ser. med. Res. Counc.* no. 283.

MEYER, K. F. (1961). Pneumonic plague. *Bact. Rev.* **25**, 249.

MINISTRY OF LABOUR (1959). Report of the Committee of Inquiry on Anthrax. London: H.M.S.O.

MORTIMER, E. A., JR, LIPSITZ, P. J., WOLINSKY, E., GONZAGA, A. J. & RAMMEL-KAMP, C. H., JR (1962). Transmission of staphylococci between newborns. Importance of the hands of personnel. *Am. J. Dis. Child.* **104**, 289.

MORTIMER, E. A., JR, WOLINSKY, E., GONZAGA, A. J. & RAMMELKAMP, C. H. (1966). Role of airborne transmission in staphylococcal infections. *Brit. med. J.* i, 319.

NATIONAL RESEARCH COUNCIL (1964). Post-operative wound infections: the influence of ultraviolet irradiation on the operating room and of various other factors. *Ann. Surg.* **160**, suppl. to no. 2.

NOBLE, W. C. & DAVIES, R. R. (1965). Studies on the dispersal of staphylococci. *J. clin. Path.* **18**, 16.

NOBLE, W. C., LIDWELL, O. M. & KINGSTON, D. (1963). The size distribution of airborne particles carrying micro-organisms. *J. Hyg., Camb.* **61**, 385.

NORMAN, P. S., RAY, J. G., JR, BRACHMAN, P. S., PLOTKIN, S. A. & PAGANO, J. S. (1960). Serologic testing for anthrax antibodies in a goat hair processing mill. *Am. J. Hyg.* **72**, 32.

NUNGESTER, W. J. & KLEPSER, R. G. (1938). A possible mechanism of lowered resistance to pneumonia. *J. infect. Dis.* **63**, 94.

NUNGESTER, W. J., KLEPSER, R. G. & KEMPF, A. H. (1943). Consideration of the respiratory pattern as a predisposing factor in the etiology of pneumonia. *J. infect. Dis.* **71**, 57.

NYKA, W. (1962). Studies on the infective particle in air-borne tuberculosis. I. Observations in mice infected with a bovine strain of *M. tuberculosis. Am. Rev. resp. Dis.* **85**, 33.

PLOTKIN, S. A., BRACHMAN, P. S., UTELL, M., BUMFORD, F. H. & ATCHISON, M. M. (1960). An epidemic of inhalation anthrax, the first in the twentieth century. *Am. J. Med.* **29**, 992.

PROCTOR, D. F. (1966). Airborne disease and the upper respiratory tract. *Bact. Rev.* **30**, 498.

RAMMELKAMP, C. H., JR, MORRIS, A. J., CATANZARO, F. J., WANNAMAKER, L. W., CHAMOVITZ, R. & MARPLE, E. C. (1958). Transmission of Group A streptococci. III. The effect of drying on the infectivity of the organism for man. *J. Hyg., Camb.* **56**, 280.

RATCLIFFE, H. L. (1952). Tuberculosis induced by droplet nuclei infection. Pulmonary tuberculosis of predetermined initial intensity in mammals. *Am. J. Hyg.* **55**, 36.

REPORT (1962). By Operating-Theatre Hygiene Subcommittee, Medical Research Council Committee on Control of Cross-Infection. Design and ventilation of operating-room suites for control of infection and for comfort. *Lancet*, ii, 945.

RICKETTS, C. R., SQUIRE, J. R. & TOPLEY, E. (1951). Human skin lipids with particular reference to the self-sterilizing power of the skin. *Clin. Sci.* **10**, 89.

RILEY, R. L., MILLS, C. C., O'GRADY, F., SULTAN, L. U., WITTSTADT, F. & SHIVPURI, D. N. (1962). Infectiousness of air from a tuberculosis ward. Ultraviolet irradiation of infected air: comparative infectiousness of different patients. *Am. Rev. resp. Dis.* **85**, 511.

RILEY, R. L. & O'GRADY, F. (1961). *Airborne infection.* New York: Macmillan.
ROBERTSON, O. H. (1938). Recent studies on experimental lobar pneumonia. *J. Am. med. Ass.* **111**, 1432.
ROSS, J. M. (1957). The pathogenesis of anthrax following the administration of spores by the respiratory route. *J. Path. Bact.* **73**, 485.
SHINEFIELD, H. R., RIBLE, J. C., DORIS, M. & EICHENWALD, H. F. (1963). Bacterial interference: its effect on nursery-acquired infection with *Staphylococcus aureus.* I. Preliminary observations on artificial colonization of newborns. *Am. J. Dis. Child.* **105**, 646.
SHOOTER, R. A., TAYLOR, G. W., ELLIS, G. & ROSS, SIR J. P. (1956). Postoperative wound infection. *Surgery Gynec. Obstet.* **103**, 257.
SOLBERG, C. O. (1965). A study of carriers of *Staphylococcus aureus.* *Acta med. Scand.* **178**, Suppl. 436.
STEWART, A. & HUGHES, J. P. W. (1951). Mass radiography in the boot and shoe industry, 1945–46. *Brit. med. J.* i, 899.
STRONG, R. P. & TEAGUE, O. (1912). Studies on pneumonic plague and plague immunization. II. The method of transmission of the infection in pneumonic plague and manner of spread of the disease during the epidemic. *Philipp. J. Sci.* **7**, Sect. B, 137.
TEAGUE, O. & BARBER, M. A. (1912). Studies on pneumonic plague and plague immunization. III. Influence of atmospheric temperature on the spread of pneumonic plague. *Philipp. J. Sci.* **7**, Sect. B, 157.
WADDY, B. B. (1957). African epidemic cerebro-spinal meningitis. *J. trop. Med. Hyg.* **60**, 179, 218.
WANNAMAKER, L. (1954). The epidemiology of streptococcal infections. In *Streptococcal Infections,* p. 157. Ed. M. McCarty. New York: Columbia University Press.
WELLS, W. F. & WELLS, M. W. (1936). Air-borne infection. *J. Am. med. Ass.* **107**, 1698, 1805.
WILLIAMS, R. E. O. (1963). Healthy carriage of *Staphylococcus aureus:* its prevalence and importance. *Bact. Rev.* **27**, 56.
WILLIAMS, R. E. O. (1966). Epidemiology of airborne staphylococcal infection. *Bact. Rev.* **30**, 660.
WILLIAMS, R. E. O., NOBLE, W. C., JEVONS, M. P., LIDWELL, O. M., SHOOTER, R. A., WHITE, R. G., THOM, B. T. & TAYLOR, G. W. (1962). Isolation for the control of staphylococcal infection in surgical wards. *Brit. med. J.* ii, 275.

THE SPREAD OF VIRUSES OF THE RESPIRATORY TRACT BY THE AIRBORNE ROUTE

D. A. J. TYRRELL

The Common Cold Research Unit, Harvard Hospital, Coombe Road, Salisbury, Wiltshire

INTRODUCTION

It is widely believed that the viruses which cause diseases of the upper and lower respiratory tract are transmitted from patient to patient though the air, by a method often loosely termed 'droplet' infection. Before techniques of virus cultivation were available this belief represented an intelligent guess, with, naturally enough, no precise data to support or refute it. However, many epidemiological observations on respiratory infections of man were reported during this period and the results obtained are still of great importance. It is obvious that any experimental work on the transmission of individual viruses or theories derived from it must be consistent with basic facts derived from 'shoe leather' epidemiology. It is proposed, therefore, to summarize some of the earlier epidemiological findings and then to describe experimental observations on the production, survival and uptake of airborne droplets containing viruses. Although these experimental results are still fragmentary an attempt will then be made to show how far they may be used to explain the known facts of epidemiology. Because of the limited knowledge of the author the article will deal almost entirely with human disease.

THE EPIDEMIOLOGY OF RESPIRATORY DISEASE IN MAN

People in Britain and the U.S.A. suffer from two to ten acute respiratory illnesses each year—the exact number depends on the age, the environment and also on the number of symptoms and signs which each investigator requires to be present before he diagnoses a respiratory illness (for review see Tyrrell, 1965). Most of these illnesses are common colds, in which the main symptoms are nasal but sometimes the throat, larynx, trachea or bronchi are involved. Pneumonia is not common. About one-third of the diseases can be shown to be due to viruses (Working Party, 1965) but, as techniques improve, a larger proportion of cases can be specifically diagnosed as being due to virus infection (Tyrrell & Bynoe, 1966). Bacteria are relatively unimportant, at least in the initiation of these diseases.

It has been shown that, in a rural area, a great many colds can be ascribed to contact a few days before with someone else who has a cold (Lidwell & Sommerville, 1951). The illness is most readily caught by and transmitted by children (Lidwell & Williams, 1961) and it seems that rather prolonged personal contact, such as occurs in the home or school, is required, rather than the casual contacts which occur elsewhere. In really isolated communities such as in the islands of Spitzbergen and Tristan da Cunha or polar research stations, waves of colds occur, beginning immediately after the arrival of ships which may not necessarily be carrying someone with an overt respiratory infection (Paul & Freese, 1933; Woolley, 1963; Andrewes, 1948). These epidemics last for a few weeks and then disappear, until the arrival of another ship. It has been found at the Common Cold Research Unit that rooms which have been used by volunteers with experimental colds are not liable to transmit the disease to other volunteers who come to live in them 4 days after they have left, even though they are in no way sterilized but merely subjected to ordinary household cleaning. This implies that cold-causing viruses do not survive long in a normal domestic environment, or cannot be transmitted from fomites. There are no reports of the transmission of colds by food or water.

In summary it may be said that the agents which cause colds are apparently common in most communities and never really disappear, and that they are: (1) transmitted by direct personal contact which is rather prolonged or close; and (2) usually transmitted by people with obvious signs of disease, but sometimes by those who seem to be well.

It is widely believed that colds are caused by cold, but the experimental evidence shows that chilling does not induce colds or increase the frequency with which volunteers develop colds after experimental infection (Andrewes, 1960; Andrewes & Allison, 1961; Dowling, 1957). Nevertheless, when the weather becomes colder the number of colds in an urban or rural community increases. It has been shown that this increase of incidence takes place simultaneously over large areas of the country and in tropical as well as in temperate areas (Van Loghem, 1928; Townsend, 1924; Sutton, 1965). Some have inferred from this that viruses are often carried in the throat or nose and that these may be stirred into activity by chilling the subject or the air he breathes (Hope-Simpson, 1958). As mentioned above, there is experimental evidence that chilling experimental subjects does not produce colds and it is therefore possible that the efficiency of transmission of virus from one patient to another is increased in cold conditions and that it is this which gives rise to an epidemic wave of colds when the weather becomes cold. Such an increase in the efficiency of transmission should lead to an increase in the secondary attack rate, i.e. the proportion of persons who are exposed to a patient with a cold and who catch one within a few days of his illness. Certainly, such evidence as there is suggests that the secondary attack rates of colds is higher in winter than summer (Brimblecombe *et al.* 1958).

POSSIBLE ROUTES OF TRANSMISSION

When a person coughs, talks or sneezes he is likely to expel small droplets of saliva or respiratory secretion, and these may become dried down rapidly and remain airborne as droplet nuclei, or attach to clothing or furniture and then be resuspended later. The airborne droplet nuclei might be inhaled and the virus they contain might then land on susceptible cells in the upper or lower respiratory tract and there initiate infection. In view of the epidemiological results we should expect to find that droplet nuclei are an important means of infection, and this view was supported by experiments performed at the Common Cold Research Unit (Lovelock *et al.* 1952). Children and adults with colds spent 2 hr. in a room where they 'were encouraged to play games involving talking, shouting or singing' and sneezing powder was released into the atmosphere half way through the experiment. By means of a fan the air of this room was circulated past a blanket barrier into an adjacent area in which volunteers sat. Of a total of twenty-five exposed, two caught colds. This is the same rate of infection as that obtained in an experiment in which the donors of the cold virus had eaten and played games together for 2 hr. (three colds in thirty-two exposed). Nevertheless, at least 30 % of volunteers are usually infected by direct intranasal instillation of virus, so transmission does not seem to be very efficient.

However, it should not be forgotten that viruses may be transported extensively in the body—they are commonly carried to the skin and the nervous system in the blood-stream. In addition, respiratory secretions may get on to the hand and thence to many other objects in a room and even into the food or on to the skin of other people. It is therefore possible that respiratory infections may be transmitted by non-respiratory routes. Indeed some viruses which cause respiratory diseases, such as enteroviruses or adenoviruses, may be shed in large amounts in the faeces; therefore, particularly among children whose hygiene may be rather perfunctory, respiratory viruses may get into the mouth from either faeces or nasal secretion. In addition, although pharyngitis or sore throat is commonly called a respiratory infection, this part of the respiratory tract actually belongs to the alimentary tract too and might well be infected by virus introduced through the mouth. However, as mentioned above, there is no epidemiological evidence for food-borne epidemics of colds and respiratory disease, so they are unlikely to occur commonly.

EXPERIMENTAL STUDY OF MECHANISMS OF DISPERSION

Granted that many different routes can be envisaged by which a virus can get from one patient to the next, one of the most important questions to be answered by experimental means is 'How *much* virus is likely to pass from one patient to the next by each of the imagined routes?' and 'How likely is it to induce an infection if it arrives?'. The experimental results bearing on this can be subdivided into several groups and are reviewed below.

Production and discharge of viruses

Acute respiratory disease may be produced by many viruses belonging to quite different biological groups and, although there are very few

Table 1. *Site of recovery of viruses causing respiratory disease from patients*

Group	Type	Virus recovered from			
		Nose	Throat	Sputum	Faeces
Myxoviruses	Influenza A and B	+	+	+	−
	Parainfluenza 1–3	+	+	?	−
	Respiratory syncytial	+	+	?	−
Adenoviruses	1, 2, 5, 6	?	+	?	+
	3, 7, 14, 21	?	+	?	+
Picornaviruses	Rhinoviruses	+	+	(+)	−
	Coxsackievirus A 21	+	+	N.D.	±
	Coxsackievirus A (other)	−	+	N.D.	+
	Coxsackievirus B	?	+	N.D.	+

quantitative results, it is clear that they are all found in respiratory secretions collected as washings or swabs from the nose or throat or as sputum. General experience in this field is summarized in Table 1. This shows that some viruses are also shed in the faeces and that it is not known whether others are usually present in the nasal secretions or not. The concentration of viruses in nasal washings and garglings from patients with influenza may be as high as 10^3 ID 50†/ml. when titrated in tissue cultures, and faecal specimens containing enteroviruses may titre 10^5/g. but there is too little information to relate these amounts to the spread of virus infections.

Some of the information obtained from the study of volunteers experimentally inoculated with rhinoviruses may be of value here. Volunteer studies at Salisbury using rhinoviruses which had not been passed in tissue culture showed a peak in the titre of virus in the nasal secretion about the time of onset of symptoms (Fig. 1), and also indicated that there could be large differences between the titres of virus

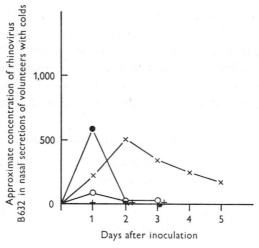

Fig. 1. The titre of virus in the nasal secretion of 4 subjects infected with a rhinovirus.

present in the secretions of different patients with colds of very similar degrees of severity (Tyrrell, 1963). In American studies it was shown that patients who have circulatory antibody excrete less virus than those who have none, but it is unlikely that this is the whole explanation of the differences observed (Mufson *et al*. 1963).

If normal subjects are given nasal drops containing bacterial spores it is possible to recover these by swabbing the throat and mouth and to assay them quantitatively (Buckland & Tyrrell, 1964). In this way it was shown that nasal secretions are carried rapidly into the throat, although the concentration there is usually much lower than in nasal secretion (Fig. 2). Some pharyngeal material may then apparently be transported into the mouth, but is rapidly transported back again into the pharynx and swallowed. These studies were followed up by

† 50% infectious doses.

investigating volunteers inoculated with coxsackievirus A 21 (Buckland & Tyrrell, 1965). This virus is known to cause colds and pharyngitis and is biologically much like a rhinovirus, although more convenient to work with in volunteers. The volunteers were inoculated in several different ways but in all cases infection was established in the nose. It

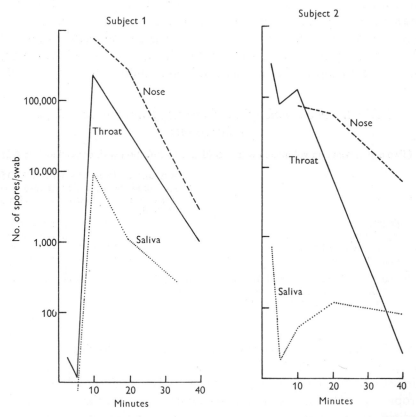

Fig. 2. *Concentration.* Number of spores recovered by swabbing normal subjects at intervals after placing 10^8 spores on the anterior nasal septum (Buckland & Tyrrell, 1964).

seemed that infected nasal secretion overflowed into the pharynx and sometimes into the mouth just as was found in the tracer experiments with spores. By far the highest concentrations of virus were found in the nose which therefore seems likely to be the main source of virus in the transmission of the infection; just as in the case of the rhinoviruses there were differences of several orders of magnitude in the concentration of virus in the nasal secretion of different patients with similar colds.

A great deal of work has been done on the dispersal of bacteria from the mouth and pharynx and from the nose of normal carriers (e.g.

Duguid, 1945; Hare & MacKenzie, 1946; Hamburger, Green & Hamburger, 1945); however, we have given elsewhere our reasons for believing that the results so obtained are not really applicable to the spread of many viruses of the respiratory tract. Experiments on normal subjects with tracers in the nose and on patients with colds due to cox-sackievirus A 21 show that infected droplets are dispersed efficiently into the air by sneezing, and not by talking or coughing (Table 2). Blowing a nose also disperses airborne droplets because a handkerchief only traps the larger droplets of 20 microns or more in diameter, which would drop out of the air rapidly in any case. Different individuals vary consider-

Table 2. *An example of the dispersal of virus by sneezing and other means*

(Two experiments on volunteers with a cold due to infection with coxsackievirus A 21.)

	Amount of infectious virus (TCD 50) recovered from plastic bag into which virus was dispersed by indicated method.	
Coughing	0	(1 replicate)
Talking (5 min.)	0 : 0	(2 replicates)
Blowing the nose (3 times)	0 : 9,000	(2 replicates)
Sneezing (10 times)	16,000 : 1,600	(2 replicates)

30,000 TCD 50 were recovered from the handkerchief used to blow the nose. Virus was found in the air of the bag only once,— 40 TCD 50 after one sneeze.
Data of volunteer B on days 3 and 4 (Buckland & Tyrrell, 1965).

ably in their ability to produce droplets on blowing their noses (Buckland & Tyrrell, 1965). In summary then, it is likely that rhino-viruses and other viruses which cause colds are dispersed as airborne droplets of infected nasal secretion, but there are likely to be large individual variations in the amount of secretion so dispersed and in the concentration of virus in the secretion, although it usually reaches a peak just after the onset of a cold. It is unlikely that the same results will apply in detail to other respiratory viruses. For example, clinical evidence suggests that coughing may play a significant part in the transmission of influenza virus (Watson, 1960). In other cases such as the enteroviruses and adenoviruses, virus is largely produced in the throat, and it is then likely that contamination of the saliva may lead to the expulsion of significant amounts of virus from the mouth, as in streptococcal infections. However, this requires experimental study and it may be impossible to recover poliovirus from the mouth of patients who are carrying it in the throat.

The fate of expelled virus

It has been shown that the tracer expelled from the nose in a sneeze is carried on droplets of many sizes. As shown in Table 3, and as might have been predicted, the majority of these fall out rapidly, and any which land on fabrics are unlikely to be readily resuspended. By the time of sampling, about half the spores are carried on droplets larger than about 4 microns which are therefore likely to be trapped in the upper respiratory tract or in a preimpinger, and the remainder are carried in droplets of less than 4 microns which would be trapped in the lower respiratory tract or an impinger sampler.

Table 3. *Fate of nasal secretion expelled by sneezing in an open room*

Means of recovery	Number of spores recovered
Glass plate 56 × 30 cm. underneath chin of sneezer	2,000,000
Sticky vertical glass slide (≡ conjunctiva)	10
Preimpinger (≡ nose)	970
Impinger (≡ lower respiratory tract)	500

10^8 spores were placed in the anterior nasal septum—about one-quarter of these are expelled by an average sneeze. Three different methods of sampling were used to mimic three different ways by which the airborne particle might reach the human respiratory tract.

The virus in these droplets is likely to be damaged in the process of desiccation and also to be inactivated after the droplet nucleus has formed. This has in fact been demonstrated in various laboratory experiments. When viruses are sprayed into containers it can be shown that the rate of loss of infectivity is influenced by temperature—for inactivation is more rapid at higher temperatures (Harper, 1963). It is also influenced by humidity, for some viruses are inactivated most rapidly at high values of relative humidity and others at low values (Hemmes, Winkler & Kool, 1960). The exact effect of humidity probably depends on the structure of the virus; in one set of studies it seemed that lipid-containing viruses survived better at low relative humidity while those containing only protein and nucleic acid survived better at high relative humidity (Buckland & Tyrrell, 1962).

In addition, it was thought possible that viruses, like bacteria, might survive better in larger droplets than in smaller ones, and this has indeed been demonstrated (Table 4), although so far no studies have been made of virus suspended in respiratory secretions. It was thought that this study might show that viruses, such as the myxoviruses, which spread particularly effectively and invade the lower respiratory tract, are not

Table 4. *Loss of infectivity of viruses mixed with tracer spores and sprayed into room air*

Log₁₀ of geometric mean loss of infectivity when sampled at indicated period after spraying

Type	No. of tests	R.H.(%)	0–4 min.		10–14 min.		Drop in 10 min. after spraying	
			Preimpinger†	Impinger	Preimpinger	Impinger	Preimpinger	Impinger
Influenza A. Swine	2	30–38	0·38	0·04	0·60	0·23	0·22	0·19
Parainfluenza 1	2	58, 72	−0·49	0·25	−0·43	0·15	0·06	−0·1
Adenovirus SV17	1	38	1·08	1·03	1·10	2·40	−0·02	1·37
Enteroviruses								
Polio 1	3	44–53	1·07	1·24	0·99	1·59	−0·06	0·35
Coxsackievirus A21	3, 1	38, 53	1·01	0·92	(2·10)	(2·22)	(1·09)	(1·30)
Rhinovirus H.G.P.	2	41, 45	−0·23	0·47	0·08	1·17	0·31	0·82

Based on unpublished experiments of Buckland, Doggett & Tyrrell (1965).

† Preimpinger samplers collected particles of roughly 4 microns in diameter and greater which would be trapped in the nose. Impinger samplers collected particles less than 4 microns in diameter which would be trapped in the lower respiratory tract. The techniques used are described by Buckland & Tyrrell (1965).

much damaged by spraying into room air and seem to be able to survive in small droplets. Similarly, the rhinovirus is well preserved in coarser droplets on spraying but inactivated in finer ones, whereas viruses which apparently spread with difficulty by the airborne route—poliovirus, coxsackievirus A21 and an adenovirus—are rapidly inactivated in large and small droplets on spraying. Obviously more studies are needed to determine whether this apparent connection between survival droplets and epidemiological behaviour is significant.

Summarizing observations on respiratory infections of man, only a tiny proportion of expelled virus is likely to remain airborne long enough to be inhaled, and in many cases this virus rapidly loses infectivity in the air.

Infection of the respiratory tract by airborne viruses

It is clear that airborne viruses are likely to become impacted on the mucociliary blanket in the nose, which possesses a quite efficient mechanism for cleansing the inspired air. However, the particles may also land on the conjunctiva, the outside of the nose and the lower respiratory tract. In order to understand fully the significance of these possible events it is necessary to know something of the amount of infectious virus likely to land in each of these areas and the likelihood that, having landed, it will initiate an infection.

In model experiments, droplets from a natural or artificial sneeze were traced with spores and it was shown that very few were impacted on a vertical sticky surface simulating the conjunctiva (Buckland & Tyrrell, 1964)—a finding consistent with the results reported by Chamberlain (p. 143). In our experiments it was also shown that the tracer was recovered roughly equally from the impinger and the preimpinger sampler. Other experiments, mentioned above, showed that much more of the coxsackievirus and the rhinovirus was inactivated in the fine particles which were trapped in the preimpinger. It can therefore be assumed that natural infection is most likely to be carried by virus incorporated in the coarser particles of the size trapped in the preimpinger sampler or in the nose.

This hypothesis is plausible only if the virus is capable of infecting the nose effectively, and this seems at first sight unlikely because of the speed and efficiency with which trapped particulate matter is transported out of the nose by ciliary action. Nevertheless, preliminary experiments showed that when a rhinovirus was swabbed on the conjunctiva or the nose there followed an infection in the nose (Bynoe *et al.* 1961), but virus swabbed on the throat did not initiate an infection. However, Papp &

Banks, 1958) believe that measles virus usually infects by landing on the
conjunctiva since the former produced more cases by placing virus on
the conjunctiva than by painting it on the buccal mucosa or throat or
instilling it into the nose. More detailed experiments with coxsackievirus A21 showed that volunteers could be readily infected with small
doses of the virus swabbed on to the nasal septum but that the pharynx
was less susceptible (Table 5). It was also shown that about the same
amount of virus—one tissue-culture infectious dose—was required to
infect the nose in the form of a droplet produced by an artificial sneeze,
or as a small drop delivered from a fine pipette. A large amount of
virus *put* on the volunteer's finger failed to initiate an infection just as in
earlier experiments uncharacterized virus put on the outer cutaneous
surface of the nose did not produce colds (Lovelock *et al.* 1952).

Table 5. *Amount of coxsackievirus A21 required to infect
human volunteers*

Mode of administration	Number of TCD50 inducing infection
Hand and nose	>1,500
Conjunctiva	≤16
Oropharynx	≥280
Nasopharynx	≥280
Nasal septum	0·8

Fine aerosols have been used by workers in the U.S.A., who have
shown that it is possible in this way to infect the lower respiratory tract
of man with coxsackievirus A21.

One of the strains of virus used induced tracheo-bronchitis in the
volunteers. Tracheo-bronchitis has also been induced with a similar
aerosol of a rhinovirus (Cate *et al.* 1965). The fact that natural infections with these viruses are usually manifested as upper respiratory tract
disease therefore suggests that they are usually transmitted as droplets
which impact in the nose.

THE RELATIONSHIP OF EXPERIMENTAL RESULTS TO THE EPIDEMIOLOGY OF UPPER RESPIRATORY DISEASE OF MAN

We may conclude from the field experiments with one coxsackievirus
and a few rhinoviruses that rather small amounts of respiratory viruses
are shed into the air during colds and that they die rapidly on drying;
this is consistent with the epidemiologist's conclusion that the diseases

are transmitted by close personal contact indoors, and not by fomites. It is nevertheless to be hoped that further experiments will investigate the shedding and uptake of other viruses which cause respiratory disease as they may not all behave in the same way.

Nevertheless, it is worth trying to apply these limited results to outstanding problems. For instance we may try to understand why respiratory diseases are more common in the autumn and winter and why they increase in frequency 2 or 3 days after the temperature of the air drops (Lidwell, Morgan & Williams, 1965). As mentioned elsewhere this may occur because more virus is shed due to an increase in the amount of nasal discharge, perhaps because of a direct reflex response of the nose. However, we do not understand fully the effects of climate and other sorts of stress on the response of man to virus infection; there is evidence that stresses such as vaccination and recruit training may increase the frequency with which men either become infected or manifest an illness if they do (Arlander *et al.* 1965) and an increase in the frequency of manifest illness would probably lead to an increase in the amount of contamination of the air. On the other hand, closing windows and reducing ventilation may be the most important factor.

This discussion so far has been based rather heavily on conclusions drawn from cases with illness with nasal discharge and infections due to picornaviruses. However, quite different diseases may well be transmitted by the airborne route. One of these, smallpox, has recently been studied carefully (Downie *et al.* 1965). It is widely believed that human beings are infected by inhalation of airborne virus. It was found in this case that relatively little virus was discharged from the mouth even when there were obvious lesions of the mucous membrane; relatively little was found in impinger samplers, but rather more in settle plates which were held near the mouth and would collect virus carried in really large droplets. Large amounts of virus were found in the pocks and in the crusts which form when these break down. Smallpox virus resists desiccation on fabrics and it was found that virus could be readily recovered from pillows and other bedding and that airborne virus could be recovered after shaking the blankets. The whole pattern resembles that observed in bacterial disease, although it is still possible that, like streptococci (Rammelkamp *et al.* 1958), the virus which has been dried may not infect man as readily as freshly shed virus does.

The transmission of measles virus is reduced by ultraviolet irradiation of classrooms while the transmission of colds is not (Reid, Lidwell & Williams, 1956). This may be because measles is transmitted by virus carried on fine particles which remain airborne a long time and travel far enough to be exposed to the light. On the other hand, it could mean that the probability of acquiring measles in the classroom is relatively much higher than that of acquiring a cold virus which might be transmitted more frequently out of school. Hope-Simpson (1966) has drawn attention to an anomaly in the way in which respiratory syncytial virus infections are usually found in infants who are often at home and virtually out of contact with other infected infants. It is known that children and adults can be infected with the virus and develop mild coryzal illnesses, but such infections are in fact rarely detected. However, it is possible that some children are infected but shed too little virus to be detected by laboratory methods although their secretions contain enough to infect the highly susceptible cells in the infants' respiratory tract, and possibly other children or adults.

It is possible also that one virus may, under different circumstances, be transmitted in different ways. For example, it is widely believed that, from time to time, poliovirus may be transmitted by 'droplet' infection rather than by the usual faecal-oral route.

One is impressed with the possibility that important elements in the epidemiological chain may depend, not on the average or the most common individual, particle or type of activity, but on a rather special one. Virus is probably spread mainly by individuals who excrete particularly high concentrations of virus. Only the tiny fraction of virus which is in particles of just the right size and composition is likely to initiate another infection successfully. It is also possible that a very small fraction of certain viruses may be more stable than we guess at present. Perhaps a new technique would enable us to detect a small, stable, airborne virus particle produced by patients infected with influenza, parainfluenza or respiratory syncytial virus and so explain how it is that they spread so efficiently and so often produce symptoms related to the lower respiratory tract. In any case we must start to consider the capacity to spread in man more seriously when evaluating which of the new serotypes of influenza virus are likely to cause epidemics. There have been several examples recently of radically new serotypes of influenza which cause localized outbreaks but never produced a big epidemic—possibly because they lacked a biological property essential for efficient airborne transmission from man to man (Pereira, 1966, personal communication).

Finally it seems necessary to escape as soon as possible from the general and qualitative descriptions of the spread of viruses and describe the process in quantitative terms. Even though it might involve some simplification of the picture it would be desirable to express the experimental results in terms which could be quantitatively related to the observed data of clinical epidemiology, and this will be attempted in the next section.

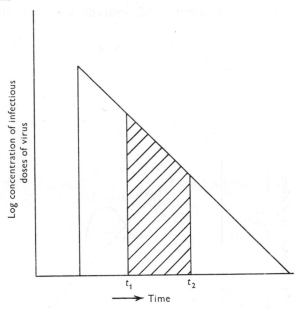

Fig. 3. Theoretical rate of decline of virus concentration in a room in which the overall rate of removal follows a simple exponential law. The shaded area shows the 'integrated' exposure of a subject in the room breathing air at unit rate between times t_1 and t_2.

THE NEED FOR A QUANTITATIVE DESCRIPTION OF THE TRANSMISSION OF INFECTION

In many ways it would be best to be able to study the airborne spread of viruses in animal experiments. Early work showed in fact that very small amounts of influenza virus sprayed into the air would infect ferrets (Bourdillon, Lidwell & Lovelock, 1948). Although Eaton (1940) described the transmission of influenza virus infections from mouse to mouse this work was not successfully repeated until quite recently. Schulman & Kilbourne (1962, 1963) showed that the rate of transmission was reduced by increasing ventilation, but also discovered that the rate was affected by ill-understood differences between strains of virus and of mice and the season. Part of the season effect was probably due to the changing temperature and humidity of the air. A slightly different system was developed by Iida & Bang (1963). On the other hand Andrewes & Allison (1961) infected chicks with a lethal strain of NDV and showed that transmission was apparently by large airborne droplets which were expelled only by sick animals and picked up only by animals standing very close to them. These systems are so different in many ways from the common respiratory diseases of man that one has to be very cautious in applying any conclusions drawn from animal experiments to the transmission of human disease. We have preferred to make quantitative analyses using data obtained from the study of air

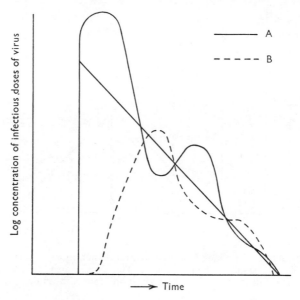

Fig. 4. Two representative curves of local concentration in a room in which a cloud of virus has been produced, by a sneeze for example, and then circulated by thermal or other currents, and is gradually dispersing. Curve A is from a point in the path followed by the cloud just after its release, while curve B is out of that path.

hygiene in normal rooms and of infections of human beings with viruses which produce colds in volunteers.

One may start by considering the consequences of a single sneeze. Much fundamental work on this subject was reported in an M.R.C. 'Green Book' some years ago (Bourdillon *et al.* 1948). A sneeze produces a population of droplets—the large ones with high sedimentation velocities and the smaller ones with low velocities. Lidwell (1964) has calculated and described the changes that take place in such a population in still air. The rate of decline of infectivity of particles would not be exponential and the proportion of smaller particles would gradually rise. However, there is often sufficient circulation in the average room to prevent sedimentation taking place except at the boundary layers and furthermore the virus infectivity in the smaller particles will often be inactivated more rapidly than in the larger particles. Bacteria also die rapidly in small particles. The concentration of infectious particles carrying bacteria and produced by a sneeze into warm air declined exponentially for 40 min., although this would not occur if the particles were of very different sizes (Bourdillon et al. 1948). Instead there would be an initially rapid rate of fall in concentration as the larger particles fell out; this rate would then slow down as the smaller particles fell out. The plot of the logarithm of concentration against time would be a curve which was concave upwards instead of a straight line. If we wish to describe the contamination of a room following a sneeze we may, therefore, as a first approximation, say that infectious particles will be removed by: (1) sedimentation—with a rate constant K_s; (2) ventilation—with a rate constant K_r (see p. 161). In addition to this physical decay, virus particles will become non-infectious with a rate K_D.

Assuming that contamination and sampling proceed at random and that large amounts of data are averaged, the 'integrated' concentration of virus, or the mean probability of inhaling a virus particle in unit volume of air at time t after the sneeze, is

$$N_t = N_0 \exp\{-(K_s + K_r + K_D)t\}.$$

The area represented by an integral between t_1 and t_2 is indicated as the shaded part of Fig. 3. This is only approximately correct as an expression of the concentration in the room as a whole. Obviously a sneeze will produce a localized cloud of infectious droplets which will disperse by sedimentation, diffusion and turbulence, and be moved round the room by circulatory currents. The concentration curve at any point will therefore oscillate and the local air concentration from which an exposed person is inhaling may have a concentration time relationship like one or other of the curves in Fig. 4B, depending on whether or not he is in the path of the cloud.

However, there are great variations in the amount of contamination produced at different stages of a cold and in different individuals. These are best described as distributions. For example, the amount of nasal secretion, correlated with the number of times the nose is blown, varies with time. Some illustrative observations on patients infected with coxsackievirus A 21 are given in Fig. 5. The dispersal of nasal secretion is of no importance in the spread of disease unless it contains infectious virus, and this has a distribution in time rather similar to that of the dispersal of nasal secretion, but if plotted on an arithmetical scale rather than on the usual logarithmic scale it can be seen that it comes to a

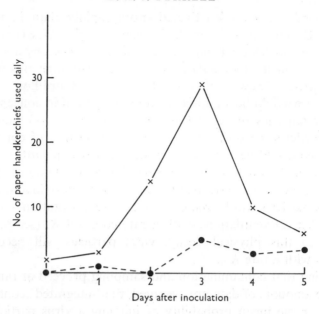

Fig. 5. This and the following figures are based on the results of experiments with colds induced by coxsackievirus A 21. Number of paper handkerchiefs used daily by two volunteers, one of whom had a moderate cold while the other had a mild cold. The handkerchiefs were all wetted with nasal secretion and the count is thus a measure of the amount of nasal secretion produced.

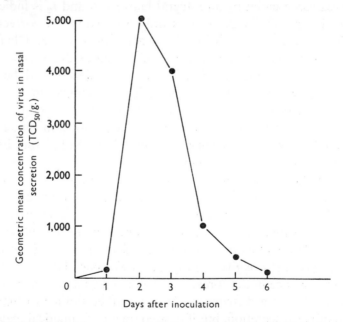

Fig. 6. The daily geometric mean concentration of virus in the nasal secretion of a group of volunteers inoculated with coxsackievirus A 21. (From Buckland & Tyrrell, 1965.)

much steeper peak than that of the amount of nasal secretion (Fig. 6). Thus concentration of virus in nasal secretion is probably of much greater importance in the epidemiology of the disease than the exact amount of nasal secretion being shed. This brings us to the last distribution, that of the numbers of subjects producing various 'peak' concentrations of virus in the nasal secretion at the height of the illness. The rather scanty data from our studies are given in Fig. 7, which shows

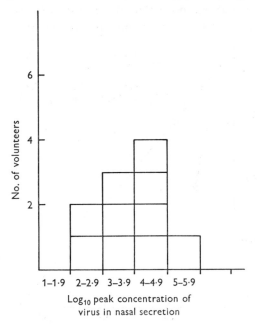

Fig. 7. The numbers of volunteers secreting various amounts of coxsackievirus A21 at the height of their colds.

that a small proportion of the population, say one-tenth may have tens or hundreds of times more virus in the nose than the rest, and may therefore be the main source of contamination in the environment. These studies showed that it was only the subject with the highest concentration who produced a detectable amount of airborne virus when sneezing into a plastic bag.

If we oversimplify and assume that most transmission of coxsackievirus A21 is due to airborne droplets produced by the uncommon 'highly infectious' volunteer we can ask whether this accords with the facts known at present.

Suppose in winter a room has three air changes per hour; that the loss of a virus by sedimentation is equivalent to five changes per hour; and that the half life of virus infectivity is about 3 min. at about

40–50% relative humidity or 10 min. at 90%. Then with $K_s = 3/\text{hr.}$, $K_r = 5/\text{hr.}$, and $K_D = 4/\text{hr.}$ at high relative humidity and the decline of infectivity is shown in Fig. 8. This is not unreasonable for we have shown also on this figure the data obtained from an artificial sneeze produced in a 'sneeze cupboard' a converted wardrobe (sampled at about two-thirds of its height) from which virus was being removed by sedimentation and biological decay, and without ventilation or air circulation. We may suppose that the room is of moderate size, say $3 \times 5 \times 3$ m., i.e. 45×10^6 l. Following one sneeze, 100 infectious doses

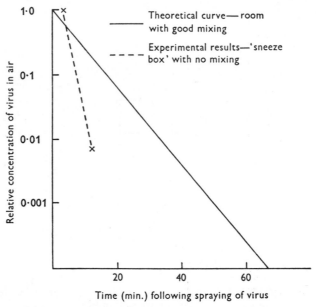

Fig. 8. The decline in concentration of infectious virus to be recovered from an experimental 'sneeze box' after an artificial sneeze, compared with some theoretical figures for a ventilated room.

might be expelled in or on respirable particles. Then there would be barely one infectious particle in the air of the room half an hour later and the probability that a man respiring at 10 l. per minute would inhale one would be very small.

CONCLUSION

It is obvious that we cannot yet give a precise description of the transmission of respiratory viruses by the airborne route; but the fact that we can begin to attempt such a description should be a valuable stimulus to future work. Ultimately it may be possible to combine this with epidemiological theory to provide an analysis of the spread of a virus in populations under various conditions.

REFERENCES

ANDREWS, C. H. (1948). The common cold. *Jl R. Soc. Arts*, **96**, 200.

ANDREWES, C. H. (1960). The viruses of the common cold. *Scient. Am.* **203**, 88.

ANDREWES, C. H. & ALLISON, A. C. (1961). Newcastle disease as a model for studies of experimental epidemiology. *J. Hyg., Camb.* **59**, 285.

ARLANDER, T. R., PIERCE, W. E., EDWARDS, E. A., PECKINPAUGH, R. O. & MILLER, L. F. (1965). *Am. J. publ. Hlth*, **55**, 67.

BANKS, H. H. (1958). Infection across the intact conjunctiva. *Lancet*, ii, 518.

BOURDILLON, R. B., LIDWELL, O. M. & LOVELOCK, J. E. with 10 others (1948). Studies in air hygiene. *Spec. Rep. Ser. med. Res. Counc.* no. 262.

BRIMBLECOMBE, F. S. W., CRUIKSHANK, R., MASTERS, P. L., REID, D. D. & STEWART, G. T. (1958). Family studies of respiratory infections. *Brit. med. J.* i, 119.

BUCKLAND, F. E. & TYRRELL, D. A. J. (1962). Loss of infectivity on drying various viruses. *Nature, Lond.* **195**, 1063.

BUCKLAND, F. E. & TYRRELL, D. A. J. (1964). Experiments on the spread of colds. I. Laboratory studies on the dispersal of nasal secretion. *J. Hyg., Camb.* **62**, 365.

BUCKLAND, F. E. & TYRRELL, D. A. J. (1965). Experiments on the spread of colds. 2. Studies in volunteers with coxsackievirus A21. *J. Hyg., Camb.* **63**, 327.

BYNOE, M. L., HOBSON, D., HORNER, J., KIPPS, A., SCHILD, G. C. & TYRRELL, D. A. J. (1961). Inoculation of human volunteers with a strain of virus isolated from a common cold. *Lancet*, i, 1194.

CATE, T. R., COUCH, R. B., FLEET, W. F., GRIFFITH, W. R., GERONE, P. J. & KNIGHT, V. (1965). Production of tracheobronchitis in volunteers with rhinovirus in a small-particle aerosol. *Am. J. Epidemiol.* **81**, 95.

DOWLING, H. F., JACKSON, G. G., SPIESMAN. I. G. & INOUYE, T. (1958). Transmission of the common cold to volunteers under controlled conditions. IV. The effect of chilling of the subjects upon susceptibility. *Am. J. Hyg.* **68**, 59.

DOWNIE, A. W., MEIKLEJOHN, M., ST VINCENT, L., RAO, A. R., SUNDARA BABU, B. V. & KEMPE, C. H. (1965). The recovery of smallpox virus from patients and their environment in a smallpox hospital. *Bull. Wld Hlth Org.* **33**, 615.

DUGUID, J. P. (1945). The number and the site of origin of the droplets expelled during respiratory activities. *Edinb. med. J.* **52**, 385.

EATON, M. P. (1940). Transmission of epidemic influenza virus in mice by contact. *J. Bact.* **39**, 229.

HAMBURGER, M., GREEN, M. J. & HAMBURGER, V. G. (1945). The problem of the 'dangerous carrier' of haemolytic streptococci. *J. infect. Dis.* **77**, 68, 96.

HARE, R. & MACKENZIE, D. M. (1946). The source and transmission of nasopharyngeal infections due to certain bacteria and viruses. *Brit. med. J.* i, 864.

HARPER, G. (1963). The influence of environment on the survival of airborne virus particles in the laboratory. *Arch. ges. Virusforsch.* **13**, 64.

HEMMES, J. H., WINKLER, K. C. & KOOL, S. M. (1960). Virus survival as a seasonal factor in influenza and poliomyelitis. *Nature, Lond.* **188**, 430.

HOPE-SIMPSON, R. E. (1958). Discussion on the common cold. *Proc. Roy. Soc. Med.* **51**, 267.

HOPE-SIMPSON, R. E. (1966). A long-term study of acute respiratory disease in a natural community. *Proc. R. Soc. Med.* **59**, 638.

IIDA, T. & BANG, F. B. (1963). Infection of the upper respiratory tract of mice with influenza A virus. *Am. J. Hyg.* **77**, 169.

LIDWELL, O. M. & SOMMERVILLE, T. (1951). Observations on the incidence and distribution of the common cold in a rural community during 1948–1949. *J. Hyg., Camb.* **49**, 365.

LIDWELL, O. M. (1964). Microbiology of the atmosphere and air-borne infection. In *Medical Climatology*. Ed. by S. Licht. New Haven, Connecticut: E. Licht.

LIDWELL, O. M. & WILLIAMS, R. E. O. (1961). The epidemiology of the common cold. I and II. Cross-infection and immunity. *J. Hyg., Camb.* **59**, 309, 321.

LIDWELL, O. M., MORGAN, R. W. & WILLIAMS, R. E. O. (1965). The epidemiology of the common cold. IV. The effect of weather. *J. Hyg., Camb.* **63**, 427.

LOVELOCK, J. E., PORTERFIELD, J. S., RODEN, A. T., SOMMERVILLE, T. & ANDREWES, C. H. (1952). Further studies on the natural transmission of the common cold. *Lancet*, ii, 657.

MUFSON, M. A., LUDWIG, W. M., JAMES, H. D. JR, GAULD, L. W., ROURKE, J. A., HOLPER, J. C. & CHANOCK, R. M. (1963). Effect of neutralizing antibody on experimental rhinovirus infection. *J. Am. med. Ass.* **186**, 578.

PAUL, J. H. & FREESE, H. L. (1933). Epidemiological and bacteriological study of 'common cold' in an isolated Arctic community (Spitzbergen). *Am. J. Hyg.* **17**, 517.

RAMMELKAMP, C. H. JR, MORRIS, A. J., CATANZARO, F. J., WANNAMAKER, L. W., CHAMOVITZ, R. & MARPLE, E. C. (1958). Transmission of Group A streptococci. III. The effect of drying on the infectivity of the organism. *J. Hyg., Camb.* **56**, 280.

REID, D. D., LIDWELL, O. M. & WILLIAMS, R. E. O. (1956). Counts of airborne bacteria as indices of air hygiene. *J. Hyg., Camb.* **54**, 524.

SCHULMAN, J. L. & KILBOURNE, E. D. (1962). Airborne transmission of influenza virus infection in mice. *Nature, Lond.* **195**, 1129.

SCHULMAN, J. L. & KILBOURNE, E. D. (1963). Experimental transmission of influenza virus infection in mice. I. The period of transmissibility. II. Some factors affecting the incidence of transmitted infection. *J. exp. Med.* **118**, 257, 267.

SUTTON, R. N. P. (1965). Minor illness in Trinidad: a longitudinal study. *J. Hyg., Camb.* **59**, 212.

TOWNSEND, J. G. (1924). Epidemiological study of minor respiratory diseases by the public health service. *Publ. Hlth Rep. Wash.* **39**, 2669.

TYRRELL, D. A. J. (1963). In *Perspective in Virology*, vol. III. Ed. by M. Pollard. New York: Hoeber.

TYRRELL, D. A. J. (1965). *Common Colds and Related Diseases*. London: Edward Arnold.

TYRRELL, D. A. J. & BYNOE, M. L. (1966). Cultivation of viruses from a high proportion of patients with colds. *Lancet*, i, 76.

VAN LOGHEM, J. J. (1928). An epidemiological contribution to the knowledge of the respiratory diseases. *J. Hyg., Camb.* **28**, 33.

WATSON, G. I. (1960). Clinical epidemiology of influenza. *J. Coll. gen. Practit.* **3**, 44.

WOOLLEY, E. J. S. (1963). Discussion. *Trans. R. Soc. trop. Med. Hyg.* **57**, 24.

WORKING PARTY ON ACUTE RESPIRATORY VIRUS DISEASES (1965). A collaborative study of the aetiology of acute respiratory infections in Britain, 1961–4. *Brit. med. J.* ii, 319.

LONG-DISTANCE SPORE TRANSPORT

J. M. HIRST

Rothamsted Experimental Station, Harpenden, Hertfordshire

G. W. HURST

Meteorological Office, Bracknell, Berkshire

INTRODUCTION

This paper is primarily concerned with the distant travel of fungus spores and pollen grains in air; its title includes the word 'transport' deliberately, to exclude the liberation and deposition of spores, and to emphasize that, as few measurements have been made of the viability of exotic airborne spores, they often have to be treated as if they were inert aerosol particles. To palynologists, and perhaps to allergists, it does not matter whether spores are alive or dead, but to plant breeders and plant pathologists only live spores are important. Our aims are: (1) to mention the evidence for distant transport and the variety of mechanisms that confuse interpretation; (2) to consider earlier methods and those we have used recently; (3) to consider possible methods of defining the biological and meteorological requirements of distant transport.

CIRCUMSTANTIAL EVIDENCE OF DISTANT TRANSPORT

The biological pollutants considered here are particles larger than bacteria and viruses, and have diameters ranging from 2 to 200 microns, although most fungus spores are within 3–30 microns and most pollens between 20 and 50 microns. Their specific gravities range from 0·5 to 1·5 but are mostly quite close to 1·0; most fungus spores have terminal velocities between 0·05 and 2·0 cm./sec. and most pollens between 1 and 10 cm./sec. In enclosed environments, concentrations exceeding 10^9 spores/m.^{3} have been recorded, but among crops, concentrations rarely exceed 10^6/m.^{3}, and 10^4/m.^{3} is an average concentration in country air during summer. Thus the spore cloud is usually invisible and special methods are necessary to detect and measure it (Gregory, 1961).

Studies of distant dispersal are best made with exotic organisms having recognizable spores and likely to be noticed when introduced to new localities; for this reason exodemic crop pathogens have received particular attention. Saprophytic fungi are much more prevalent and

20-2

some have recognizable spores but, over land, spores produced locally are usually indistinguishable from those of distant origin. However, their ubiquity itself provides the strongest evidence of the success of dispersal, given enough time (Hirst, 1965). Although soils are less permanent than the rocks from which they are derived, the soils of Northern Canada have had some 25,000 years since the Ice Age to accumulate their present microflora as Bisby (1943) commented. Occasionally the beginnings of colonization can be watched on a more practical time scale, as in Krakatoa after the devastating eruption of 1883 (Bisby, 1943) or on the recently formed volcanic islands off Iceland (Fridriksson & Kolbeinsson, 1965).

The history of colonization seldom proves the mode of transport because it is as impossible to detect all airborne dissemination as to exclude the role of man (Baker, 1966), migrant birds or possible introductions on flotsam, etc. Conversely, the possibility of distant spore transport confuses the interpretation of ancient pollen accumulations, which palynologists use to indicate past vegetation and climates. Proof of aerial dissemination requires either interception of migrant spores or an incontrovertible association between the source and new colonies. An alternate host with a halo of prematurely infected plants is usually convincing evidence. So are many maps of the spread of pathogens from the point of their first introduction; for example, the recent spread of tobacco blue mould (*Peronospora tabacina*) in Europe (Rayner & Hopkins, 1962; Populer, 1964); of maize rust (*Puccinia polysora*) in Africa (Cammack, 1959); and of banana leaf spot (*Mycosphaerella musicola*) within the Caribbean area (Stover, 1962). Painstaking examination of contemporary publications has even reconstructed the original spread of potato blight (*Phytophthora infestans*) in Europe during the mid-nineteenth century and suggested a probable area of introduction (Bourke, 1964). The common feature of successful maps is a sufficient density of observations, including nil records, for the scale of study, but as observations become wide-spaced and the length of the dispersal steps increases, confidence quickly declines.

Where observations are few, it is tempting to let conjecture assume undue importance. Stover's (1962) chronological account of the discovery of banana leaf spot throughout the world is valuable and the course of intercontinental dissemination he suggests is reasonable, but because the distances are great and because the proposal is supported only bibliographically it is not wholly convincing. After *Peronospora tabacina* appeared at several places in Great Britain and in the Netherlands during the autumn of 1958, it was generally accepted that the outbreaks originated from a licensed introduction into England shortly before. However, it is not easy to believe that airborne spores spread from one glasshouse to the other distant ones in which the disease was noticed, because both the known source and sink were so small. Human vectors cannot be discounted and other possible, but equally unproven explanations, seem not to have been considered. For example, 1958 was the first year in which the fungus was reported attacking field crops (rather than seed beds) in the north-eastern U.S.A.; is trans-Atlantic spore transport from a powerful source a possible explanation? Fortunately the movements of some other pathogens are much better documented, but most are not examples of air dispersal (Zadoks, 1966). The best known and best supported example of distant air dispersal is the northward migrations of *Puccinia graminis* uredospores from the southern U.S.A. that cause wheat stem rust in the wheat belt (Stakman & Harrar, 1957; Johnson, 1961). With most others there are alternative methods of travel; for example, *P. antirrhini* the cause of antirrhinum rust (Close, 1958) and many other pathogens are seed-borne (see Malone & Muskett, 1964). Also, the jet aircraft is a probable 'vector' of chrysanthemum white rust (*P. horiana*) carried in infected cuttings and this may explain recent major extensions in the distribution of this fungus (see Zadoks, 1966). Examples of past spread cannot prove the route of new introductions and there is need for quantitative information about the various dispersal mechanisms to assess their feasibility and frequency. This is particularly true of airborne dispersal because it evades quarantine precautions.

INTERCEPTION OF SPORES REMOTE FROM SOURCES

The problem

At first, plant pathologists studied the movement of spores in or near crops, and perhaps this is why they were slow in understanding the movement of spores in air. Fortunately, it is no longer commonly assumed that distance of travel can be estimated simply from the resultant of terminal velocity and wind speed. Similarly, exaggerated claims for the effect of forcible spore liberation become rare as it is realized that few spores are projected more than 1 cm. through air before being carried passively. The advances are largely an indirect benefit of aerodynamics, as applied first to meteorology and then to biological problems. For example, the diffusion and deposition of spores close to sources is well defined by modifying eddy-diffusion theories to allow for deposition from near-ground sources (Gregory,

1945, 1961; Waggoner, 1952; Chamberlain, 1956). However, there is still disagreement about the importance of gravitational settling, and estimates of 'probable flight range' (the distance from the source by which half the cloud is deposited) differ by factors up to several thousand-fold (Gregory, 1962; Schrödter, 1960).

In moderately turbulent conditions, Chamberlain (1956) estimated that the 'velocity of deposition' of a *Lycopodium* spore cloud approximated to the terminal velocity of the particles (p. 139). But Sreeramulu & Ramalingam (1961) showed large differences in the proportion of spores deposited in 'day' or 'calm night' tests. Plainly, variable proportions of spores may escape local deposition, and Gregory (1962) estimated that 'commonly a fraction of the order of 10% "escapes" into the atmosphere'.

Both wind and convection can transport aerosol particles upwards many times faster than they fall. Convection probably occurs in bubbles or rising air between 300 and 2,000 m. across (Scorer & Ludlam, 1953) (p. 4). A single large convection cloud will probably contain several bubbles at different heights with consequent up and down currents within the cloud: upward speeds well above the ground can exceed 6 m./sec., although in shower clouds speeds probably exceed 1·5 m./sec. only briefly; near the ground velocities of about 0·3 m./sec. would be much commoner. Pasquill (1961) found that windborne particles would move upward little if at all in light winds at night, but stronger winds (> 5 m./sec.) would take some material to a height of 10 m. within 100 m. of the source. At the same distance downwind of the source, on calm sunny days, material was detected at a height of 25 m., but in stronger winds (> 5 m./sec.) it only reached 15 m. high. If at least 90% of spores from near-ground sources are often deposited within 100 m. (Gregory, 1952, 1958) and some of the 'escapers' ascend at angles up to 20° from the horizontal, it is understandable that spores emitted from weak sources become undetectable after travelling a short distance. The actual distance must depend on the strength of convective and frictional turbulence and on the form of the surface, for a pine forest would presumably remove many more spores than open water (Tauber, 1965; Ogden, Raynor & Hayes, 1966). It is difficult to measure the fraction escaping other than by the difference between the number liberated and the estimated number deposited within a specified distance of the source. Few detailed experiments have been reported in which the measurements extend beyond 30–100 m. from the source. The greater the distance, the more difficult it becomes to make them comprehensively three-dimensional, because aircraft must be used and costs prevent frequent or continuous sampling. Simpler and cheaper methods had therefore to be devised to learn the principles of distant dispersal and their effects.

Methods of detecting spores

Spores can be collected from natural deposits on vegetation and in water, or caught on variously prepared trapping surfaces. The choice of method is influenced by the information required, the time scale of the observations, difficulties of identifying organisms and the variable frequency of spores. Some spores will not grow in culture, others can be named only after growth. Cultural methods are less perfected than those suited to visual recognition. Gregory & Stedman (1953) showed that all freely exposed, sticky spore traps select spores of particular sizes and are affected by orientation and wind speed. Power-assisted traps usually catch spores with a greater and more uniform efficiency, and also improve the discrimination of the time when spores are caught (see Hirst, 1959; Gregory, 1961; U.S. Department of Health, 1959).

Palynologists simplify the problem of detecting distant dispersal by measuring the result rather than the act of transport, namely, spore deposition instead of spore concentration. Pollen grain extines survive in peat and in lake deposits long enough for very rare occurrences to be recorded, and this survival has shown deposits of pollens far from their parent plants, for example, the pollen of the southern beech (*Nothofagus*) in peat on Tristan da Cunha (Hafsten, 1951). Unfortunately the analysis of sediments does not record the sources, routes, frequency of arrival or means of spore deposition; it is less well suited to fungus spores than pollen, and cannot give answers quickly.

Plant pathologists have used many methods to catch spores at times when crops are threatened, but their records tend to be fragmentary. Allergists are interested in a longer season and often sample continuously and with less variable methods. For both these purposes, freely exposed surface traps are being gradually replaced by power-assisted types. Whereas the earlier traps required at least a day to accumulate enough of even the large spores to merit counting microscopically, recent types need less than an hour. Exposure of culture plates has traditionally been brief, because few colonies can be accommodated on a plate without overcrowding.

The catches from any type of trap take a long time to analyse, so it is natural to wonder whether the appearance of infection on growing crops might not provide more sensitive, simpler and more direct indications of distant spore transport. Wheat has often been planted in 'rust nurseries' (Ogilvie & Thorpe, 1961; Zadoks, 1961), but usually to determine the spectrum of physiologic races rather than to detect spore dissemination, for which the method has serious disadvantages. Trap crops must be of varieties susceptible to all races. They can be used only where there are no local sources of spores, and to detect only the first introduction. (If this is slight there is a danger that the first lesions may not be found and that a false date will be suggested when multiplication eventually makes the disease detectable.) Also deposition is recorded only when infections occur, which may depend more on the leaf surface conditions soon after spores are deposited rather than on the number deposited, and changes in susceptibility of host plants with age, nutrition or environment make it uncertain that results will be similar throughout a network of stations.

SPORE TRAPPING AT SURFACE LEVEL

A two-dimensional grid of ground spore traps can reveal the movement, extent and concentration of spore clouds, as in the demonstration that uredospores of *Puccinia graminis* were carried from the southern U.S.A. to the wheat belt (Stakman & Harrar, 1957). Extensive trapping networks of this kind are not easily maintained and can usually be operated only over land.

Surface traverses or 'transects' are less trouble but provide less comprehensive information about the movement of spore clouds. They should be normal or coaxial with the direction of movement of the spore cloud but are often randomly oriented. On land, the traps have either been static or moved along roads (Johnson, 1961; Craigie, 1945), but locally produced spores predominate and only the few spores that can be confidently recognized as of distant origin are useful. Ship-borne traps have the advantage that all the spores caught must have come from land sources (unless derived from the ship itself). Ships travelling only a few hundred miles a day cannot sample long transects quickly, so catches are affected by the real and apparent wind. Nevertheless, there are reports enough to confirm that catches decrease rapidly after leaving coasts until, except for marine bacteria (ZoBell, 1942), very few microorganisms are caught in mid-ocean (Erdtman, 1937; Sack, 1949; Sreeramulu, 1958). As catches become smaller, the importance of a few contaminants increases and elaborate precautions become necessary to exclude them. It is not difficult to ensure that trapping surfaces and containers are sterile, but for visual examination it is much more difficult to ensure that they are completely clean and free from dead as well as live spores.

Were there no contamination, catching a few pollen grains and spores in mid-Atlantic would be important and raise the question whether spores are truly ubiquitous and reach even to polar regions. Published evidence is slight (see Gregory, 1961) but suggests that very few are ubiquitous. This suggestion is supported by catches made in 1961 with the co-operation of Dr D. L. Easty of the British Antarctic Survey. A rotorod trap (Perkins, 1957) was operated for 24 hr. periods in the bows of the supply ship *Kista Dan* during her passage south along the eastern seaboard of South America to Montevideo and via South Georgia and the South Orkney Islands to Halley Bay in Antarctica. Several hundred miles off the South American coast the concentration ranged from 10 to $10^2/m.^3$ (cf. concentrations typical over land, p. 307) and its constituents varied greatly with latitude. Near South Georgia and the South Orkney Islands concentrations averaged $10^{-1}/m.^3$, but a single sample collected during the approach to Halley Bay had 2×10^2 spores/m.^{3}, all probably of two species of *Aspergillus* and almost certainly contaminants. Samples collected on the ice at Halley Bay had only 10^{-2} to $10^{-3}/m.^3$ and even so we are not certain that all contamination was excluded.

Analysis of trajectories

Most measurements of spore concentrations refer neither to networks nor to transects but to fixed positions. Occasionally, during the analysis of catches at fixed points, exotic spores may be noticed but it is seldom possible to substantiate their origin without detailed meteorological analysis (Hyde & Adams, 1961). Attempts to explain probable sources in terms of prevailing winds or the direction of the local wind at the time of deposition are very liable to be incorrect. Air usually moves nearly parallel to curved isobars of pressure systems which are themselves moving with individual speed and direction. From the probable height of spore travel, as well as the time and position of catch and synoptic weather charts, meteorologists can estimate the past tracks of spore-bearing air, or 'air trajectories'. Weather maps were used to help interpret the *Puccinia graminis* uredospore catches of traps in U.S.A. and Canada, and although trajectories were not drawn, it was noticed that migration often accompanied the broad northward airflow between an anticyclone and a depression following it slowly east over southern and central U.S.A. (Craigie, 1945). Mehta (1952) claimed a relationship, in India, between the arrival of uredospores and air trajectories from potential source areas, but the association was weakened by relating trajectories to catches made from 2 to 5 days after the arrival of the trajectory, on the incorrect assumption that spores could remain over the trapping station while slowly settling from the height at which they were assumed to have travelled. Canadian workers also found that the spore content of air masses over Montreal and the Arctic was determined more by their history than by their position (Pady & Kapica, 1956).

Extensive use has also been made of trajectories in Great Britain to help explain movements of both fungi and insects (Hogg, 1962; Hurst, 1965). Detailed synoptic charts of surface pressure distribution are prepared every 6 hr., and comparable charts for the 700 and 500 mb. levels (approx. 3,000 m. and 5,000–6,000 m.) every 12 hr. only. Consecutive pairs of these charts, starting as nearly as possible from the place and time of spore capture, are used to estimate back-tracks of air movement. Both the geostrophic and observed winds are considered in estimating the position of the air at the start of the interval between charts, and the procedure is repeated for preceding 6 or 12 hr. intervals. Plainly this is a subjective process open to many errors, some of which are fairly constant in magnitude and result from turbulence and diffusion, but other large and less predictable errors depend on topography and individual weather systems. Durst & Davis (1957) estimated the radius within which there was a specified probability that the air sampled had been located at a particular time earlier. In areas with adequate wind observations they concluded that the vector error was about 27 miles in 6 hr. and increased to 36 miles where observations were scarce. In 24 hr. this leads to standard deviations of 80–110 nautical miles, estimates which can be extrapolated for longer travel by multiplying by the square root of the number of days. Such errors are implicit in all trajectories although, for clarity, they are omitted from diagrams. Because vector errors represent the radii of circles enclosing the previous estimated positions of the sampled air, they may affect not only the time when spores arrive but also their track. A few traps may prove almost as informative as an extensive network of traps, provided their catches are interpreted in the light of air trajectories, and indeed are superior for recording the track of spores over the sea.

Hogg first used trajectories to explain occasional large catches of pine and hornbeam pollen on traps exposed on the Bishop Rock Lighthouse (Hyde & Adams, 1961). He then used catches from the Bishop Rock and Cardiff to identify possible European sources of *Puccinia graminis* uredospores (see Ogilvie & Thorpe, 1961; Hirst, Stedman & Hogg, 1967a). Early in the season (from May to July) few north-bound tracks carried uredospores but later a closer relation developed between tracks from Europe and spore catches in Britain

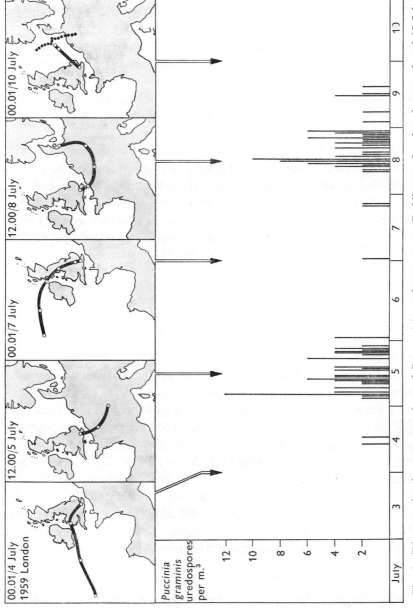

Fig. 1. Diagram showing concentrations of *P. graminis* uredospores over Paddington, London, between 3 and 1C July 1959 and related surface air trajectories. Circles show estimated positions of the air sampled, at the time indicated, a:d at previous 12 hr. intervals.

and finally, when the disease was established in Britain, catches were made in winds from all directions. Hour-by-hour catches of suction traps showed when spores began and ceased arriving and, as Fig. 1 shows, provided a more precise time-base for estimating and interpreting air trajectories. In 1959 each of the two occasions when *P. graminis* uredospores were brought to the London area was related to air trajectories passing over western and then northern France around two small anticyclones which moved eastwards. The first anticyclone moved slowly east from the Bay of Biscay on 2 July, crossed northern France by 4 July and weakened over the Baltic on 6 July. A second and faster-moving anticyclone passed eastward over the English Channel on 7 July and into Russia by 9 July. Each uredospore introduction we have studied in detail has involved a precise synchronization of liberation and deposition with the movement of weather systems and the speeds of the winds within them. Later we shall consider the feasibility and value of defining the spore movements in pressure systems well enough to allow occasions of spore migrations to be identified meteorologically. Before doing so, we need to discuss how the vertical spore distribution can vary and be measured.

SPORE TRAPPING ABOVE SURFACE LEVEL

The extensive bibliographies quoted by Wolfenbarger (1959) and Gregory (1961) show how spores were first collected above ground with kites and balloons in the late nineteenth century. Kites work only during winds, usually at fixed positions and with limited lift and height. Balloons are usually carried by air but do move through it as they rise and fall, so power-assisted traps are required to catch spores. However, balloons have provided the only published information on the microbiology of the stratosphere (Rogers & Meier, 1936; Green, Pederson, Lundgren & Hagberg, 1964). Aeroplanes have a unique ability for sampling vertical and horizontal spore density profiles quickly, but their great cost and short flight duration restrict sampling to infrequent and brief occasions. Nevertheless, information about spore distribution throughout the troposphere chiefly derives from aircraft observations.

Airborne traps (see also p. 77)

Most spore traps carried in aircraft have used air speed to improve the efficiency of spore impaction on sticky surfaces such as slides (Stakman, Henry, Curran & Christopher, 1923; Heise & Heise, 1948), thin cylinders or square rods (Rempe, 1937; Asai, 1960) or Petri dishes (Mischustin,

1926; Dillon Weston, 1929; Polunin & Kelly, 1952). Few have measured the volume of air sampled or the efficiency of spore deposition at aircraft speeds which far exceed those tested by Gregory & Stedman (1953), and may be of an order where 'blow-off' from small surfaces is important. However, observations by Heise & Heise (1949) suggested that, as air speed increased, proportionally more ragweed pollen and *Alternaria* spores were caught on microscope slides than expected from the distance travelled in unit time, but the slide was close to the cockpit window and its orientation unspecified. Some suction traps have been used (Pady & Kelly, 1953) but they probably sampled at intake velocities very different from airspeed. Because methods have varied so much in kind and efficiency, the results of different workers can rarely be compared directly.

During the past ten years we have collaborated with the Meteorological Research Flight, Farnborough, Hants. trapping spores from aircraft. The Hastings and Varsity aircraft used are well equipped for meteorological measurements and carried suction traps (Pl. 1). Air was sampled through a forward-facing 3 mm. diameter orifice projecting about 0·6 m. clear of the fuselage. Sampling rates of 35–39 l./min. gave theoretically isokinetic collection at speeds between 160 and 180 knots. The orifice (Pl. 2) tapered to a $10 \times 0·33$ mm. slit separated by 0·5 mm. from the sticky surface of a transparent film wrapped around a drum, which can be set to any of 120 positions from within the aircraft. The methods used, and the precautions taken both to decrease and estimate contamination, have been described elsewhere (Hirst *et al.* 1967*a*). Because the sampling was volumetric and approximately isokinetic, it is justifiable to express catches in terms of spore concentrations in air. A single spore in a 1 min. sample represented approximately 30 spores/m.^{3}, but often three replicate samples were taken to estimate sampling errors and to decrease the detection threshold concentration to about 10 spores/m.^{3}, similar to that in routine sampling on the ground with a Hirst trap.

Horizontal transects by aircraft

Most sampling by aircraft has included measurements of spore numbers at a sequence of points along a level track. The results, although few and fragmentary, show that spores of many genera occur and that some are alive. To the reports quoted by Gregory (1961) can be added those of Asai (1960), Harrington (1965) and ours. Flights over the sea have confirmed the expectation that, far from land, few spores were caught (Newman, 1948; Pady & Kelly, 1954) but the flights added little to previous conclusions from shipboard observations, except for the suggestion that, at height, concentrations often exceed those at sea level. Over land, horizontal transects have been used to demonstrate extensive dispersal and to add the support of actual spore interception. Flights over north Canada also helped to demonstrate how important the history of an air mass is in determining the concentration of spores it bears (Kelly & Pady, 1953; Pady & Kapica, 1956). However, it cannot be claimed that any of these flights defined the cross- or down-wind dimensions of spore clouds. The story is incomplete mainly because aircraft cannot be obtained often enough or fly long enough to demonstrate the processes involved. The horizontal transects made in our uredospore interception flights at 600 m. over the English Channel were little better; some revealed one edge of the spore cloud, but they were too short to measure its whole width across the wind (Hirst *et al.* 1967a).

Vertical profiles of spore concentration

Enough vertical spore distributions have been reported to show that spores of many genera are abundant, especially close to the ground; that some are alive (see Gregory, 1961); and to lend support to the suggestion that there may be a 'biological zone' of maximum concentration commonly a few hundred metres above ground. However, they provide very little evidence to support the idea of an endemic 'aeroplankton'.

Many spore collections are not accompanied by vertical temperature soundings, so the probable activity or ceiling of convection is unknown. Nevertheless, even these flights reinforced the evidence that concentration decreases with height until spores become undetectable at heights ranging from 2 to 6 km. and that pollens, algae, bryophytes and pteridophytes are represented in addition to fungi and bacteria. The flights have been diverse enough to represent a wide range of climates and vegetation. Polunin and his co-workers (Pady & Kelly, 1953) showed that micro-organisms were often plentiful over the Arctic when the air-mass sampled had come from the south, excellent evidence of long distance transport at considerable height. In four trans-Atlantic flights made in summer, at about 3 km. above sea level (Pady & Kelly, 1954), fungi were widespread at concentrations reaching up to $200/m.^3$ and pollens reached $25/m.^3$, i.e. several orders of magnitude greater than those Erdtman (1937) estimated from volumetric catches on a ship when in mid-Atlantic.

Valuable though these studies were, they were too few and, as most lacked adequate meteorological observations, their contribution to our understanding of the atmospheric processes governing spore distribution was small. Sequences of better documented flights have contributed more; for example the series made over forested areas of Germany by Rempe (1937). By day, concentrations of tree pollen were often very uniform up to 1 km. when thermal turbulence was active, but concentration diminished greatly in the upper part of profiles in high winds, at layers of stratus cloud (presumably associated with layers of stable air) and at night. The night profiles were attributed to sedimentation of the pollen when air was not turbulent, and there was evidence that pollen grains were stratified by size. In contrast to the changes at stratus cloud level, several night flights showed increased concentrations *above* temperature inversions at 100–300 m., but the conclusion that pollens *congregate* above inversions because these are as difficult to penetrate downwards as upwards seems unlikely to be correct. Heise & Heise (1948, 1949, 1950) also reported sequences of ascents, in some of which they caught fewer spores at 500 m. than above during early evening but the height of the maximum concentration then decreased throughout the night. Temperature profiles measured in later daytime flights showed that inversions, which restrict convection during active spore liberation, retained unusually large concentrations of airborne allergens near the ground and limited their ascent.

During the period when spore-trapping methods for use in aircraft were being developed we took every opportunity to measure vertical spore profiles. These flights were scattered geographically so it was seldom possible to make concurrent measurements at ground level. Preliminary inspection of results showed that, with a few notable exceptions to be mentioned later, all the spore types counted tended to have similar profiles of concentration, so it is reasonable, first, to consider how the total spore concentration was related to the temperature profiles. In unstable air the spore concentration often decreased approximately logarithmically with height and it was convenient to plot $\log (n+1)$ spores/m.^{3} against height on a linear scale (Fig. 2). This convention accommodates large concentrations without losing the sensitivity to small ones, and allows easy comparison with temperature lapse rate which is idealized in the International Standard Atmosphere as a decrease of 6·5 °C per km. up to 11 km.

When turbulence was active in the lowest 1 km. the spore concentrations there were often almost uniform. We did not find a consistent inverse relation between temperature lapse rate and the rate of decrease in spore concentration up to 3 km., such as Johnson (1957) found up to 1 km. for aphids. Besides the difference in heights between his observations and ours, we measured fewer profiles at various times of day and year, and over both land and sea. Spore concentration invariably decreased upwards within stable air (Fig. 2) and the bottom of the zones of relative scarcity often coincided with a visible 'haze top'. Sometimes spore concentration increased again above the stable layer, as also did haze. Spores have been reported to concentrate in cloud (Dillon Weston, 1929; Heise & Heise, 1948), but this conclusion may

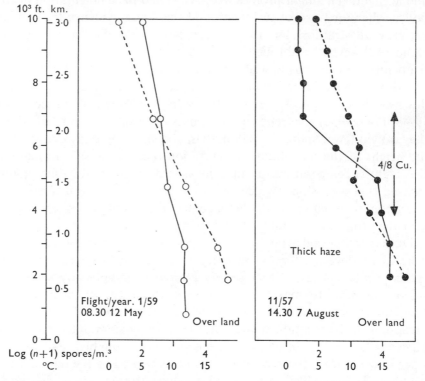

Fig. 2. Examples of vertical profiles of concentration of all spores (solid lines) through unstable air, flight 1/59, and through a stable layer, flight 11/57. Hollow circles indicate ascent and solid circles indicate descent, temperature profiles in dotted lines. Cumulus (Cu) cloud layer indicated by arrows with cover in 'oktas' (eighths).

have reflected the method of trapping: spores captured in cloud droplets would be more readily deposited on the freely exposed surface traps used, than would spores in air free from water droplets. Our observations suggest that spore concentrations decreased only in cloud layers that were associated with stable air, and a few flights did show slight increases at cloud level (Hirst et al. 1967a). In one of these, unreplicated samples suggested that there were 6,500 spores/m.³ at 2,100 m. near cumulus tops but only 500/m.³ near cloud base at 1,000 m. and approx. 4,500/m.³ at 600 m. Such differences could result from spore capture by falling water drops, a process which could account for both apparent

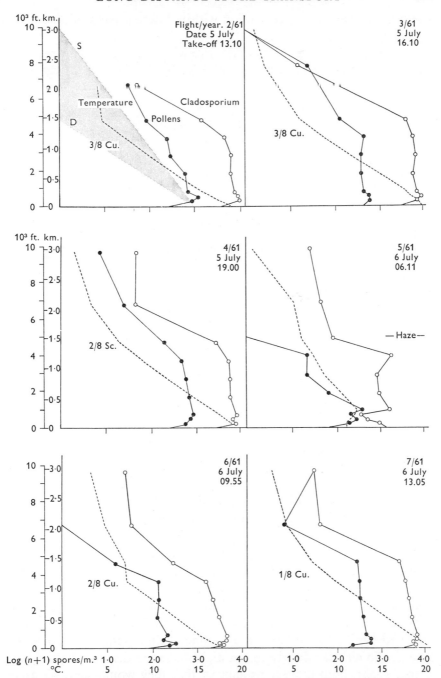

Fig. 3. Profiles of temperature (dotted), concentration of pollen (solid circles) and *Cladosporium* spores (hollow circles) in a sequence of ascents over Farnborough, Hants on 5 and 6 July 1961. Lower edge (D) of shaded wedge on diagram of flight 2/61 indicates the slope of dry adiabatic lapse rate and upper edge (S) the approximate saturated adiabatic lapse rate, temperature profiles in dotted lines. Cloud types shown with standard abbreviations and cover in oktas.

and real increases in concentration within different parts of clouds and in the air beneath (p. 332).

In a series of ascents over Hampshire within a single 24 hr. period in July 1961 (Hirst *et al.* 1967*a*, and Fig. 3) the profiles of the small conidia of *Cladosporium* spp. and the relatively large and heavy pollen grains were almost identical while the air was unstable, confirming that gravitational settling of spores of all sizes was insignificant compared with convective ascent. This conclusion is not new but is repeated

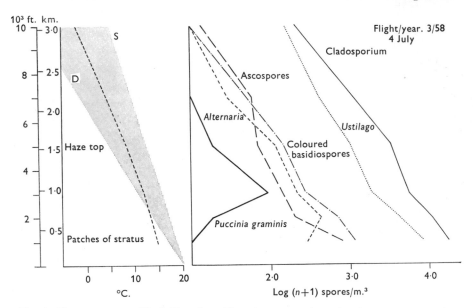

Fig. 4. Temperature profile (left) and profiles of concentration of various spore types in an ascent over the English Channel on 4 July 1958 (flight 3/58 in Hirst *et al.* 1967*a*).

because it is important to later discussion of the probable role of gravitational settling during long-distance transport. The only ascent of this series that probably reflected night conditions began at 0600, through a strong inversion in the lowest 500 m. The densest part of the pollen cloud was found at about 500 m. (Fig. 3), whereas *Cladosporium* concentration was as great at 1,200 m. as at 500 m. (see Rempe, 1937, and below). There is no comparable sequence of profiles of night-liberated fungus spores, and unfortunately too few were caught in these flights to merit inclusion in Fig. 3. Some of these spores are often very common in air near the ground at night but soon disappear after dawn (Hirst, 1953); both these facts suggest that they would serve as useful markers of night-time diffusion, and of the rate of convective ascent the next morning.

Not all the features of vertical spore distribution can be explained by contemporary temperature profiles and it may be necessary to know the changing rates of spore liberation and deposition, previous temperature profiles and the past movements of the air-mass being sampled. Flights in 1957, 1958 and 1959 designed to intercept immigrant *Puccinia graminis* uredospore clouds provided good examples of anomalous profiles (Hirst *et al.* 1967*a*). Figure 4 shows the temperatures and spore profiles of an ascent over the English Channel in flight 3/58 at approx.

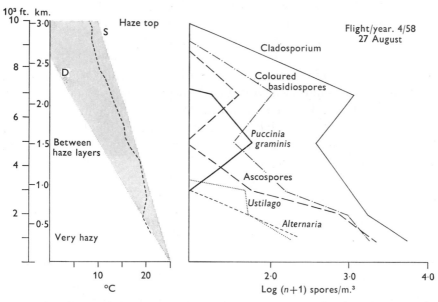

Fig. 5. Temperature profile (left) and profiles of concentration of various spore types in an ascent over the English Channel on 27 August 1958 (flight 4/58 in Hirst *et al.* 1967*a*).

1230 G.M.T. on 4 July 1958. Temperature lapse rates were consistent with moderate convection, except perhaps below 300 m. where patches of stratus suggested stable air near the sea. Above 600 m. the profiles of log. spore concentration were almost straight lines for most spore types, with the notable exceptions of *P. graminis* uredospores, which were few and mostly at 900 m.; and *Alternaria* spp. which were most abundant at 600 m. Comparable profiles for flight 4/58 (Fig. 5) show that from about 600 to 1,200 m. air was stable and then not very unstable up to 3,000 m. An ascent was again made over the English Channel at about 1400 G.M.T. on 27 August 1958, with winds coming from France. If the stable layer extended far over France it could account for the concentration of most spore types decreasing up to 1,500 m., but the spores comprising the subsidiary peak concentrations at 2,100 m. must be assumed to have risen before the stable layer existed. Air trajectories suggested that the upper spores could well be the residue of those, raised by active convection over England on 25 August or France on 26 August, which had been retained in suspension by slight instability above the inversion. But these assumptions still leave the contrasting profile of *Puccinia graminis* uredospores unexplained.

Many factors besides the degree of atmospheric stability must play a part in determining the vertical distribution of spores and hence the rate at which they are deposited. Most of our flights were intentionally made in fine convective weather: first, because this was likely to place spores high enough to favour distant transport; secondly, to avoid rain, which not only complicates profiles by washing-out spores irregularly but also interfered with our sampling. Trajectories at several heights showed that directional wind shear was rare (except perhaps flight 4/57; see Hirst *et al.* 1967*a*). Differences in wind velocity at different heights were more common and may have been important in flight 1/64 (Hirst, Stedman & Hurst, 1967*b*). The time of day when spores are liberated certainly affects the proportion deposited near their source, but probably has little effect on their final destination because spores which remain suspended long enough to be affected by active turbulence will be influenced similarly, irrespective of whether they first ascended by day or night. If it is assumed that spore concentrations often decrease approximately logarithmically in unstable air above source areas, then the frequent 'erosion' or decrease in spore concentration at the base of the profiles has to be explained. Often all spore types are affected in this way and stable air near the surface could offer an explanation. But sometimes, as in flight 3/58 (Fig. 4), only some components show 'eroded profiles'. *P. graminis* uredospores often did this and because they were also among the few recognizable distant immigrants, Hirst *et al.* (1967*a*) suggested that erosion and a distant source might be related. The suggestion could be tested by comparing the profiles over source areas and at increasing distances from them. Instead of attempting this with sparse and infrequent uredospore clouds, it proved simpler and more convenient to measure profiles of various common components of the spore flora produced by the whole of England, first at the downwind coast and then over the sea at increasing distances downwind. The flight plan used for intercepting uredospores above the English Channel was inadequate for measuring spore concentrations along vertical sections long distances over the sea.

Spore concentrations in vertical cross-sections over the sea

Vertical sections to heights of 1,800 to 3,000 m. over the North Sea were sampled with the hope of revealing the processes by which spore clouds were depleted as they moved away from source areas in the British Isles (Hirst *et al.* 1967*b*). It was assumed, with some support from previous flights, that the few spores which may have come over the Atlantic in westerly weather, from very distant sources, could be ignored but this assumption needs to be tested. The flights were made around midday in summer and were planned to coincide with fine weather and steady winds between south and west with little change of direction with height or distance from the coast. When these conditions were met, totals of *Cladosporium* conidia and pollens represented in successive vertical profiles decreased soon after leaving the coast, as expected; but, rather unexpectedly, numbers began increasing again to a maximum several hundred miles out (e.g. Hirst *et al.* 1967*b*, Fig. 4). Analysis of the previous trajectories of the air sampled showed that the possibility of alternative source areas could be rejected. As both these spore types are chiefly liberated in daytime it also seemed probable that as the aircraft flew out from the coast it first sampled the spores liberated during the current day and then, farther out, those liberated the preceding day. This hypothesis would be supported if longer flights revealed even older clouds farther from the coast or if night-liberated spores were commonest between the day-liberated clouds produced on successive days. The latter situation did occur in one flight (1/64, see Fig. 6) and reasons are suggested for its absence in others. Flight 1/64 probably sampled spore clouds liberated on 2 nights and 2 days but our hope of detecting more is not bright. Light winds vary too much in direction for trajectories to be estimated confidently and spore clouds liberated on successive days may become confused if all spores from the source area have not crossed its downwind coast when liberation begins again next day. Conversely, strong winds stretch the day's liberation over a greater distance and carry it beyond the range of the aircraft or right across the North Sea in less than 2 days. We were perhaps fortunate in studying dispersal from the British Isles, which has a length of wind run over source areas of only a few hundred miles so that steady winds of 10–20 knots blow across it in half a day, and carry out to sea discrete and detectable spore clouds. However, working downwind of an island source, where spore liberation is known to vary enormously both within and between days, has prevented any calculation of the rate at which the spore cloud is depleted with increasing distance from the coast.

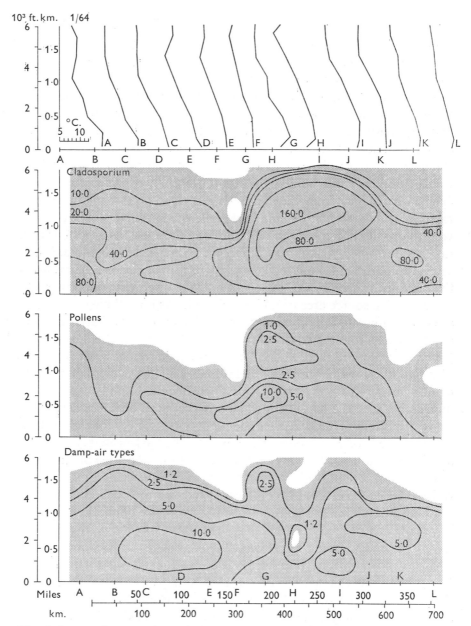

Fig. 6. Isopore diagrams of a vertical section over the North Sea between Yorkshire and the Skagerrak on 16 July 1964 (flight 1/64 in Hirst *et al.* 1967*b*). At top, vertical temperature profiles related to distance from the coast (origins displaced as indicated by letters below axis). Below, isopore lines (in hundreds of spores/m.³ and separated by a geometric progression increasing by a factor of 2, i.e. log₂ scale) show concentrations of *Cladosporium*, pollen and damp-air types related to height and distance from the English coast.

Perhaps further studies would probably best be made from the downwind coast of a land mass large enough to have smoothed away the contributions of spores from small areas on individual days. The discovery of recognizable clouds where the meteorological analysis suggests they should be, not only gives confidence in the methods but shows that distant dispersal of extensive spore clouds is a daily occurrence in that season and weather. The quantity of spores transported is also impressive; had all spores been instantaneously washed-out of the air at the point some hundred miles from the Danish coast where totals were greatest in flight 1/64, approximately ten spores of some kind would have been deposited per square millimetre* of surface.

The sections in Fig. 6 were constructed from sloping profiles which, taking considerable liberties, we regarded as vertical. They confirmed the importance of convection and showed that vestiges of its activity 1 or 2 days previously were still detectable. They added unique information about the fate of the damp-air spores which, in the fine weather we selected, were almost certainly liberated at night. This group, comprising Sporobolomyces, Tilletiopsis and hyaline ascospores, often attains large concentrations near the ground on calm nights but dissipates rapidly at dawn. That these spores disappear because they disintegrate (as suggested by Rich & Waggoner, 1962) seemed unlikely, so it was reassuring to find that those not deposited were diluted upwards by daytime turbulence. Far away from the coast the 'isospore' contours for all types indicated 'eroded' profiles (Fig. 6), with concentrations several times greater higher up than at the surface. In the same regions the pollen cloud was most dense about 300 to 600 m. lower than *Cladosporium*, suggesting that gravitational settling was producing stratification according to spore size. This suggests that the residence time of pollen is shorter than that of *Cladosporium*, but unfortunately the observations do not provide a reliable way of measuring residence time or the rate of deposition.

SPECULATIONS ON THE BIOLOGY OF DISTANT TRANSPORT

Facts about distant dispersal can be acquired only with difficulty, so there is perhaps a need and certainly a temptation to generalize on less evidence than would be acceptable for studies of local dissemination. Occasions like the present Symposium provide an opportunity to speculate from the basis of our experience in and around the British Isles, which we realize may not apply everywhere.

* Not per square centimetre as erroneously stated on p. 135 of *Rep. Rothamsted exp. Stn. for 1965* (1966).

Our intentional omission of any detailed consideration of spore liberation and deposition processes and our inability to measure spore viability, dispose of most of the biological factors that must eventually be considered, but a few must be mentioned because they affect the meteorological interpretation. In midsummer, the freezing level over the British Isles can be as low as 1 km. or as high as 5 km. and in most of our flights it was above 3 km. In winter the freezing level varies with air-mass between the surface and 3 km. It is more difficult to generalize about relative humidities at flight levels but important to remember that they may vary between 100% in cloudy frontal weather and 25% or less in settled anticyclonic conditions. Desiccation may increase slightly the specific gravities of spores, which cover only a small range when hydrated so that their mass is almost a function of size; and terminal velocities may also be influenced by the shrinking and folding of desiccated spores. Eddy velocities in turbulent air are usually large compared with terminal velocities of all but the largest spores, so we expect, and find, that size makes little difference to *ascent* once spores have escaped local deposition. The evidence suggests that spore size may be more important for *descent*. In calm air, all spores must sink at rates depending on their mass and shape, and our results probably show larger differences than those quoted by Rempe (1937) and Harrington (1965) because we selected groups differing widely in size. However, spores continue to fall through convection currents carrying them aloft, so there must always be a tendency for different-sized spores to stratify. Over source areas this tendency will usually be obscured by replenishment from the ground.

Erosion of the base of vertical spore profiles seems usual after long travel over both land and sea, so the spores carried highest during active convection will have the best chance of going far. However, the North Sea sections show that even damp-air types liberated at night can travel far provided they remain suspended long enough to experience convection the next day. The damp-air spore types are liberated after rain as well as at night, so the proportion of these deposited by raindrop capture may be greater than for spores liberated in dry air. Although the proportion of either group lost by rain wash-out is unknown, this is one of the most efficient deposition mechanisms (Hirst, 1959; Gregory, 1961; May, 1958). Concentrations of most spore types vary diurnally over long periods and erratically in response to weather, and such variations may result from variable turbulent mixing as well as directly from changed rates of liberation (Hirst, 1953; Kramer, Pady & Wiley, 1964).

SPECULATIONS ON THE METEOROLOGY
OF DISTANT TRANSPORT

The simultaneous processes that influence the movement and depletion of aerosols are confusing to biologists, so it may be helpful to illustrate their separate effects by cartoons of idealized vertical distributions.

Vertical distribution processes
Source and ascent

Organisms growing on soil, decaying organic matter and vegetation all add to the spore concentration near the ground, where most spores are expected when liberation is active.

Both frictional and thermal turbulence can carry spores upward; frictional turbulence is the more uniform but varies with wind speed, surface roughness and topography. Convection acts irregularly in time, height and horizontal distribution so that both the thoroughness of mixing and the layer affected vary greatly. When spores are liberated into spore-free unstable air, they will ascend progressively (as t_0, t_1, t_2, t_3 in Fig. 7a) giving profiles that often decrease approximately logarithmically with height. Conversely, there is little lift in stable air, so that spores not quickly deposited form dense clouds near the ground, as do water drops in fog.

The effect stable air layers have on spore profiles depends on whether the stability developed before or after the spores ascended. Figure 7b illustrates the profile expected when spore ascent into clear air (t_0, t_1, t_2) is limited (t_3) by a stable layer (shaded). In Fig. 7c the change from (t_0) to (t_1) illustrates the theoretical effect of a stable layer developing within a preformed spore cloud by subsidence or by advection. The gain in concentration beneath the layer would usually be obscured by mixing and greater changes of concentration at the surface. Convective mixing may occur both above and below the stable air. This latter situation occurs quite often, either when warm air overlies cold air at a warm front or as a result of upper air subsiding, circumstances distinguishable by the relative humidity of the warm air. Most temperature inversions are effective barriers to the vertical ascent of air, but very active convection may break through to form isolated towers of cumulus clouds, resulting in irregular additions to the aerosol above the stable layer. Figure 7d (t_1) illustrates the situation expected when a stable layer develops near ground level within a preformed spore cloud (t_0). Allowing for some preferential deposition on the ground, it is easy to see how a situation (t_2) could develop like that claimed by Rempe (1937) to indicate an accumulation above an inversion, and equally clear that it is vestigial rather than the result of congregation. Profiles exactly like those shown by solid lines in Fig. 7*b*, *c* or *d*, would probably never develop naturally because the boundaries of stable layers are less abrupt than indicated.

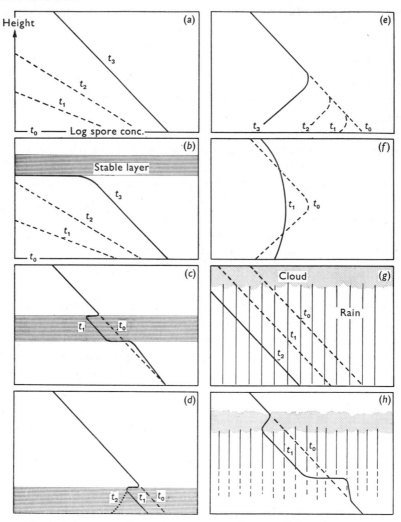

Fig. 7. Diagrams to illustrate meteorological factors likely to influence the shape of vertical spore profiles. For details see text.

Air can also ascend up frontal slopes. Such 'frontal lifting' is more uniform and slower than ascent in convective bubbles, perhaps averaging 0·15 m./sec., but as little as 0·05 m./sec. in weak frontal systems. Nevertheless, these slow rises may be important because they are of the same order as the terminal velocity of spores, the lift is extensive, uniform and persistent. This effect has not yet been detected in our flights and indeed would be very difficult to measure.

Transport and deposition

Before discussing horizontal transport, changes which may modify vertical profiles need mention. Rates of transport in turbulent air have already been mentioned (p. 310). The terminal velocity of spores is unlikely to be much affected by changes in the viscosity of air over the range of temperatures and pressures experienced up to 4 km. in temperate latitudes. Shrinkage of spores through desiccation would probably have larger effects (Wienhold, 1955). Apart from these minor variations, gravitational settling should bring about a uniform downward displacement of the profiles at speeds ranging from less than 3 m./hr. to more than 300 m./hr. but with a mode at about 30 m./hr. 'Subsidence' or widespread, uniform sinking of air, comparable but with opposite effects to frontal lifting also occurs, particularly in association with high or rising pressure. Velocities are again small compared with those in turbulent eddies but may average 2–5 cm./sec. (approx. 70–150 m./hr.) and in special circumstances, such as behind a fast-moving depression, may locally be as great at 1,000 m./hr. Thus at times, subsidence is likely to be at least as important a cause of descent as sedimentation but, like the effects of frontal lifting, it would not be easy to measure or predict.

The decrease of spore concentrations up to 3 km. implies that mixing becomes less thorough well above the ground, and that spores at the base of the profile are more likely to be deposited than those at the top. When spore clouds leave source areas, or when liberation ceases, the bottom of the cloud is no longer replenished and this preferential deposition becomes evident in the development of 'eroded' profiles (Fig. 7e). The degree of erosion may not indicate how much deposition has occurred. Variable surface roughness changes both the efficiency of deposition and the surface area presented. A pine forest would, for example, remove spores more efficiently than a calm water surface, so near-surface concentrations would diminish faster over the forest and leave fewer spores to be deposited later, at least until the near-surface layers are replenished by downward diffusion. Both the efficiency of deposition and the frictional turbulence depend on wind speed, whereas the transfer of spores from higher layers will depend on turbulence, sedimentation and downdraughts. Both upward and downward currents must attenuate peak concentrations and so decrease the degree of erosion visible at the base of the profiles (Fig. 7f (t_0–t_1)). Thus profiles developed during travel over the sea will be modified each day by convection, and changes in their shape provide a much less reliable measure of spore deposition than changes in the total spores forming the profile.

Winds at different heights often differ in speed and direction; this shearing must modify spore profiles occasionally (see flight 4/57 in Hirst et al. (1967a) and flight 1/64 in Hirst et al. (1967b)).

Spores could be washed out of the air by rain either because they act as condensation nuclei or because falling raindrops act as spore traps (p. 155). Condensation occurs preferentially on hygroscopic nuclei; spores might act as 'giant condensation nuclei' but they seem unlikely to play a major role in rain making because they are many fewer (10^2 to 10^4/m.^{3}) at cloud heights than the smaller hygroscopic nuclei (10^6 to 10^{10}/m.^{3}) (Mason, 1962). The efficiency of wash-out (Gregory, 1961) depends on the size of spores and raindrops (Langmuir, 1948) and the rate of rain (Best, 1950). Chamberlain (1956) and May (1958) assessed the process experimentally and theoretically, and McDonald (1962) suggested that large spores would be more efficiently deposited by persistent light rain than by the same amount of thunder rain, because there are more drops. However, Gregory stressed that even large drops would catch small fungus spores rather inefficiently.

In speculating on the modification of vertical spore profiles by rain we may ignore minor variations and assume initially that uniform rain falling from high cloud would decrease spore concentrations by the same proportion at all heights (Fig. 7g). Raindrops often fall from cloud but evaporate before they reach the ground, which can increase the concentration of dry but displaced spores where the drops evaporate (Fig. 7h). This provides one of the very few mechanisms for concentrating spores while suspended in air. As convection is likely to accompany evaporation, the concentrated layer will be simultaneously attenuated as in Fig. 7f and the final shape of the profiles will depend on the balance between wash-out and mixing.

Horizontal distribution processes

Although vertical transport mechanisms are important in deciding the period spores will remain suspended in air and when they will be deposited it is horizontal movement that decides where they will go. As distance from the source increases, the small eddies important in diffusion become relatively unimportant compared to the movement of air in large pressure systems. Inability to predict the development and movement of large systems is a major difficulty in weather forecasting but past records are adequate for estimating spore trajectories. Hence it is worth examining whether the principles of air movement within pressure systems would help to define the times and conditions in which distant spore transport is likely and the direction it will follow.

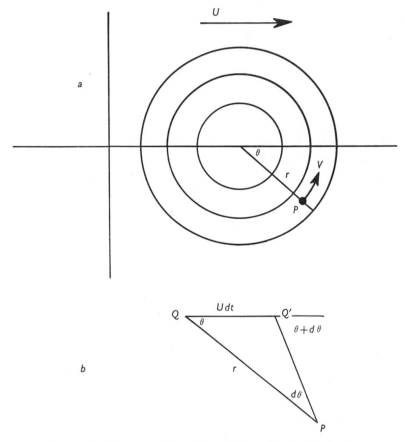

Figs. 8 *a*, *b*. Movement of a particle within an idealized depression. For details see text.

Flights in temperate climates suggest that most spores occur at heights where air movement is best represented by 'surface' pressure distribution (i.e. at about 500 m.). Several factors divert low-level winds from the direction of the isobars (see Meteorological Office, 1960), but we may begin by ignoring these and considering the motion of a particle suspended in an idealized circular depression (Fig. 8*a*). This is regarded as unchanging in intensity and moving east at a uniform velocity, *U*, with an angle θ between the direction of depression movement and the line, r, between its centre and P. Ignoring convergence towards the centre, winds will move at a steady speed, V, parallel to the isobars nearest them. The acceleration of a particle, P, radially inwards by the wind rotating round the depression is V^2/r and the acceleration from the movement of the depression can be obtained from Fig. 8b. Here the change in direction in time, dt, is $d\theta$ where

$$d\theta = \frac{U dt}{r} \sin \theta$$

and the radial change of speed is therefore

$$V d\theta = \frac{UV}{r} \sin \theta \, dt,$$

so the acceleration inwards is $- UV/r \sin \theta$. The resultant acceleration can therefore be expressed in the form

$$\frac{V^2}{r'} = \frac{V^2}{r} - \frac{UV}{r} \sin \theta,$$

where r' is the radius of curvature of the trajectory. Pettersen (1956) quoted a similar equation in a different form.

The equation gives curves of the type shown in Fig. 9a where the curvature is least when V is in the same direction as U, but increases with increase of $\sin \theta$. With eastward movement, therefore, the curvature is greater to the north and hence the trajectory is approximately cycloidal with the size of the loop depending on: (1) the ratio of the speed of the depression to that of the circulating wind (U/V); and (2) the point in the south-east quadrant at which the trajectory begins. If stationary, such an idealized depression would have particles circulating within it without change of radius. Figure 9b shows the effects of different depression speeds with a constant circulating wind. Particles liberated in other parts of the depression would follow similarly shaped tracks but starting at different positions; thus those liberated in the north-east quadrant describe only a partial loop. Trajectories starting from the western sector do not loop initially but can be regarded as the latter part of a looped path, and so on (Fig. 10).

In considering northward migrations of the type described for uredo-spores of *Puccinia graminis*, trajectories within depressions moving east would effect most northward movement when U/V is small and also when the particles are liberated into the south-east quadrant of an approaching depression rather than into its centre. Rapid northward movement of the depression would enhance northward transport but is unusual in west Europe where most depressions move with an eastward component. Hogg (1961, 1962; and see Hirst *et al.* 1967*a*) found that

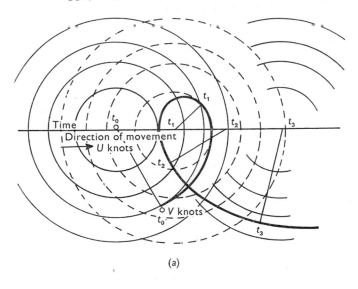

(a)

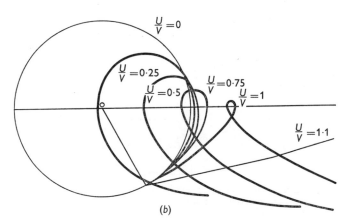

(b)

Fig. 9. (*a*) Trajectory of a particle around a steadily moving idealized depression (explanation in text). (*b*) Trajectories of particles from the same starting point in an idealized depression but with different values of U/V (further explanation in text).

large depressions centred near the Bay of Biscay and moving slowly north were often associated with uredospore catches in south-west Britain. Similar movement could occur around the west side of a slow-moving anticyclone centred over France, but this situation is less important because it is less frequent, seldom persists for long and is usually accompanied by light winds. Pressure systems moving quickly east are unlikely to introduce spores from sources far to the south but may do from less distant ones: e.g. France was probably the source of the uredospore introduced to England by the passage of two small anticyclones in July 1959 (Fig. 1).

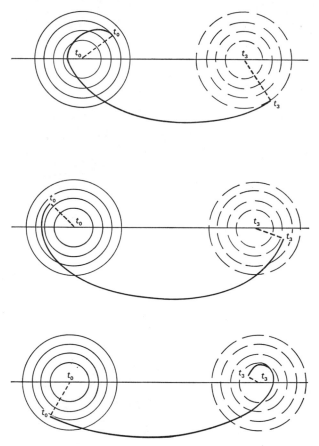

Fig. 10. Trajectories of particles starting from different positions in the same idealized depression (further explanation in text).

In practice, pressure systems are never ideal and change constantly, so although a theoretical treatment helps to illustrate principles and to classify situations, it will not replace detailed examination of individual episodes. Hogg (1961) considered all possible introductions of uredospores into south-west England from Spain or beyond during May, June and July of 1947 to 1959 and at heights up to 6 km. On average there was an interval of 8·6 days between one favourable flow and the

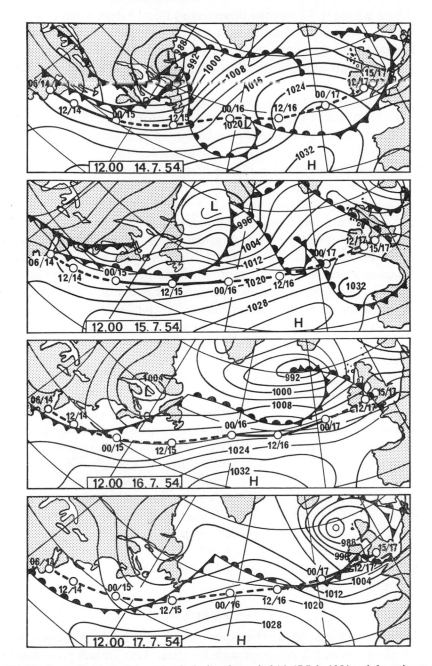

Fig. 11. Synoptic maps of the Atlantic during the period 14–17 July 1954 and the estimated track of an American species of moth trapped in Wales. Track is dotted except in the section applying to each chart. Further explanation in text.

next, and within the 3 months there were 11 or 12 days when transport between north Spain and south-west Britain was possible. This may not be a great frequency but the evidence (Ogilvie & Thorpe, 1961) suggests that it is enough to introduce *Puccinia graminis* in most years. Movements of moths such as *Laphygma exigua* have provided similar evidence of a southern origin (Hurst, 1965), but less often.

It is not difficult to show that exotic organisms reach England from European sources to the south and east, so it is natural to inquire whether spores can travel farther, for example, from North America. As yet there is no critical evidence of this because the history of air sampled on or above the eastern Atlantic has been unknown. Difficulties of tracking are enormously increased by the longer distances and continued spore transport is subject to increased risk of wash-out by rain. However, the above theoretical considerations suggest that most eastward movement with least northward diversion would be found where U approaches V, namely on the southern flank of active depression systems. Then, particles within the warm sector could transfer allegiance from one depression to another succeeding it; such particles, being south of the active frontal system, would escape most or all of the frontal rain. There is not yet evidence that spores can move in this way, but we are grateful to Mr R. A. French of the Entomology Department at Rothamsted for information about an American moth *Phytometra biloba* caught near Aberystwyth on 19 July 1954 (Miles, 1955). Examination of synoptic charts suggested that the moth had probably arrived in the afternoon of 17 July while warm south-westerly winds were blowing over the Irish Sea. Arrival earlier than this would have occurred to the rear of a cold front with north-easterly winds and no possible long-distance track from the west. Assuming the moth arrived on 17 July, two days before it was caught, the estimated track of the moth, at heights never exceeding 600 m., would have led back to South Virginia just over 3 days earlier (Fig. 11). Despite the complex meteorological situation over the North Atlantic at that time, this track would have always been in warm air to the south of the depressions and was surprisingly direct.

CONCLUSIONS

This review of long-distance transport, like its predecessors, shows how incomplete are our knowledge and abilities. Our failure to measure viability is one example, but scarcely more important than the lack of numbers relating airborne spore concentration to deposition on exposed surfaces. Experiments measuring spore deposition near sources need extending to measurements involving the effects of wind speed, convection and precipitation over both smooth and rough surfaces. Recent contributions depend mainly on improved methods for catching spores, longer and more complex flights, and improved meteorological documentation. Even these improvements did not provide accurate estimates of the rates of erosion, vertical particle transport or the atmospheric residence times for spores of different sizes. Nevertheless, further development of techniques, and a careful choice of localities where larger source areas have smoothed the diurnal variations in spore production, should allow the processes we now begin to discern to be studied more precisely.

Biologists have relied too much on generalizations about prevailing winds and climates. Close examination shows that transport depends upon a delicate synchrony of biological and physical processes governing the activity of sources, and the ascent, transport and descent of spores within the atmosphere. Distant transport is governed by weather, not by climate or prevailing winds, which merely indicate the most frequent weather. Meteorology can answer many questions provided biologists can pose them precisely; thus air trajectories help to explain the catches of ground traps that can discriminate the time of catch accurately. Biologists need to know how often spores are introduced if they are to estimate the risks to crops. Long series of observations of uredospore introduction, such as that made in U.S.A., eventually provide this information but it would be quicker to understand the mechanism of spore transport, to define types of suitable weather and then to recognize them meteorologically.

Warm air masses are often stable but may be either cloudy and very moist, or clear, much depending on whether their history was maritime or continental. Vertical transport of aerosols is often limited by inversions, although daytime heating does cause some convection. In contrast, many cold air masses are unstable with strong vertical currents and develop showers, so that provided the spores avoid washout in rain they may be well placed to go far. However, some cold air is much less unstable, and in the evening or at night, light winds decrease and the sky clears.

Although most of our flights were made during active convection, the catches support previous evidence that spores are often transported far and in great numbers. Conditions in flight 1/64 may have been unusual but the potential deposit of 10 spores/mm.^{2} after almost crossing the North Sea would still demand attention even if it occurred on 1% of days, if only 1% were pathogens and only 1% of those were viable.

22-2

It is plain that migrations occurred in many directions and we detected movement with, against and across the direction of the prevailing westerly winds and extending more than 1,000 miles.

Although erosion of vertical spore profiles seemed a typical result of travel away from sources, we cannot yet compare its activity over land and sea or by day and night. However, after a night over the sea, the greatest concentrations occurred between 500 and 1,500 m.; these were several times greater than those measured at 30–60 m., and concentrations on the surface may have been even smaller. Under such conditions spore concentrations estimated with surface traps must grossly underestimate the total spore transport and the possible density of deposit in rain. Although continuous sampling by surface traps increase their sensitivity in detecting small concentrations it cannot make them more able to estimate the total spores within the profiles above. Thus both aircraft sampling and the collection of spores from rain-water seem necessary additions to ground sampling in comprehensive studies of spore migration.

Variations in spore liberation, turbulent dilution and spore deposition have been recognized as possible variables in studies of diurnal periodicity of spore liberation near the ground. Recent evidence from flights over the North Sea suggests that previous fetch of the wind over sources must also be considered. Even moderate winds can blow right across the British Isles in half a day, so during the night the air over land may be purged of day-liberated spores as 'clean' maritime air moves across, and accumulates a characteristic night flora. At ground level the magnitude and timing of such changes would be determined by wind speed, distance from the windward coast, the spore load of the air approaching it, the decrease in near-ground concentrations resulting from erosion during travel over land, and the degree to which turbulence and sedimentation replenish them from above. Contrasting diurnal periodicities of *Cladosporium* have been reported (Hirst, 1953; Cammack, 1955; Hamilton, 1959; Rich & Waggoner, 1962; Pady, Kramer & Wiley, 1962). Some of the differences might be explained geographically. For example, an overland wind fetch of several days may give a nearly uniform spore content, without the amplitude typical of an island source, and erratic fluctuations at coastal stations could result from alternating land and sea breezes. A knowledge of large-scale atmospheric transport may, therefore, prove as necessary to understanding local aerobiology as it is to distant dispersal.

REFERENCES

ASAI, G. N. (1960). Intra- and inter-regional movement of uredospores of black stem rust in the upper Mississippi river valley. *Phytopathology*, **50**, 535.

BAKER, G. E. (1966). Inadvertent distribution of fungi. *Can. J. Microbiol.* **12**, 109.

BEST, A. C. (1950). The size distribution of raindrops. *Q. Jl R. met. Soc.* **76**, 16.

BISBY, G. R. (1943). Geographical distribution of fungi. *Bot. Rev.* **9**, 466.

BOURKE, P. M. A. (1964). Emergence of potato blight, 1843–46. *Nature, Lond.* **203**, 805.

CAMMACK, R. H. (1955). Seasonal changes in three common constituents of the air spora of S. Nigeria. *Nature, Lond.* **176**, 1270.

CAMMACK, R. H. (1959). Studies on *Puccinia polysora* Underw. II. A consideration of the method of introduction of *P. polysora* into Africa. *Trans. Br. mycol. Soc.* **42**, 27.

CHAMBERLAIN, A. C. (1956). Aspects of travel and deposition of aerosol and vapour clouds. *A.E.R.E. Rep.* HP/R 1261. 35 pp. London: H.M.S.O.

CLOSE, R. (1958). Antirrhinum rust in New Zealand. *N.Z. Jl Agric.* **97**, 551.

CRAIGIE, J. H. (1945). Epidemiology of stem rust in Western Canada. *Scient. Agric.* **25**, 285.

DILLON WESTON, W. A. R. (1929). Observations on the bacterial and fungal flora of the Upper Air. *Trans. Br. mycol. Soc.* **14**, 111.

DURST, C. S. & DAVIS, N. E. (1957). Accuracy of geostrophic trajectories. *Met. Mag., Lond.* **86**, 138.

ERDTMAN, G. (1937). Pollen grains recovered from the atmosphere over the Atlantic. *Acta Horti. Gothoburg.* **12**, 185.

FRIDRIKSSON, S. & KOLBEINSSON, A. (1965). A report on the first isolation of micro-organism on Surtsey. Appendix I of *Proc. Surtsey Biol. Congr. Reykjavik*, pp. 15–17.

GREEN, V. W., PEDERSON, P. O., LUNDGREN, D. A. & HAGBERG, C. A. (1964). Microbiological exploration of stratospheric results of six experimental flights. *Proceeding of the Atmospheric Biology Conference*, p. 199. Ed. H. M. Tsuchiya & A. H. Brown. University of Minnesota.

GREGORY, P. H. (1945). The dispersal of air-borne spores. *Trans. Br. mycol. Soc.* **28**, 26.

GREGORY, P. H. (1952). Fungus spores. *Trans. Br. mycol. Soc.* **35**, 1.

GREGORY, P. H. (1958). A correction. *Trans. Br. mycol. Soc.* **41**, 202.

GREGORY, P. H. (1961). *The Microbiology of the Atmosphere*, 251 pp. London: Leonard Hill Ltd.

GREGORY, P. H. (1962). The dispersal distance problem. *Pollen Spores*, **4**, 348.

GREGORY, P. H. & STEDMAN, O. J. (1953). Deposition of air-borne *Lycopodium* spores on plane surfaces. *Ann. appl. Biol.* **40**, 651.

HAFSTEN, U. (1951). A pollen-analytic investigation of two peat deposits from Tristan da Cunha. *Results Norweg. Exped. T. da Cunha*, 1937–1938, **22**, 1–42.

HAMILTON, E. D. (1959). Studies on the air spora. *Acta allerg.* **13**, 143.

HARRINGTON, J. B. (1965). *Atmospheric Pollution by Aeroallergens: Meteorological Phase. Final Report.* Vol. II. *Atmospheric Diffusion of Ragweed Pollen in Urban Areas.* Text. University of Michigan. Dep. of Meteorology and Oceanography, ORA Project 06342. Off. Res. Admin. Ann Arbor.

HEISE, H. A. & HEISE, E. R. (1948). The distribution of ragweed pollen and *Alternaria* spores in the upper atmosphere. *J. Allergy*, **19**, 403.

HEISE, H. A. & HEISE, E. R. (1949). The influence of temperature variations and winds aloft on the distribution of pollens and molds in the upper atmosphere. *J. Allergy*, **20**, 378.

HEISE, H. A. & HEISE, E. R. (1950). Meteorologic factors in the distribution of pollens and molds. A review: Geographic Influence. *Ann. Allergy*, **8**, 641.

HIRST, J. M. (1953). Changes in atmospheric spore content: Diurnal periodicity and the effects of weather. *Trans. Br. mycol. Soc.* **36**, 375.

HIRST, J. M. (1959). Spore liberation and dispersal. In *Plant Pathology Problems and Progress*, 1908–1958, pp. 529–38. University of Wisconsin Press.

HIRST, J. M. (1965). Dispersal of soil micro-organisms, In *Ecology of Soil-borne Plant Pathogens*, pp. 69–81. Prelude to biological control. Ed. K. F. Baker & W. C. Snyder. University of California Press.

HIRST, J. M., STEDMAN, O. J. & HOGG, W. H. (1967*a*). Long distance spore transport: methods of measurement, vertical spore profiles and the detection of immigrant spores. (In the Press.)

HIRST, J. M., STEDMAN, O. J. & HURST, G. W. (1967*b*). Long-distance spore transport: Spore concentration in vertical sections over the sea. (In the Press.)

HOGG, W. H. (1961). The use of trajectories in Black rust epidemiology. *2nd Coloquio Europeo sobre la roya negra de los cereales*. Madrid.

HOGG, W. H. (1962). The use of upper air data in relation to plant disease. *Mem. Univ. Coll. Wales, Aberystwyth*, **5**, 22.

HURST, G. W. (1965). *Laphygma exigua* immigrations into the British Isles, 1947–1963. *Int. J. Biomet.* **9**, 21.

HYDE, H. A. & ADAMS, K. F. (1961). Spore trapping in relation to epidemics of black rust 1947–1959. *2nd Coloquio Europeo sobre la royo negra de los cereales*, 7 pp. Madrid.

JOHNSON, C. G. (1957). The vertical distribution of aphids in the air and the temperature lapse rate. *Q. Jl R. met. Soc.* **83**, 194.

JOHNSON, T. (1961). *Rust Research in Canada and Related Plant-Disease Investigations*, pp. 1–69. Res. Branch, Canada Dep. Agric.

KELLY, C. D. & PADY, S. M. (1953). Microbiological studies of air over some non-arctic regions of Canada. *Can. J. Bot.* **31**, 90.

KRAMER, C. L., PADY, S. M. & WILEY, B. J. (1964). Kansas aeromycology. XIV: Diurnal studies 1961–62. *Trans. Kans. Acad. Sci.* **67**, 442.

LANGMUIR, J. (1948). The production of rain by a chain reaction in cumulus clouds at temperatures above freezing. *J. Met.* **5**, 175.

MALONE, J. P. & MUSKETT, A. E. (1964). Seed-borne fungi, description of 77 fungus species. *Proc. int. Seed Test. Ass.* **29**, 176.

MASON, B. J. (1962). *Clouds, Rain and Rain Making*. Cambridge University Press.

MAY, F. G. (1958). The washout by rain of *Lycopodium* spores. *A.E.R.E. Rep.* HP/R 2198.

McDONALD, J. E. (1962). Mechanism of raindrop washout of airborne pollen and spores. *Pollen Spores*, **4**, 365.

MEHTA, K. C. (1952). Further studies on cereal rusts in India. *The Indian Council of Agricultural Research Sci. Monog.* no. 18, 363 pp.

METEOROLOGICAL OFFICE (1960). *Handbook of Aviation Meteorology*, 404 pp. Air Ministry, Meteorological Office M.O. 630 (A.P. 3340). London: H.M.S.O.

MILES, P. M. (1955). *Phytometra biloba* Stephens (Lep. Plusiidae) in Wales. *Entomologist's Mon. Mag.* **91**, 89.

MISCHUSTIN, E. (1926). Zur Untersuchung der Mikroflora der höheren Luftschichten. *Zbl. Bakt.* (II. Abt 67), 347.

NEWMAN, I. V. (1948). Aerobiology on commercial air routes. *Nature, Lond.* **161**, 275.

OGDEN, E. C., RAYNOR, G. S. & HAYES, J. V. (1966). Travels of airborne pollen. *Progress Report, New York State Museum and Science Service*, no. 6, 23 pp. The University of the State of New York, Albany N.Y. Research Grant. AP-81 Public Health Service.

OGILVIE, L. & THORPE, I. G. (1961). New light on epidemics of black stem rust of wheat. *Sci. Prog.* **49**, 209.

PADY, S. M. & KAPICA, L. (1956). Fungi in air masses over Montreal during 1950 and 1951. *Can. J. Bot.* **34**, 1.

PADY, S. M. & KELLY, C. D. (1953). Studies of microorganisms in Arctic air during 1949. *Can. J. Bot.* **31**, 107.

PADY, S. M. & KELLY, C. D. (1954). Aerobiological studies of fungi and bacteria over the Atlantic Ocean. *Can. J. Bot.* **32**, 202.

PADY, S. M., KRAMER, C. L. & WILEY, B. J. (1962). Kansas Aeromycology. XII. Materials, methods and general results of diurnal studies 1959–1960. *Mycologia*, **54**, 168.

PASQUILL, F. (1961). Estimation of the dispersion of windborne materials. *Met. Mag., Lond.* **90**, 33.

PERKINS, W. A. (1957). The roto-rod sampler. *2nd Semi-Annual report, Aerosol Laboratory, Dep. of Chemistry and Chemical Engng, Stanford University*, C.M.L. 186.

PETTERSEN, S. (1956). *Weather Analysis and Forecasting*. London: McGraw-Hill.

POLUNIN, N. & KELLY, C. D. (1952). Arctic aerobiology. Fungi and bacteria etc. caught in the air during flights over the geographical North Pole. *Nature, Lond.* **170**, 314.

POPULER, C. (1964). Le comportement des epidemies de mildiou du Tabac, *Peronospora tabacina* Adam. I. La situation en Europe. *Bull. Inst. agron. Stns Rech. Gembloux*, **32**, 339.

RAYNER, R. W. & HOPKINS, J. C. F. (1962). Blue mould of tobacco. A review of current information. *Commonw. mycol. Inst. Misc. Publ.* no. 16, 1.

REMPE, H. (1937). Untersuchungen über de Verbreitung des Blütenstaubes durch die Luftstromungen. *Planta*, **27**, 93.

RICH, S. & WAGGONER, P. E. (1962). Atmospheric concentration of *Cladosporium* spores. *Science, N.Y.* **137**, 962.

ROGERS, L. A. & MEIER, F. C. (1936). The collection of microorganisms above 36,000 feet. *Nat. geogr. Soc. Strat. Ser.* **2**, 146.

SACK, S. S. (1949). How far can wind-borne pollen be disseminated. *J. Allergy*, **20**, 453.

SCHRÖDTER, H. (1960). Dispersal by air and water—the flight and landing. Chapter 6 in *Plant Pathology: An Advanced Treatise*, vol. III, pp. 169–227. Ed. by J. G. Horsfall & A. E. Dimond. New York: Academic Press.

SCORER, R. S. & LUDLAM, F. H. (1953). Bubble theory of penetrative convection. *Q. Jl R. met. Soc.* **79**, 94.

SREERAMULU, T. (1958). Spore content of air over the Mediterranean sea. *J. Indian bot. Soc.* **37**, 220.

SREERAMULU, T. & RAMALINGAM, A. (1961). Experiments on the dispersion of *Lycopodium* and *Podaxis* spores in the air. *Ann. appl. Biol.* **49**, 659.

STAKMAN, E. C. & HARRAR, J. G. (1957). *Principles of Plant Pathology*, 581 pp. New York: The Ronald Press Co.

STAKMAN, E. C., HENRY, A. W., CURRAN, G. C. & CHRISTOPHER, W. N. (1923). Spores in the Upper Air. *J. agric. Res.* **24**, 599.

STOVER, R. H. (1962). Intercontinental spread of banana leaf spot (*Mycosphaerella musicola* Leach). *Trop. Agric., Trin.* **39**, 327.

TAUBER, H. (1965). Differential pollen dispersion and the interpretation of pollen diagrams. *Geol. Sur. of Denmark*, II, Series, no. 89.

U.S. DEP. OF HEALTH, EDUCATION AND WELFARE (1959). Sampling microbiological aerosols. *Public Health Monograph*, no. 60, 53 pp.

WAGGONER, P. E. (1952). Distribution of potato late blight around inoculum sources. *Phytopathology*, **42**, 323.

WEINHOLD, A. R. (1955). Rate of fall urediospores of *Puccinia graminis tritici* Erikss. and Hem. as affected by humidity and temperature. *Tech. Report of Office of Naval Research. ONR Contract N9 onr* 82400, 104 pp.

WOLFENBARGER, D. O. (1959). Dispersion of small organisms. Incidence of viruses and pollen; dispersion of fungus spores and insects. *Lloydia*, **22**, 1.

ZADOKS, J. C. (1961). Yellow rust on wheat. Studies in epidemiology and physiologic specialization. *Tijdschr. PlZiekt.* **67**, 69.

ZADOKS, J. C. (1966). International dispersal of fungi. *Neth. J. Plant Path.* **72** (in the Press).

ZOBELL, C. F. (1942). Microorganisms in Marine Air. *Aerobiology*, p. 55. Publication 17, Amer. Assoc. Adv. Sci.

EXPLANATION OF PLATE

PLATE 1

(a) Sampling head of impactor extruded through the fuselage of a Hastings aircraft of the Meteorological Research Flight. (Photograph: Royal Aircraft Establishment, Crown Copyright reserved.)

(b) Sampling head of aircraft impactor. The orifice is pointing towards a protective cover which is removed before operation; spores are impacted on sticky transparent tape wrapped around the drum. (Photograph: Royal Aircraft Establishment, Crown Copyright reserved.)

PLATE 1

Fig. 1*a*

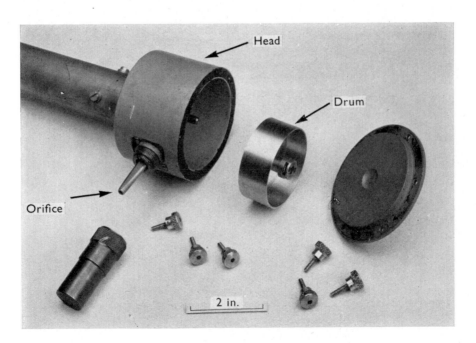

Fig. 1*b*

MICROBES IN THE UPPER ATMOSPHERE AND BEYOND

CARL W. BRUCH*

National Aeronautics and Space Administration, Washington, D.C.

One of the important conclusions that can be reached from all of the microbiological data that have accumulated during the past 300 years is the ubiquity of microbial life on this planet. Micro-organisms abound in the soil and water of the Earth and are prevalent in its atmosphere. The boundaries of microbial ecology are still vague in that the extreme environmental limits for microbial life on this planet have not been established.

In the envelope of air close to the Earth's surface there can be 100 micro-organisms per cubic foot on average, and during disturbances such as dust storms the number can increase dramatically. To date, there is no good estimate as to what range of altitude constitutes the upper boundary for the terrestrial biosphere. Can microbial life be found at heights of 100,000 ft., 200,000 ft. or even higher in going from the Earth's surface? If micro-organisms can be found at reaches from the Earth beyond those accepted by considerations of known physical processes, new mechanisms for their presence at these altitudes will have to be postulated. Possibilities that can be suggested are recent volcanic eruptions, nuclear bomb explosions, and the activities of man in space exploration. Even more challenging is the concept that evidence of microbial life will be found in the upper atmospheric regions and on other planets because life pervades the universe.

Man's efforts to sample the upper atmosphere have progressed rapidly in recent years under the stimulus to assay the particulate matter as well as the hazardous gases resulting from atomic or hydrogen bomb explosions in the upper atmosphere. Although these techniques were developed to monitor radioactivity in the atmosphere, they have now been reviewed for their applicability to the sampling of other matter, particularly micro-organisms. These sampling tools, when combined with the current advances in rocketry and spacecraft instrumentation, provide a means to determine the presence of micro-organisms in the Earth's upper atmosphere.

* Now with Division of Microbiology, Food and Drug Administration, Washington, D.C.

OBJECTIVES OF THE NASA PROGRAMME

The National Aeronautics and Space Administration (NASA) programme for determining the boundaries of the Earth's biosphere has been undertaken to furnish data relative to these topics:

(1) Sterile planetary-impacting spacecraft must be shrouded during passage through the Earth's atmosphere to maintain their sterility. No information is available as to how long this protection must be afforded to the sterile payload.

(2) The upper terrestrial atmosphere can be used as a test bed for instrumentation capable of the detection in real time of extremely small samples of living organisms or their biochemical by-products. Some of these life-detecting instruments will comprise the scientific payloads in the search for extra-terrestrial life on planetary surfaces.

(3) As a corollary to the detection of micro-organisms, microbial specimens can be carried to the upper atmospheric regions to measure their ability to survive in these environments. If micro-organisms remain viable during long exposures to the full spectrum of physical and chemical factors in the upper atmospheric regions, some of the theoretical objections to their occurrence in these environments will have been removed.

(4) This research can monitor the extent of biological contamination resulting from the activities of manned spacecraft in orbits near the Earth.

(5) This effort could detect the existence of an extra-terrestrial microbiota that is capable of transferring life between the planets of the solar system (theory of panspermia).

GENERAL ASPECTS OF THE UPPER
ATMOSPHERIC ENVIRONMENT

The Earth's atmosphere is a vast churning mixture of gases and trace quantities of liquids and solids. The major properties of the atmosphere, apart from its composition, are its temperature, pressure, and density. For convenience, the scientist has divided the atmosphere into regions differentiated by their temperature distribution. The lowest region, which extends from ground level to the first temperature minimum, is the troposphere. The next higher region, which extends to the second temperature maximum, is the stratosphere. The following region, which extends to the second temperature minimum, is the mesosphere. The region directly above this is the thermosphere. The region beyond the thermosphere has not been defined by its temperature and is called the exosphere.

The prime force producing the multitude of changes in the upper atmosphere is the radiant energy of the Sun. The Sun's ultraviolet radiation breaks down molecules into atoms. It converts molecules and atoms into ions and causes the transformation of oxygen into ozone and the splitting of hydrogen from water vapour. Since these normally unstable species are usually produced at high altitudes where gas density and rates of recombination are low, they can persist for long intervals. The upper atmosphere receives a continual influx not only of electromagnetic radiation but also of electrons and protons from the Sun. It is also constantly bombarded by cosmic rays from outer space. At the same time, it is exposed to a steady shower of meteors and meteoric debris, an amount estimated to be as much as a thousand tons per day. From this cursory description the following question can be composed: What is the capability of micro-organisms to survive in this environment for long periods of time?

RESPONSE OF MICRO-ORGANISMS TO SOME OF THE CONDITIONS OF OUTER SPACE

The survival of micro-organisms in interplanetary space has been largely a matter of speculation and extrapolation of data obtained in the laboratory. Several studies have been supported by NASA relative to the effect of ultraviolet radiation and ultra-high vacuum on the viability of microbial spores. Portner, Spiner, Hoffman & Phillips (1961) were among the first to show that ultra-high vacuum would not kill various populations of micro-organisms. Pressures as low as 2×10^{-10} mm. Hg. were reached in these studies. Confirmation of this work in studies with *Bacillus subtilis* var. *niger* came from the Jet Propulsion Laboratory of NASA in a paper by Morelli, Fehlner & Stembridge (1962). In a later extensive study, a group directed by G. J. Silverman has reported in several papers (Davis, Silverman & Keller, 1963; Silverman, Davis & Keller, 1964) on the ability of microbial spores to tolerate low dosages of ionizing radiation and/or ultraviolet radiation in the presence of ultra-high vacuum. These studies showed that, although ultraviolet radiation can destroy a sizable fraction of the spore populations, the material on which the specimens were prepared usually provided enough shielding so that sterilization was never achieved. Imshenetsky (1963) has shown that microbial spores mixed with dust particles will readily survive the combined presence of ultra-high vacuum and ultraviolet radiation

Thus, mechanisms exist for spores to withstand the rigours of deep space. Although some flight programmes are now under way to expose micro-organisms fully to the harsh conditions of the upper atmosphere and deep space (Hotchin, Lorenz & Hemenway, 1965; Hotchin, Lorenz, Markusen & Hemenway, 1967), it is now agreed that many flight experiments will be needed to establish conclusively the microbial response to this environment. The general view is that deep space conditions will not cause the total inactivation of a population of terrestrial micro-organisms. The degree to which inorganic agents such as micrometeorites may afford protection to atmospheric microbes is completely unexplored.

ANALYSIS OF THE THEORY OF PANSPERMIA

It has already been stated that one of the goals of the NASA programme of microbiological research in the upper atmosphere is to determine whether microbial spores do migrate between the planets of this solar system. This idea was first proposed early in this century by Arrhenius (1908), the famous Swedish physicist and chemist. He envisaged spores of living organisms drifting through space and seeding hospitable planets upon which they came to rest. The living forms are imagined to have moved from a planet by electrostatic ejection and to have been propelled by radiation pressure through interstellar space. At the time it was proposed, the panspermia hypothesis had a certain appeal. There was then very little evidence concerning abiogenic processes by which life might have come into being on the primitive Earth, and the experiments of Pasteur, who had disproved the theory of spontaneous generation, allowed a ready acceptance of spores as an origin of terrestrial life. An extraterrestrial source for terrestrial life at least postponed answering the difficult question of the origin of life.

The credibility of the panspermia hypothesis can be attacked mainly on two issues: (1) the lack of a plausible natural mechanism for impelling a spore or spore-bearing particle out of the gravitational field of a planet as large as the Earth or any planet large enough to sustain a significant atmosphere; and (2) the vulnerability of such a particle to destruction by solar radiation. Sagan (1961) has estimated the radiation pressure requirements and the panspermic transit times for living particles of various sizes. Micro-organisms escaping the solar system would be in a size range of 0·2–0·6 microns, while micro-organisms seeding the Earth would be larger. The former size range would allow all viruses, some bacteria, and the smallest of bacterial spores in the vicinity of the

Earth's orbit to be propelled away by the radiation pressure of the Sun and to arrive at the orbit of Mars in a few weeks, at Jupiter in months, and at Neptune in years. Sagan raises the question of microbial survival during these transits because of the doses of ultraviolet, X-rays and proton radiation that would be encountered.

In view of the dormancy of micro-organisms in high vacuum at low temperatures and of their relatively low cross-section for ionizing radiation, the hazards to exposure in space may have been exaggerated. The chief danger to a microbe should come from solar ultraviolet radiation and the proton wind (Lederberg, 1960), but a thin layer of overlying material would shield a spore from both types of radiation. Micro-organisms ejected from planets at great distances from a star such as Uranus or Neptune in our own solar system should encounter negligible radiation hazards (Sagan, 1961). The tenability of the panspermia hypothesis for ejection from or arrival on to many planets cannot be rejected by radiation sensitivity arguments alone.

Sagan (1961) has calculated from geometrical considerations that in order for the Earth to have received one micro-organism from a stellar source during the first billion years of Earth's history, each one of 10^{11} assumed planets in the galaxy must have ejected into interstellar space about one ton of micro-organisms. Because little is known about the present rate of ejection of micro-organisms from the planets, especially by electrostatic mechanisms, the probability of these values cannot be judged. Studies of the microbial population of the terrestrial upper atmosphere and interplanetary space would be very useful in analysing such considerations.

EXOBIOLOGY AND THE ORIGIN OF LIFE

Underlying previous discussions of panspermia was the fundamental question, 'How did life originate?' Space exploration can provide man with an opportunity to obtain data relevant to this question. As man journeys into space, he can gain a perspective not only of this planet, but a prospect of what has occurred in other parts of this universe. Thus, the new field of exobiology—the study of life beyond the Earth (Lederberg, 1960)—is the most subtle and demanding of the new opportunities placed in man's hands by space rocketry.

Since the time of Pasteur, biology has experienced remarkable growth as a scientific discipline, particularly in the analysis of the biochemical mechanisms of life. The key to these advances has been the concept of evolution, for it is this magnificent concept that helps to explain how structures as diverse as the microscopic amoeba and as complex as man could have developed. Despite the outward differences of terrestrial organisms their chemistry is the same. In all organisms the genetic material consists of nucleic acids, while the cell structures are composed mainly of proteins. The comparison of these similarities has led to the theory of the unity of biochemistry throughout terrestrial life. The tools are now at hand for determining whether the sequence of biochemical events and structures that prevail in terrestrial life are common to life wherever it may have originated, or whether life has evolved as a function of different environmental and chemical backgrounds in the universe.

The need for spacecraft sterilization in exobiological exploration

The search for extraterrestrial life with unmanned space probes requires the total sterilization of the landing capsule and its contents. If microbial contaminants should be landed on a planet that has an evolving form of life, the ecology of these planets might be greatly disrupted. There would be the danger of competition to the point of extinction of the indigenous organisms. In the absence of a planetary biota, the terrestrial invaders might completely metabolize any stores of non-living organic matter, thus confusing the status of abiogenesis on such a planet. Terrestrial biologists as yet lack enough information on biological theory to interpret fully the hazards that are involved in the biological contamination of a planet.

Because it has been shown in preceding paragraphs that some micro-organisms can tolerate the conditions prevalent in interplanetary environments, it is a requirement that planetary probes be sterilized (Hall & Bruch, 1965). The sterilized spacecraft is protected by a microbiologically tight canister, and the ejection of this protective canister cannot occur until the spacecraft has safely passed through the Earth's biosphere. This situation was an immediate impetus for determining the vertical extent of the biosphere, but more recent plans for planetary exploration missions indicate that the canister will not be released until the spacecraft is deep into interplanetary space. Still, one must be certain that any life (detectable by exobiological instrumentation) on a planet is due to the presence of life on the planet's surface and not to living organisms moving about in interplanetary space.

Space exploration as a form of panspermia

As a corollary to the discussion of panspermia, it should be noted that the flight of non-sterilized unmanned and manned spacecraft could be a vehicle for panspermia. Already, there are many satellites in near-Earth orbit that can allow the escape of the micro-organisms thereon. In the manned spaceflight programme a small amount of waste material is lost to the space environment. It is possible that these activities of space exploration already may have confused the investigations for micro-organisms in the upper atmosphere. Justification for this pessimism can be enhanced from the possibility that nuclear explosions may have propelled micro-organisms into the upper atmosphere.

CURRENT APPROACHES TO BIOLOGICAL SAMPLING OF THE UPPER ATMOSPHERE

A primary difficulty in performing microbiological sampling of the upper atmosphere has been the lack of consistently reliable methods for carrying instruments to high altitudes. There are three means by which sampling apparatus can be carried into the stratosphere and beyond: aircraft, balloons, and rockets. Each of these methods has been used in the past for successful sampling of non-biological particles.

Aircraft-borne samplers

Aircraft are practical up to altitudes of 40,000 ft. Lundgren, Mc-Farland & Greene (1964) have described the U-2 hatch sampler and the isokinetic cascade impactor probe (p. 66) that have been used for particulate samplers carried by aircraft. Because most aircraft-borne samplers operate at altitudes that are of low priority in the NASA programme for determining the vertical extent of the biosphere, only brief mention will be given to microbiological data that have been obtained in sampling the troposphere.

Holzapfel & Gressitt (1964) have described results obtained with an air-plankton trap that was designed primarily for the collection of insects and pollen. Of great interest was their comment on the finding of irregular-shaped particles that were rich in silicon, chromium, or aluminium in their sampler. Timmons, Fulton & Mitchell (1966) have described an aircraft-borne isokinetic air sampler that collects micro-organisms on soluble gelatin foam filters. The results of sampling with this device up to altitudes of 11,000 ft. have been reported by Fulton (1966), who found a range of 5–200 micro-organisms per cubic metre of air space at the highest altitude sampled. *Hormodendron* (*Cladosporium*), *Aspergillus* and *Alternaria* comprised approximately 75% of the fungal isolates at the altitudes sampled. The predominant bacterial genera that comprised 75% or more of the bacterial isolates were *Bacillus* and *Micrococcus*.

Balloon-borne samplers

As vehicles for stratospheric sampling experiments, balloons have been used for many years and can lift relatively large payloads to altitudes as high as 45 km. Although the use of balloons has proved to be somewhat unreliable, they offer the only medium-priced method of obtaining instrument flights of long duration at altitudes above 20 km. Recent

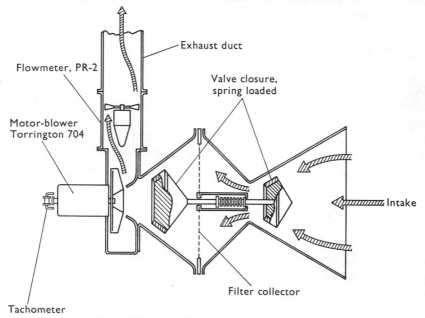

Fig. 1. Diagram of the direct-flow balloon-borne
sampler used in the NASA programme.

balloon technology and materials have extended the limitations of instrument weight, power and time aloft, constraints which applied to stratospheric sampling devices in the past.

Until 1962, the highest profile biologically sampled in the terrestrial atmosphere was from 69,000 to 39,000 ft. A single successful sampling run was made during the Explorer II balloon programme sponsored by the National Geographic Society in 1935. From a collection volume of approximately 2,400 ft.[3] Rogers & Meier (1936) retrieved 10 micro-organisms.

In January 1962, the NASA undertook a programme of unmanned balloon flights under contract with the Electronics Division of the General Mills Company (this division is now part of Litton Systems, Inc.) to sample stratospheric air for viable micro-organisms. The basic sampling process to be employed was air filtration through high efficiency, low pressure-drop material from which the entrapped viable particles could be extracted and cultured quantitatively. The balloon-borne unit shown in Fig. 1 was developed from the direct flow sampler that had been employed by the U.S. Atomic Energy Commission for the determination of radioactive fallout in the stratosphere.

Studies with NASA direct flow sampler

The NASA direct flow sampler is about 0·7 m. in diameter by 1·3 m. long and is fabricated entirely from aluminium. The sampler skin and inlet cone are aluminium spinnings, and the frame is aluminium tubing. Each unit weighs approximately 25 kg. (without associated apparatus). A blower pulls air through a filter, and the volume of sample air is monitored by an anemometer-type flowmeter located at the discharge of the blower (Lundgren et al. 1964). The unit was designed to acquire sample volumes in the order of 20,000 to 100,000 ft.^{3} of ambient air and to measure the air flow rates and air volumes sampled.

The sampling payload consists of four direct-flow sampling units mounted vertically on the four corners of a gondola. The air inlets point downward for sampling during descent. Total weight of the gondola with flight units, batteries, and instrumentation is about 300 kg. During the early sampling flights one unit was used for control purposes and three units were used for sampling; in later flights the gondola had four samplers and one control unit. Prior to the launch, each of the assembled samplers is wrapped in surgical wrapping paper and auto-claved at 121° for 1 hr. The inlet and outlets of the unit are covered with jettisonable aluminium dust covers. In addition, the inlets are also protected by jettisonable nylon shrouds (Pl. 1). The dust covers and shrouds protect the unit during the launch and ascent through the atmosphere.

When favourable weather for a balloon launch is forecast, the paper wrappers on the sterilized units are removed, and the samplers are mounted on the gondola. After the necessary wiring has been completed, the gondola is placed in the portable plastic chamber, inflated with a gaseous mixture of ethylene oxide-Freon 12. The payload is kept in this decontamination chamber for a minimum of 12–14 hr. Just prior to the launch, the plastic chamber is removed, and the gondola attached to the balloon. Sampler inlets and outlets are still protected by the aluminium dust covers; the inlets have the additional protection of the nylon shrouds. Samples of the surfaces of the exterior skin yield less than one organism per 6 in.^{2}. The filter pads inside the samplers are sterile. The interiors of the samplers are never exposed to contamination between the time of autoclaving and the time of jettisoning the dust covers and nylon shrouds in the stratosphere.

Just before take-off, the dust cover and shroud are removed from the inlet of one sampler and the spring-loaded closure door of that sampler is released. It slams shut and locks in the closed position. This sampler provides a ground control.

The system is designed to sample during the descending portion of the flight. The balloon carries the package to maximum altitude (Pl. 2), at which point the jettisonable dust covers and inlet shrouds are released. Simultaneously, sufficient helium is vented from the balloon to permit a controlled descent of about 150 m./min. Shortly after descent starts, two samplers are energized. The first one samples for a period of about 3 min. before being shut off, and then its spring-loaded closure door is released. The sample collected by this unit serves as an in-flight control. The other unit samples through a pre-programmed altitude range, then is shut off and sealed. The remaining unit samples over a lower altitude increment. The balloon continues on its descent until the total package impacts, whereupon the balloon is cut loose to avoid dragging the payload. Each sampler body has a small pressure-equilibrium port fitted with an absolute filter so that during ascent and descent only sterile air will enter into the unit (Lundgren *et al*. 1964).

The direct-flow sampler as originally developed for sampling of stratospheric particulates for radioactivity employed IPC 1478 filter paper (Beadle, 1964). In the NASA direct-flow sampler, 1·3 cm. thick 80-pore polyurethane foam is used as the collection medium. It has the advantages of being chemically and biologically inert, withstands autoclaving, and permits quantitative removal of organisms.

Greene, Pederson, Lundgren & Hagberg (1964) demonstrated the efficiency of this polyurethane foam against artificially generated microbial aerosols in an altitude simulation chamber. High rates of microbial recovery were obtained with low levels of extraneous contamination. Additional studies by the same group showed that lyophilized *Serratia marcescens* exposed to air flows of 1,000 ft./min. for as long as 1,000 min. showed no greater loss of viability than replicate controls not exposed to such air flows. These data indicate that polyurethane foam could retrieve viable aerosolized organisms, allowing the cells to maintain their viability at high air flow rates, before being extracted quantitatively.

Microbiological analysis of filters from direct flow samplers

The following protocol was developed for the recovery and analysis of the microbiological samples (Greene *et al.* 1964):

(1) At the impact site, the sampling units were examined for obvious leaks and malfunctions, detached from the gondola, shrouded in clean polyethylene bags, and then returned to the laboratory.

(2) In the laboratory the bags were removed, the exterior surfaces of the units were thoroughly cleaned, and a phenolic detergent-germicide applied to disinfect the exterior.

(3) The sampling unit was aseptically disassembled in a clean room, and the filter pad was exposed for the first time since completion of the sampling run in the atmosphere.

(4) The filter was dissected into segments; each segment was immediately placed in a sterile polyamide (capran) bag with 100 ml. of sterile water; the bags were then heat sealed.

(5) The filter material was repeatedly and thoroughly extracted with the sterile water diluent by manual manipulation of the sealed bag.

(6) Samples of the diluent were then removed and filtered through membrane filters (Millipore HA) which were then cultured on the following media under the described incubation conditions: (A) Tryptone glucose yeast extract agar (Difco); 35° C for 48 hr. followed by 20° C for 10 days. (B) Eugon agar (BBL); 35° C for 48 hr. followed by 20° C for 5 days. (C) Thioglycollate agar (BBL); 35° C for 48 hr. followed by 20° C for 5 days (anaerobic conditions). (D) Mycophil agar (BBL); 20° C for 7 days.

(7) A laboratory control was obtained by performing steps (4), (5) and (6) on a freshly autoclaved sheet of polyurethane foam.

Because this paper is concerned with descriptions of a broad research programme and the results achieved to date, it is not possible to provide in detail those aspects of each experiment that are more suitable for publication in original research manuscripts. The approach in this programme was to elevate sterile samplers into the stratosphere, to filter a large volume of air without contaminating the samplers with organisms carried on the balloon and gondola, to seal the exposed filters against subsequent low altitude and ground-based contamination and, finally, to culture any viable material trapped on the filters.

The engineering problems that were imposed on the designing of the sampler were rather formidable. The sampler had to tolerate autoclaving, operate in the low temperatures and low pressures of the stratosphere, sample approximately 100,000 ft.³ of ambient air and then seal itself, withstand the stress of launch and impact while preventing internal contamination, and work at remote distances automatically and reliably. The data to be presented will indicate that much remains to be accomplished in achieving all of the desired aspects for sampling in the stratosphere.

Results from the balloon-borne direct flow sampler

The quantitative data for all balloon flights on this programme to date are summarized in Table 1. It must be remembered that the data as

Table 1. *Quantitative results from the balloon-borne direct flow samplers*

(After Green *et al.* 1964; Sanders & Pederson, 1966.)

Altitude (thousand feet)	Flight date	No. of colonies cultured	Volume sampled (10^3 ft.^{3})	Volume per microbe (ft.^{3})
10–30	1 Aug. 1962	112	6 ⎫	
	22 July 1965	463	18 ⎪	
	19 Aug. 1965	60	13 ⎬	Average 50–100
	1 Oct. 1965	212	37 ⎭	
30–60	19 Oct. 1962	196	20 ⎫	
	31 July 1963	310	133 ⎪	
	18 Nov. 1963	10	17 ⎪	Minimum 100,
	7 June 1965	0	35 ⎬	average 330–500
	22 July 1965	8	43 ⎪	
	4 Aug. 1965	117	18 ⎪	
	19 Aug. 1965	37	17 ⎭	
60–90	19 Oct. 1962	128	140 ⎫	
	18 Nov. 1963	24	101 ⎪	
	7 June 1965	14	80 ⎬	Minimum 1,000,
	22 July 1965	16	45 ⎪	average 2,000
	4 Aug. 1965	26	45 ⎪	
	1 Oct. 1965	96	105 ⎭	

reported for the various altitudes for each flight are usually based on one sampler; on the later flights (those of 1965), paired samplers were employed. One sampler in the flight package was always used as a ground control. This control sampler was sealed just before take-off of the gondola and remained sealed throughout the flight programme (including the hard landing). During the early phases of the programme, one sampler was also employed as an in-flight control. Although attempts were made to keep all the techniques consistent, the very nature of this work prevented each flight from being a duplicate of any other. It is not possible in this paper to provide a detailed description of the performance of each flight. The original research papers published on this effort have been cited, and it is anticipated that additional papers will be forthcoming.

Analysis of the data in Table 1 shows variation in the microbial

Table 2. *Qualitative results from the balloon-borne direct flow samplers*

(After Greene *et al.* 1964; Sanders & Pederson, 1966.)

Altitude (thousand feet)	Flight date	Predominant moulds	Predominant bacteria (includes Actinomycetes and yeast)	Total no. moulds	Total no. bacteria
10–30	1 Aug. 1962	*Penicillium*	Diphtheroids; gram-positive rods	55	56
	22 July 1965	*Cladosporium, Alternaria*	Yeast; gram-positive rods	395	67
	19 Aug. 1965	*Alternaria*	Micrococci; gram-negative rods	3	52
	1 Oct. 1965	Unidentified moulds	Micrococci; gram-negative rods; diphtheroids	5	207
30–60	19 Oct. 1962	*Aspergillus, Cladosporium*	Micrococci	56	140
	31 July 1963	*Cladosporium, Alternaria*	Spore-forming rods; gram-negative rods	190	120
	18 Nov. 1963	*Cladosporium, Alternaria*	Gram-positive rods; diphtheroids	1	9
	7 June 1965	None	None	0	0
	22 July 1965	None	Diphtheroids; actinomycetes	0	8
	4 Aug. 1965	*Cladosporium, Alternaria*	Micrococci; gram-negative rods	3	114
	19 Aug. 1965	*Cladosporium*	Gram-negative rods; diphtheroids	2	35
60–90	19 Oct. 1962	*Aspergillus*	Micrococci	22	106
	18 Nov. 1963	*Cladosporium*	Gram-positive rods; diphtheroids	2	15
	7 June 1965	*Alternaria*	Gram-positive rods; sporeformers	2	12
	22 July 1965	None	Gram-negative rods; diphtheroids	2	16
	4 Aug. 1965	*Alternaria*	Yeast; diphtheroids	3	23
	1 Nov. 1965	*Cladosporium*	Diphtheroids; gram-negative rods; micrococci	3	93

recoveries with each flight at similar altitudes. Thus, at 30,000–60,000 ft. altitude the probable average is two to three organisms per 1,000 ft.³. At 60,000–90,000 ft. altitude the average is five organisms per 10,000 ft.³. It is the author's judgement that the average for the 60,000–90,000 ft. level is probably closer to one organism or less per 10,000 ft.³ of ambient air sampled. Since there was always some low level background contamination on the filters of the control samplers, the data are presented as the best estimates of the upper limits of the number of organisms that could be present.

The data in Table 2 are a summary of some of the qualitative micro-biological results that have been obtained for the various altitudes sampled. Fungi, primarily *Alternaria* and *Cladosporium*, and micrococci predominated at the highest altitude sampled. It is felt that the very consistent recovery of *Alternaria* and *Cladosporium* on every successful flight at altitudes from 90,000 to 60,000 ft. is of some significance, particularly since it verifies the isolation of these fungi by other workers at considerably lower altitudes (Fulton, 1966).

Other balloon-borne sampling instrumentation

The current effort on the balloon-borne samplers is directed towards a modification of the direct flow sampler that will utilize an air ejector pump to move atmospheric air through the polyurethane foam filter material (Sanders & Pederson, 1966). A diagram of this new system is shown in Fig. 2. The air ejector system has been used by the U.S. Atomic Energy Commission for their high altitude samplers. The air ejector is a separate unit and is bolted to the rectangular filter material container, which can be autoclaved. The filter module is loaded with a strip of filter-material approximately 1 ft. wide by 7 ft. long. The rolled-up filter is stored on the left side of the container and is fed through guide tracks to the take-up section on the right side. In the take-up section the filter is interleaved with one layer of plastic film to separate the layers of filter and to hold the particulate matter in place. The upper and lower doors of the filter module are pre-programmed to open and close at specific altitudes during a sampling flight. The take-up section has a special door that enables that portion of the filter container to be tightly sealed during recovery operations.

A previous attempt was made by the NASA to sample biologically the Earth's upper atmosphere with an air impactor type of collecting instrument built by the Jet Propulsion Laboratory (JPL). The JPL impactor was flown on three balloon-borne missions at altitudes of 125,000–135,000 ft. during 1963 (Soffen, 1964). A globular package consisted of two hemispheres, one of which housed a continuous sampling air impactor operating at high efficiency. The ambient air was drawn into the instrument, passed through a narrow slit at high velocity and impacted against a 1 in. wide strip of Whatman no. 42 filter paper.

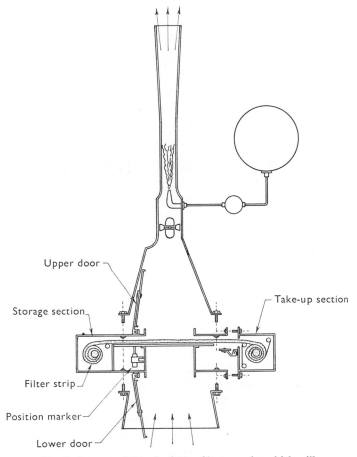

Fig. 2. Layout of the air ejector-filter sampler which will be used in future balloon flights.

Particles with sufficient inertia became attached to the surface where adhesive and electrostatic forces held them. The duration of the flights was 24 hr. each.

Upon retrieval, the sample collector was decontaminated on all exterior surfaces with formalin and 70% ethyl alcohol. The port-holes were sealed, and the instrument transported to the laboratory. It was placed in a sterile glove box, and the hemispheres were opened and decontaminated. The sealed chamber with the filter paper strip was opened, and the paper was removed aseptically for culturing in broth or on solid media.

This JPL balloon flight programme has been discontinued; a description of the sampler, the analytical procedures and micro-biological results were published by Soffen (1964). The sampling capacity of this unit was small (after 10 hr. of sampling, a total of 1,000 ft.³ of ambient air was sampled at 130,000 ft.).

The experiment was flown on three successful balloon flights. During the second flight, however, the motor mechanism of the collecting impactor malfunctioned, and no organisms were collected. From the first flight, seven *Penicillium* colonies were obtained; five *Penicillium* colonies were found on the agar culture plates from the third flight. Thus, twelve organisms were recovered from approximately 2,000 ft.³ of ambient air sampled. In spite of the special precautions taken and the various controls employed, these results are subject to question. This experiment would have to be repeated several times before the data could be accepted. If micro-organisms do exist at 130,000 ft., their numbers are very small. Other corroborative balloon studies at these altitudes should be forthcoming.

Rocket-borne samplers

The next type of vehicle that can be used to transport microbial sampling instrumentation into the mesosphere, thermosphere and beyond is the rocket. Two important biological problems are encountered in the use of rockets for microbial sampling in the atmosphere. Since the most desirable profile for a sampling flight involves a supersonic trajectory, the micro-organisms must pass through a normal shock wave with the concomitant release of energy. During this collection process they are exposed to elevated temperature for a few milliseconds. This problem can be minimized by carefully selecting trajectories with low Mach numbers.

The second biological problem concerns the relatively small number of micro-organisms to be expected at altitudes that can be reached by rockets. Should micro-organisms be extremely rare, as indicated by balloon data (less than one organism per 10,000 ft.³), a very large volume of ambient air must be sampled to detect such small numbers without confusion from background contaminants during laboratory assay of the sampling units.

Developments for a cryogenic whole air sampler

A cryogenic whole-air sampler is under development for use with inorganic particulate matter (micrometeorites) and gases in the upper atmosphere (Denton, Hord, Jacobs & Martell, 1966) and is being investigated for its adaptability to the gathering of micro-organisms. A number of technical features make this sampler desirable for microbial collection by rockets. A particular advantage is that it will obtain a whole-air sample from a predetermined altitude range. The sampler retains 100% of the gases and particulates intercepted by the inlet. This is accomplished by condensation of all the atmospheric gases entering the sampler, a process which keeps the back pressure around the pump low and, in turn, prevents spillage around the inlet. The detailed knowledge of the volume of air collected and the technical ability to gather all of the air intercepted can allow a very accurate determination of the number of micro-organisms in the atmosphere at any given altitude.

The collector will be travelling at supersonic speed during that portion of its trajectory in which the sampling will occur. In its operation in the supersonic region, there will be a shock wave generated somewhere between the inlet of the collector and the heat exchanger. From the shock waves at an altitude of 100,000 ft. and Mach of 2·5, the temperature will reach approximately 220° for a few milliseconds. Some of the micro-organisms, especially the heat-resistant spores, should be able to withstand such high temperatures without any untoward effects.

Effects of supersonic shock waves on micro-organisms

The NASA has supported research with Melpar, Inc., to determine qualitatively the survival of several microbial species to shock wave exposure similar to that which would occur during cryogenic whole-air sampling. The following eight micro-organisms were chosen for these experiments: *Cladosporium resinae, Aspergillus niger, Penicillium notatum, Bacillus subtilis* var. *niger, Serratia marcescens, Clostridium pasteurianum, Nocardia asteroides*, and *Streptomyces griseus*. The physical conditions to which these micro-organisms were subjected were chosen from those suggested by the design of an existing cryogenic whole-air collector system (Plattner, 1965) to be used by the U.S. Air Force in sampling the particulate content of the upper atmosphere. This system utilizes a low temperature (4–30° K.) metal surface which at high speeds condenses all the air in its path. From this it was assumed that successful collection of micro-organisms in the atmosphere would depend upon the ability of the organism to survive:

(1) Near vacuum in the upper atmosphere.

(2) Rapid heating in passage through the shock wave generated by the sampling vehicle.

(3) High-speed impaction on the metal surface.

(4) Rapid cooling to a few degrees Kelvin.

(5) Rewarming to room temperature and subsequent storage for a period of time.

The cultures of bacteria previously cited were grown for 3 days at 28° C on appropriate solid media, whereas the fungal cultures were grown for 10 days at 28° C on solid media. The microbial growth was harvested and washed with distilled water prior to lyophilization. The lyophilized cells for each species were exposed to liquid H_2 for 12–15 min. (actual exposure time of 5–8 min. at 20° K.) and then warmed (some rapidly, some slowly) to room temperature. All cultures except *Serratia marcescens* had survivals in the range of 20–100% following these variations in treatment.

The shock tube was made from 2·5 in. I.D. aluminum tubing with 0·25 in. wall thickness. The driver section was a single tube 5 ft. in length. The test section was 10 ft. long and ended in an evacuated dump tank, 1 ft. in diameter by 2 ft. long. The dump tank was connected to a 4 in. diffusion pump which rapidly reached 10^{-3} mm. Hg. A liquid-hydrogen Dewar mounted in the dump tank held a Millipore filter facing the outlet of the shock tube. Helium in the driver section was exploded into the test section in which the micro-organisms were suspended on thin collodion or nitrocellulose lacquer membranes that cover the internal diameter of the tube. In a majority of the twenty-five shock tests, the shock speed was held close to 1·56 m./msec. required to give an exposure time of 2·0 msec. and a temperature of 1,200° C.

All seven species of micro-organisms listed survived the shock experiments when tested as mixed cultures. The experimental instrumentation did not permit quantitative measurement of survival. When they were tested as pure cultures, the spore-forming species exhibited a definite pattern of greater survival than the vegetative species. *Serratia marcescens* was never recovered when it was tested as a pure culture. Thus these data indicate that many micro-organisms could survive the heating during passage through a shock wave under some conditions of high-speed cryogenic collection in the upper atmosphere. Further refinement of the testing apparatus is necessary before quantitative data can be obtained on this particular aspect of upper atmospheric sampling.

Use of bioprobes on Aerobee sounding rockets

At the Goddard Space Flight Centre of the NASA, an Aerobee 150 rocket has been used to carry an impact low-velocity particle-collector for micro-organisms at altitudes above 150,000 ft. The collection principle of this instrumentation is based on the exposure of sterile

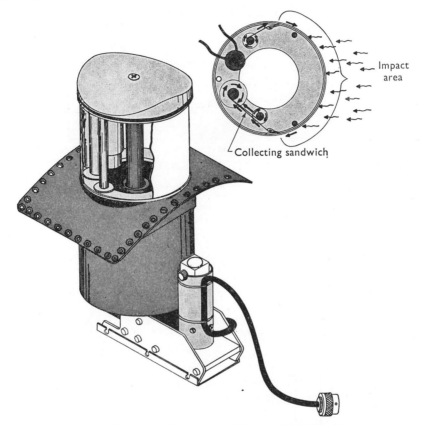

Fig. 3. Diagram of Bioprobe 1 which is a microbial sampling device used on Aerobee sounding rockets.

impactor film mounted on a movable circular cam which can be pushed out from its sterile housing and exposed during the flight of the rocket. The mechanical design and physical hardware employed in this device were developed originally for the collection of micrometeorite dust particles (Berg, 1965).

The mechanical details of this collector (called Bioprobe 1) are illustrated in Fig. 3. The cylinder (piston) contains three spools: one is empty, one contains the sterile collecting film, and the last one has a sterile film to sandwich against the face of the collecting film. The sterile collecting film passes over one-half of the outer circumference of the cylinder (piston) and is wound on to the empty spool. This mechanism is analogous to the winding of exposed film in a box camera. As the exposed film is wound on the initially empty spool, its collecting surface

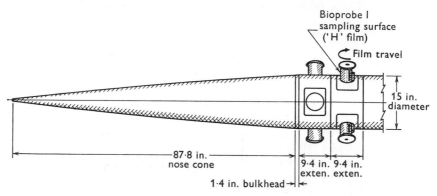

Fig. 4. Location of the Bioprobe 1 on the Aerobee sounding rocket.

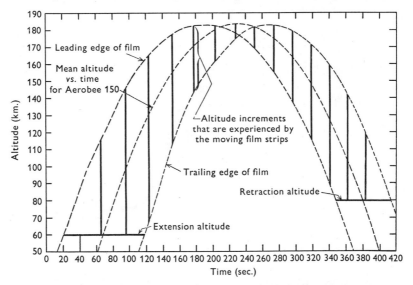

Fig. 5. Altitude sampling profile for Aerobee sounding rocket with attached Bioprobe 1. The collection time can be calculated from the abscissa of this plot.

is sandwiched with sterile film from the third spool. When the film is removed from the piston, its collection surface is always protected.

Upon completion of the rocket sampling run the piston with the impactor film is moved back into the sterile housing of Bioprobe 1 and sealed by means of an O-ring gasket. The relationship of Bioprobe 1 on the Aerobee rocket relative to the position of several similar devices used for the collection of micrometeorite dust particles is shown in Fig. 4. The micro-organisms are collected on a polyamide film called Capton or 'H' film (1 mm. thickness). Bioprobe 1 (including housing) with Capton film is sterilized by dry heat at 135° C for 24 hr. (see Hall & Bruch (1965) for background of this sterilization cycle).

To date, only one flight has been made with the Bioprobe 1 on an Aerobee 150 rocket (Picciolo, Powers & Rich, 1966). The altitude sampling profile for this flight is shown in Fig. 5, and the sampling time

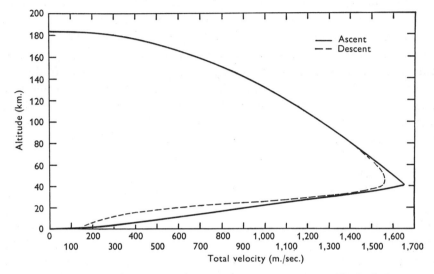

Fig. 6. Plot of the velocity of the Aerobee sounding rocket versus altitude during ascent and descent of the rocket. The highest speeds obtained during exposure of Bioprobe 1 approached Mach 5.

was approximately 310 sec. The velocity of the rocket during the sampling profile is presented in Fig. 6. The shock waves generated during the high velocity portions of the sampling profile in Fig. 6 should not be detrimental to microbial viability. This assumption is based on the qualitative results from the shock-wave microbial study of Melpar, Inc., described previously. After the sampling runs the collectors (including housing) are removed from the skin of the rocket and returned to the laboratory for analysis.

The types of analysis that were performed on this first sampling run were the cultivation of microbes on the film by standard microbiological plating techniques as well as the use of biochemical procedures to detect the ATP (adenosine triphosphate) associated with any biological material that was rinsed from the film. As noted in the discussion of the results from the balloon programme, extreme precautions must be taken during the preparation of the sampler for rocket flight, and during recovery and analysis, to eliminate extraneous contamination. The results of the first Bioprobe 1 flight will not be published until several additional flights have been performed (Picciolo *et al.* 1966).

Other rocket and satellite programmes for the collection of atmospheric micro-organisms

For many years astronomers and geophysicists have tried to collect and analyse micrometeorites, the dust particles small enough to survive entering the Earth's atmosphere. With the advent of high altitude balloons and sounding rockets, it has been possible to reliably collect micrometeorites since the particle residence times are relatively short in the upper stratosphere and mesosphere. The sampling altitude for micrometeorites is determined by the size range of micrometeorites that are to be collected. Balloon altitudes seem to be sufficient for particles with diameters of 5 microns or larger; for submicron particles, sounding rocket altitudes (up to 150 km.) must be sampled; at satellite altitudes (200 km. and higher) it is calculated that the size range of the particles is from 50 to 100 Angstroms.

During the past few years the Dudley Observatory at Albany, N.Y., has carried on an active programme of micrometeorite research. The micrometeorite collection techniques which have been developed by this group require extreme precautions and cleanliness (Hemenway, Fullam, Skrivanek, Soberman & Witt, 1964) in order to preserve the exact nature of the material collected. The collecting surfaces usually consist of a film thin enough to permit easy penetration by the electron beam of an electron microscope. One of the cleanest types of substrate film for these collections is nitrocellulose. The films and their supports are firmly held in place in sealed, small, flat, rectangular boxes ranging in area from 250 to 1,000 cm². (Hemenway & Soberman, 1962).

In order to determine the presence or absence of micro-organisms in micrometeorites, it is necessary to mount sterile collecting surfaces within separately sterilized compartments of the collection devices. The use of two compartments allows greater flexibility and care during loading and unloading of the biological filters versus the micrometeorite collecting films. Modifications of existing micrometeorite collecting equipment for biological experiments has been described by Hotchin *et al.* (1965, 1967).

Because it is doubtful whether micro-organisms can survive total exposure to the space environment, three balloon and three rocket flights have been made in which representative micro-organisms could be exposed during micrometeorite collection studies. Organisms used include T1 coliphage, poliovirus I, spores of *Penicillium roqueforti* Thom., *Escherichia coli* B, and spores of *Bacillus subtilis*. In the initial studies of exposure to balloon and rocket flights (Hotchin *et al.* 1965), a few large area (1–1·5 cm.²) samples of micro-organisms were exposed on nylon reinforced Millipore filter discs or squares cemented to aluminium plates. In the later series of flights (Hotchin *et al.* 1967), a total of 756 separate exposure units (each approximately 5 × 5 mm.) were flown in experiments that allowed total exposure, inverted exposure (screened by 2 mm. of aluminium), or filter protection of the micro-organisms seeded on vinyl-coated metal surfaces or Millipore filter units. The altitudes of the exposures varied from 35 km. in the balloons to 150 km. in the rockets. Time of exposure was 6 hr. in the balloon flights and about 3 min. in the rocket flights.

The results from these flights show that the environment of deep space is not immediately lethal to the micro-organisms tested. The microbial spores showed little or no loss in viability. Highly dispersed and fully exposed virus was rapidly inactivated during the rocket exposures. Solar radiation appears to be the primary cause of microbial inactivation, but thin layers of filtering or shielding materials can afford enormous protection. These results verify the laboratory studies of the effect of deep space conditions on micro-organisms described earlier.

These studies of microbial survival have provided a justification and stimulus for the sampling of micrometeorites for the presence of micro-organisms. Developments are under way to expose sterile Millipore filters and vinyl-coated metal surfaces as part of the experimental package during micrometeorite collecting experiments on several sounding rocket programmes. In addition to the sterile collecting surfaces, additional microbial specimens will be flown to determine the rates of survival following different conditions of space exposure.

Use of manned satellite vehicles for exposure and collection experiments

Manned satellite vehicles now provide an unusual opportunity to extend the micrometeorite detection experiments to heights at which very small micrometeorites can be detected. The collecting devices for micrometeorites and microbes and the exposure surfaces for microbes that have been used on the balloon and sounding rocket flights by the Dudley Observatory group can be applied to manned satellite vehicles. It is planned on the Gemini 9 flight to have the astronauts open from inside of the spacecraft an externally attached micrometeorite and microbial collecting package that also contains microbial specimens for exposure in deep space. This collection package will be retrieved after some 8 hr. of exposure and returned by the astronauts to the inside of the Gemini spacecraft. Upon return to Earth, the samples will be analysed microbiologically like the previous balloon and rocket flight collection boxes (Hotchin *et al.* 1965, 1967).

In addition, the Agena target vehicle for the Gemini series of flights can hold micrometeorite and microbial collection as well as microbial exposure boxes. During the rendezvous of the Gemini spacecraft with the Agena target vehicle, the astronaut, while performing extravehicular activity, can open the micrometeorite and microbial collection devices carried in the Agena target vehicle. The exposed packages could orbit the Earth for 60–120 days; during the next or succeeding Gemini flights, they would be closed and removed by the Gemini astronaut during extravehicular activities after rendezvous of the spacecraft and target vehicle. The Agena target vehicle used on the Gemini 8 flight contains such a micrometeorite and biological collection and exposure package. A similar collection box was attached to the Agena target vehicle for the Gemini 9 flight, but this experimental package was lost when the target vehicle failed to orbit.

BIOCHEMICAL ASSAYS FOR REAL-TIME DETECTION OF ATMOSPHERIC MICRO-ORGANISMS

It has been implicit in all the previous discussion that the determination of microbial numbers depends on classical viability assays (except for the mention in the Goddard rocket programme of the use of a biochemical assay for ATP). It has been noted also that much additional research needs to be done to determine the quantitative survival of micro-organisms that are collected at supersonic speeds in collectors aboard sounding rockets or in orbiting satellites. When these samples are returned to terrestrial laboratories for analysis, severe constraints are placed upon the assay systems to detect the entrapped organisms with a minimum of interfering contamination. A serious problem of signal-to-noise level in the classical viability (plate count) assays has been prevalent in all the data reported in this paper. These problems have encouraged microbiologists to look at instrumentation that could yield real-time detection of micro-organisms during the sampling flights in the upper atmosphere. Because microbial growth involves lengthy periods of time, these procedures would be based on rapid biochemical assays.

The substance ATP is a biochemical constituent of all known living cells. The ubiquity of this compound in living organisms renders it an excellent indicator of the presence or absence of terrestrial life. The detection of ATP is evidence of the presence of cellular products or debris from either living or recently deceased cells.

Strange (1961) has derived a concentration of 1 μg. ATP per mg. cell dry weight for starved *Aerobacter aerogenes*. If it is assumed that *A. aerogenes* has a wet weight of 100 times its dry weight, and that one cell is 10^{-12} g., then 1 g. of wet *A. aerogenes* cells contains 10^{-5} g. ATP and there is 1×10^{-17} g. ATP per fresh cell. Additional calculations show that each fresh cell would have approximately 1,000 molecules of ATP. If a limit is placed on the number of ATP molecules immediately available for reaction in a cell, and if each ATP molecule could generate one light photon, then approximately 200 photons per cell would be available for detection by a photomultiplier in the instrumentation. In the preliminary analyses for determining the feasibility of this approach, the biologists were assured by electronic engineers that instrumentation could be built to detect this number of photons and thus detect, theoretically, one living cell.

These calculations on the amount of light energy that could be produced per microbial cell are based on a bioluminescent reaction requiring ATP that occurs in the tail lantern of fireflies (*Photinus pyralis*). This particular reaction has been well established by the work of W. D. McElroy and his associates (1947, 1964). In brief, the light emission during firefly bioluminescence is the result of the reaction of oxygen with an oxidizable substrate (luciferin) catalysed by an enzyme (luciferase). Luciferin must react initially with ATP before it can be oxidized with the production of light. The first step of the reaction is as follows:

$$LH_2 + ATP + E \overset{Mg^{2+}}{\rightleftharpoons} E.LH_2 - AMP + PP, \qquad (1)$$

where LH_2 = luciferin, E = enzyme (luciferase), PP = pyrophosphate, L = dehydroluciferin, AMP = adenylic acid. The kinetics of the reaction indicate that ATP is not yielding energy but acts in an unknown catalytic fashion to change the electronic configuration of one or all of the energy states of luciferin (Rhodes & McElroy, 1958). In the presence of oxygen the light emission step takes place as follows:

$$E.LH_2 - AMP + O_2 \longrightarrow E.L - AMP + (H_2O_2)? + h\nu \text{ (photon)}. \quad (2)$$

The regeneration of the enzyme may be effected by either or both of the following reactions:

$$E.L - AMP + CoA \longrightarrow E + AMP + CoA - L, \qquad (3)$$

where CoA = co-enzyme A;

$$E.L - AMP + PP \longrightarrow L + E + ATP. \qquad (4)$$

On examination of reactions (1), (2), (3), and (4) it can be seen that the total light emitted during the course of the reaction is a function of the concentration of luciferase, luciferin, ATP, CoA, O_2 and pyrophosphate. It has been shown, however, that the rate-limiting step in the sequence is the reaction between ATP and luciferin. In the presence of excess luciferase, the maximum light intensity is a direct function of the concentration of luciferin and ATP. If all the components of this reaction (with the exception of ATP) are present in excess, the emission of light is quantitatively specific for the amount of ATP added.

The Hazleton Laboratories, Inc., have designed an ATP detection instrument to be used as a flexible tool in the study of the parameters which influence the progress of the firefly-lantern enzyme reaction upon the injection of ATP and the subsequent emission of light (Chapelle & Levin, 1965). The instrumentation provides for the introduction of a quantity of purified biochemical components known as the enzyme mixture which contains the components described in the above equations with the exception of ATP. The enzyme mixture is contained in a cuvette which is placed in a temperature-controlled unit in front of a light-collecting optical system. The cuvette assembly is contained in a light-tight reaction chamber which also includes a precision syringe that is filled with a sample of ATP dissolved in water. The syringe is positioned directly over the cuvette and is driven by a hydraulic drive to discharge a controlled quantity of ATP into the enzyme mixture. This injection results in the immediate emission of light quanta which are collected by the optical system and directed on to the photocathode of a photomultiplier vacuum tube. The photomultiplier tube is operated to obtain a high signal-to-noise ratio at low light levels. The photocathode is cooled to reduce the thermal noise, and pulse amplitude discrimination is employed to reduce the effects of photomultiplier noise.

Under optimal reaction conditions, the maximal sensitivity of the enzyme assay with this instrumentation was found to be $10^{-9} \mu$g. with confidence limits of 28–78 % at this level. The ATP responses are not linear at quantities of $10^{-7} \mu$g. or less. Because there are many factors which could influence the variations in light response at low ATP concentrations, additional studies will be necessary to establish conclusively the nature of the variations when the amount of ATP is less than $10^{-7} \mu g$.

Another bioluminescent system that can be used to complement the firefly ATP assay is that of bacterial luminescence. Strehler and his associates were among the first to show that a cell-free extract of luminescent bacteria (*Achromabacter fischeri*) was capable of emitting light (Strehler & Cormier, 1953). As a result of studies conducted by a number of investigators over the past years the following reaction mechanism has been established:

$$NADH + H^+ + FMN \overset{\substack{NADH \\ oxidase}}{\rightleftharpoons} FMNH_2 + NAD^+, \qquad (5)$$

$$2FMNH_2 + RCHO + O_2 \overset{luciferase}{\longrightarrow} light\ (0\cdot49\ microns), \qquad (6)$$

where NADH = reduced pyridine nucleotide, FMN = flavin mononucleotide, RCHO = long chain aldehyde.

FMN is a biologically significant compound which is widespread in terrestrial living systems, and therefore a candidate for extraterrestrial life detection.

Research at the Goddard Space Flight Centre of NASA is being carried out on bacterial luciferase as an assay for FMN by using a chemical reductant as a substitute for equation (5). Various bacteria are being compared for luminescence, growth, and production of active luciferase on extraction with subsequent biochemical purification. Linearity and sensitivity studies are being run and determination of the amounts of FMN in various micro-organisms will follow.

CONCLUSIONS

This review of the current NASA programme to establish the vertical extent of the biosphere should be considered as an introduction to a broad effort of microbiological research in space. The upgrading of the balloon-borne samplers will continue so that additional data will be available to confirm the quantitative data that have been reported.

The use of sounding rockets and space satellites for the collection, as well as the exposure of micro-organisms in space, should help the microbiologist to characterize some of the environmental limits for terrestrial microbes.

Throughout this review, the author has attempted to show the severe problems that face research activities in space. Furthermore, the difficulties of assaying for microbes in samples that contain very small numbers of viable organisms constantly challenges the interpretation of quantitative results.

New biochemical approaches to the real-time detection of micro-organisms must be thoroughly investigated for their applicability to space flight instrumentation. If significant advances can be made in such instrumentation for use in space flight, many of the controversies about the presence of micro-organisms in the upper atmosphere can be resolved.

REFERENCES

ARRHENIUS, S. A. (1908). *Worlds in the Making.* New York: Harper Brothers.

BEADLE, R. W. (1964). Atomic Energy Commission high altitude samplers. *Proceedings of the Atmospheric Biology Conference* (University of Minnesota, 13–15 April, 1964), pp. 37–47. National Aeronautics and Space Administration, Washington, D.C. (Accession no. N 65–23980.)

BERG, O. E. (1965). Unpublished data from the Goddard Space Flight Center, National Aeronautics and Space Administration.

CHAPELLE, E. W. & LEVIN, G. V. (1965). The design and fabrication of an instrument for the detection of adenosinetriphosphate (ATP). Final Report on Contract No. NAS 5–3799 between Hazleton Laboratories, Inc., and the National Aeronautics and Space Administration, Washington, D.C. (NASA CR–411).

DAVIS, N. S., SILVERMAN, G. J. & KELLER, W. H. (1963). Combined effects of ultrahigh vacuum and temperature on the viability of some spores and soil organisms. *Appl. Microbiol.* **11**, 202.

DENTON, E. H., HORD, J., JACOBS, R. B. & MARTELL, E. A. (1966). Preliminary design, ENCAR–1 rocket-borne cryogenic air sampler. Report NCAR–TN–18 from National Centre for Atmospheric Research to National Aeronautics and Space Administration on Contract NASr–224.

FULTON, J. D. (1966). Microorganisms in the upper atmosphere. 3. Relationship between altitude and micropopulation. *Appl. Microbiol.* **14**, 237.

GREENE, V. W., PEDERSON, P. D., LUNDGREN, D. A. & HAGBERG, C. A. (1964). Microbiological exploration of stratosphere: Results of six experimental flights. *Proceedings of the Atmospheric Biology Conference* (University of Minnesota, 13–15 April, 1964), pp. 199–211. National Aeronautics and Space Administration, Washington, D.C. (Accession no. N 65–23980.)

HALL, L. B. & BRUCH, C. W. (1965). Procedures necessary for the prevention of planetary contamination. *Life Sciences and Space Res.* **3**, 48.

HEMENWAY, C. L. & SOBERMAN, R. K. (1962). Studies of micrometeorites obtained from a recoverable sounding rocket. *Astr. J., N.Y.* **67**, 256.

HEMENWAY, C. L., FULLAM, E. F., SKRIVANEK, R. A., SOBERMAN, R. K. & WITT, G. (1964). Electron microscope studies of noctilucent cloud particles. *Tellus,* **16**, 96.

HOLZAPFEL, E. P. & GRESSITT, J. L. (1964). Airplane trapping of organisms and particles. *Proceedings of the Atmospheric Biology Conference* (University of Minnesota, 13–15 April, 1964), pp. 151–62. National Aeronautics and Space Administration, Washington, D.C. (Accession no. N 65–23980.)

HOTCHIN, J., LORENZ, P. & HEMENWAY, C. (1965). Survival of micro-organisms in space. *Nature, Lond.* **206**, 442.

HOTCHIN, J., LORENZ, P., MARKUSEN, A. & HEMENWAY, C. (1967). The survival of microorganisms in space: further rocket and balloon borne exposure experiments. *Life Sciences and Space Res.* 5 (in the Press).

IMSHENETSKY, A. A. (1963). Life in space. *Vestnik Akademii nauk SSSR*, 9, 23.

LEDERBERG, J. (1960). Exobiology: approaches to life beyond the earth. *Science*, 132, 393.

LUNDGREN, D. A., McFARLAND, A. R. & GREENE, V. W. (1964). Mechanical methods for collecting stratospheric aerosols. *Proceedings of the Atmospheric Biology Conference* (University of Minnesota, 13–15 April, 1964), pp. 49–65. National Aeronautics and Space Administration, Washington, D.C. (Accession no. N 65–23980.)

McELROY, W. D. (1947). The energy source for bioluminescence in an isolated system. *Proc. natn. Acad. Sci., Wash.* 33, 342.

MORELLI, F. A., FEHLNER, F. P. & STEMBRIDGE, C. H. (1962). Effect of ultrahigh vacuum on *Bacillus subtilis* var. *niger*. *Nature, Lond.* 196, 106.

PICCIOLO, G. L., POWERS, E. M. & RICH, E. (1966). Unpublished data from the Goddard Space Flight Center, National Aeronautics and Space Administration.

PLATTNER, C. M. (1965). Super-cooled paddles used in high altitude air sampler. *Aviation Week and Space Technol.* (11 January, 1965), p. 44.

PORTNER, D. M., SPINER, D. R., HOFFMAN, R. K. & PHILLIPS, C. R. (1961). Effect of ultrahigh vacuum on the viability of micro-organisms. *Science*, 134, 2,047.

RHODES, W. C. & McELROY, W. D. (1958). Synthesis and function of luciferyl-adenylate and oxyluciferyl-adenylate. *J. biol. Chem.* 233, 1,528.

ROGERS, L. A. & MEIER, F. C. (1936). In *National Geographic Society (Technical paper)*, *U.S. Army Air Corps Stratosphere Flight of 1935 in Balloon Explorer II*, pp. 146–51. National Geographic Society, Washington, D.C.

SAGAN, C. (1961). Interstellar panspermia. *Symposium on Extraterrestrial Biochemistry and Biology*, American Association for the Advancement of Science, 128th Annual Meeting, Denver, Colorado, 26–30 December, 1961.

SANDERS, R. & PEDERSON, P. D. (1966). Unpublished data from Contract NAS–3888 between Litton Systems, Inc., and National Aeronautics and Space Administration, Washington, D.C.

SELIGER, H. H. & McELROY, W. D. (1964). The colors of firefly bioluminescence: Enzyme configuration and species specificity. *Proc. natn. Acad. Sci., Wash.* 52, 75.

SILVERMAN, G. J., DAVIS, N. S. & KELLER, W. H. (1964). Exposure of micro-organisms to simulated extraterrestrial space ecology. *Life Sciences and Space Res.* 2, 372.

SOFFEN, G. A. (1964). Atmospheric collection at 130,000 feet. *Proceedings of the Atmospheric Biology Conference* (University of Minnesota, 13–15 April, 1964), pp. 213–18. National Aeronautics and Space Administration, Washington, D.C. (Accession no. N 65–23980.)

STRANGE, R. E. (1961). Induced enzyme synthesis in aqueous suspensions of starved stationary phase *Aerobacter aerogenes*. *Nature, Lond.* 191, 1,272.

STREHLER, B. L. & CORMIER, M. J. (1953). Factors affecting the luminescence of cell-free extracts of the luminous bacterium, *Achromobacter fischeri*. *Archs Biochem. Biophys.* 47, 16.

TIMMONS, D. E., FULTON, J. D. & MITCHELL, R. B. (1966). Microorganisms of the upper atmosphere. 1. Instrumentation for isokinetic air sampling at altitude. *Appl. Microbiol.* 14, 229.

EXPLANATION OF PLATES

Pl. 1. The balloon-borne gondola package used in the flights during 1965 carried five direct-flow samplers.

Pl. 2. Gondola package is shown in ascent stages of balloon flight.

PLATE 1

PLATE 2